Engineering Materials

THEIR MECHANICAL PROPERTIES AND APPLICATIONS

PRENTICE-HALL ENGINEERING DESIGN SERIES

John A. Hrones, *Editor*

Engineering Materials

THEIR MECHANICAL PROPERTIES
AND APPLICATIONS

by JOSEPH MARIN

PROFESSOR AND HEAD,
DEPARTMENT OF ENGINEERING MECHANICS
THE PENNSYLVANIA STATE UNIVERSITY
STATE COLLEGE, PENNSYLVANIA

PRENTICE-HALL, INC.
Englewood Cliffs, N. J.

First Printing......March, 1952
Second Printing......June, 1953
Third Printing...September, 1954
Fourth Printing...January, 1956
Fifth Printing ...... May, 1957

Preface

In recent years a number of developments have made it necessary for the engineer to consider more completely the properties of materials. These developments include the invention of new types of machines and structures, the introduction of new kinds of materials, the use of higher speeds and temperatures, the increase in the severity of operating conditions, and the decrease in the factors of safety used. Designers of machines and structures must, therefore, utilize more thoroughly information on mechanical properties. Although at one time the engineer could design machines and structures based on the static tensile yield or ultimate strength, it is essential today that he consider the influence of numerous types of possible operating and stress conditions to insure a safe and economical design.

This text is concerned with the mechanical properties of engineering materials. Its objective is to provide the student with sufficient knowledge of the behavior of stressed materials to permit the intelligent selection and use of materials. The book was written in an attempt to make the subject more analytical, more rigorous, and more directly applicable to design than is done in existing books on the subject.

The mechanical properties of materials, their definition, determination and utilization are treated in Part One. In the general treatment of mechanical properties, static, fatigue, impact, and high and low temperature loading conditions are considered. The behavior of materials under various types of loading conditions such as tension, compression, bending, and torsion are treated. The utilization of mechanical properties in simple machine and structural design problems is strongly emphasized and the material presented attempts to give necessary background for subsequent design courses.

In Part Two, a brief treatment of a number of important engineering materials is given. In the discussion of specific materials, emphasis is placed on the mechanical properties and the factors influencing the mechanical properties. A chapter is also included on the structure of materials and the control of their properties.

Part Three presents a discussion of the more important materials testing machines and strain gages that are used for the determination of the mechanical properties of materials.

In line with recent trends in engineering education, emphasis has been placed on the fundamental ideas underlying the subject. Descriptive material concerning manufacture and fabrication of materials has been kept to a minimum and every attempt has been made to confine the text to a concise presentation of the determination, significance, and use of mechanical properties.

In a first course on materials, sufficient time is usually not available to cover all the subject matter of this text. For this reason, parts of the book are in small print, and for the usual introductory course these parts can be omitted without destroying the continuity of the remaining subject matter.

The writer sincerely appreciates the many helpful suggestions made by Professors J. W. Breneman, D. E. Hardenbergh, P. B. Kapp, P. K. Roos, J. A. Sauer, and R. K. Vierck, members of the Department of Engineering Mechanics at the Pennsylvania State College. He acknowledges the use made of various books and other publications in the preparation of this text, particularly *Properties of Engineering Materials* by Professor Glenn Murphy. The introductory material in Chapter 1 was patterned on that excellent text, and several illustrations were adapted from it. The help of Mrs. Jean Marin in editing and typing the manuscript is also greatly appreciated.

JOSEPH MARIN

Contents

Part One: Mechanical Properties—General

1. STATIC PROPERTIES IN TENSION AND COMPRESSION   3

1-1: Introduction. 1-2: Mechanical properties in simple tension. 1-3: Mechanical properties in simple compression. 1-4: Design or working stresses. 1-5: Utilization of tension and compression properties. 1-6: True stress-strain relations in simple tension. 1-7: Factors which modify stress-strain relations. 1-8: Special properties. 1-9: Problems.

2. STATIC PROPERTIES IN SHEAR AND BENDING   79

2-1: Mechanical properties in direct shear. 2-2: Mechanical properties in torsion. 2-3: Utilization of torsion properties. 2-4: Mechanical properties in bending. 2-5: Utilization of bending properties. 2-6: Problems.

3. STATIC PROPERTIES UNDER COMBINED STRESSES   116

3-1: Principal stresses, strains and strain energy. 3-2: Theories of failure for yield. 3-3: Theories of failure for ultimate strength. 3-4: Theories for plastic stress-strain relations and ductility. 3-5: Comparison of theories and test results. 3-6: Design stresses for static combined stresses. 3-7: Utilization of theories in design. 3-8: Stress concentration. 3-9 Problems.

4. FATIGUE PROPERTIES   178

4-1: Nature of fatigue. 4-2: Fatigue strength for repeated axial stresses—determination of fatigue strength. 4-3: Fatigue strengths for repeated torsional stresses. 4-4: Fatigue strength for repeated bending stresses. 4-5: Members subjected to repeated bending and axial loads. 4-6: Fatigue strengths for combined stresses. 4-7: Factors affecting the fatigue strength. 4-8: Types of fatigue test data. 4-9: Problems.

5. IMPACT PROPERTIES   222

5-1: General comments.   5-2: Notched-bar impact testing.   5-3: Impact testing.   5-4: Design impact stresses.   5-5: Impact stresses in members subjected to simple tension, bending and torsion.   5-6: Utilization of impact properties in design.   5-7: Problems.

6. CREEP AND TEMPERATURE PROPERTIES   250

6-1: Introductory comments.   6-2: Temperature properties.   6-3: Long-time creep properties in tension.   6-4: Creep-stress relaxation in tension.   6-5: Creep strains and stresses in simple bending.   6-6: Creep strains and stresses in torsion.   6-7: Creep strains for combined stresses.   6-8: Problems.

Part Two: Specific Materials

7. STRUCTURE OF MATERIALS AND CONTROL OF THEIR PROPERTIES   299

7-1: Introduction.   7-2: Structure of matter.   7-3: Influence of chemical composition and mechanical treatment.   7-4: Cooling curves.   7-5: Equilibrium diagrams.   7-6: Influence of fabrication methods on properties.   7-7: Problems.

8. FERROUS METALS AND ALLOYS   320

8-1: Introduction.   8-2: Composition of ferrous alloys.   8-3: Equilibrium diagram for the iron-carbon system.   8-4: Manufacture of ferrous metals and alloys.   8-5: Shaping and fabrication of steel. 8-6: Heat treatment of steel.   8-7: Mechanical properties of steel. 8-8: Factors affecting the mechanical properties of steel.   8-9: Mechanical properties of cast iron.   8-10: Problems and questions.

9. NON-FERROUS METALS AND ALLOYS   349

9-1: Introduction.   9-2: Copper and its alloys.   9-3: Aluminum and its alloys.   9-4: Magnesium and its alloys.   9-5: Lead and its alloys. 9-6: Tin and its alloys.   9-7: Zinc and its alloys.   9-8: Nickel and its alloys.   9-9: Problems and questions.

10. NON-METALLIC MATERIALS   373

10-1: Introduction.   10-2: Wood.   10-3: Stone.   10-4: Clay products.   10-5: Cementing materials.   10-6: Concrete.   10-7: Plastics. 10-8: Miscellaneous materials.   10-9: Problems and questions.

Contents

Part Three: Materials Testing Machines and Strain Gages

11. MATERIALS TESTING MACHINES   417

11-1: Introduction. 11-2: Methods of application of loads. 11-3: Methods of load measurement. 11-4: Simple stress machines. 11-5: Combined stress machines. 11-6: Creep testing machines. 11-7: Fatigue testing machines. 11-8: Impact testing machines. 11-9: Machines for tests of structural and machine members. 11-10: Hardness testing machines.

12. STRAIN GAGES   467

12-1: Types of strain gages. 12-2: Mechanical strain gages. 12-3: Optical strain gages. 12-4: Electric strain gages.

NAME INDEX   483

SUBJECT INDEX   487

PART ONE

Mechanical Properties—General

Chapter 1

Static Properties in Tension and Compression

1-1. INTRODUCTION

An airliner crashes into a mountain, a train is wrecked, a bridge collapses, and the loss of life and cost of destruction may sometimes be the grave responsibility of the engineer. To avoid these possibilities, engineers must not only know how to determine the stresses and strains produced in structures and machines under a variety of possible external loading conditions, but they must also know how well the selected material of construction will resist these loading conditions. In our daily lives the importance of suitable materials of construction is constantly before us. We are sometimes reminded of the importance of suitable material properties when household equipment fails, when a road becomes rutted, when a building needs repair or is on fire, or when a train, ship, bus or plane departure is delayed due to some structural failure of the material.

A complete knowledge of the properties is not only required by the engineer to prevent failure of structures and machines but such knowledge is also required in a modern civilization and in a competitive world in order to utilize materials most economically. In recent years a scarcity of certain materials, and the more effective use of new substitute materials, has necessitated a more thorough consideration of material properties. The science of engineering materials has led to the development of many alloys having greatly improved resistance to various loading conditions. This has been necessitated by a number of modern changes, such as the increase in speed and size of various transportation units, the special material requirements in equipment used in the chemical industry, including resistance of materials to corrosion and temperature, and the ever changing advances in various kinds of machinery and household equipment. For many products made of nonmetallic materials as, for example, the tremendous volume of articles manufactured using plastics, a consideration of engineering properties may be very important. Our survival is dependent upon the development of military articles of war that require information on properties of materials subjected to most severe conditions of temperature, impact, corrosion and fatigue. These conditions become important in the design of gas and steam turbines for military ships, rockets, jet engines, and equipment for the construction of atomic weapons.

The development of materials required for the construction of the many machines, structures and products used in our modern civilization is provided by many kinds of engineers and scientists. Geologists explore the sources of materials, and they are aided by the mining engineer in obtaining the raw materials from the earth's surface. The metallurgist and chemist are concerned in part with the refinement of the raw materials and the development of new types of engineering materials. Industrial engineers deal with the processing and fabrication of the materials into their final form or into forms that can be directly used in constructions. The size and shape of a member used in a construction then becomes one of the responsibilities of the civil, mechanical or aeronautical engineer who, as structural or machine designer, has also the responsibility of selecting the most suitable material. In selecting the most suitable material and in the determination of the sizes of the required members, the designer may utilize the services of a materials engineer in order to consider completely the properties of the material to be used in a particular design.

Some factors that must be considered are the durability, appearance and cost of the material. The appearance may sometimes be important, as in the case of buildings, bridges, domestic equipment, or other machines and structures that are not hidden from view. The durability of a material refers to its resistance to destructive internal or external conditions. These destructive conditions may be chemical, electrical or mechanical in nature. Sometimes heat or light will be destructive. Conditions of variation in temperature, as alternate freezing and thawing, produce destruction of concrete. Wearing of machine parts due to contact of these parts, corrosion of metal structures and machines due to chemical action are important considerations in evaluating durability. The cost of a material may be a deciding factor in its selection; initial, maintenance, and replacement costs should all be considered.

In addition to cost, appearance and durability there are many properties of materials that must be considered in engineering design. These properties may be classified as physical or chemical. Physical properties include a number of properties such as mechanical, thermal, electrical and acoustical properties.

Mechanical properties are those properties concerned with the behavior of materials when subjected to loads. Mechanical properties represent the resistance of materials to loads and are expressed in terms of stress and strain or as a function of both stress and strain. These properties are obtained on samples of materials for various kinds of simple and combined stresses that may be encountered in structures and machines. Laboratory specimens used for obtaining mechanical properties give only approximate values of the material behavior in a structural or machine member. This is the case since the complete member may have properties quite different from the laboratory specimen. These differences may be caused by surface conditions not being the same, residual stresses in the member being greater than in the specimen, stress gradients and stress concentration being present in the member and not in the specimen, and dissimilarity in loading and other external conditions. In many cases the foregoing differences between laboratory specimen and fabricated member are not too great, and the properties based on laboratory specimen test data can be used for a design. In other instances the specimen tests are accompanied by comprehensive tests of the members of a structure or machine.

The values of the mechanical properties obtained from tests of samples do not represent the correct values of these properties, since the laboratory specimen is made up of a number of small units of the material with many flaws and cracks. It is perhaps for this reason that the tensile strength of a very fine glass fiber is found to be about three million pounds per square inch, while the strength of a glass rod is about one per cent of this value. In addition to the influence of cracks and flaws on the mechanical properties, the structure of materials has an important influence on properties.

The Structure of Materials. The structure of materials has been studied by use of the X-ray and more recently by the electron microscope. Although the engineer is primarily concerned with the behavior of specimens of materials, a basic knowledge will require a study of the smallest unit of matter. The structure of matter is not completely known, but theories have been presented to explain

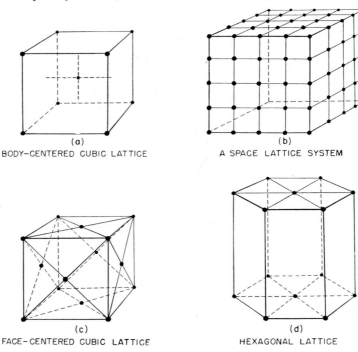

(a)
BODY-CENTERED CUBIC LATTICE

(b)
A SPACE LATTICE SYSTEM

(c)
FACE-CENTERED CUBIC LATTICE

(d)
HEXAGONAL LATTICE

Fig. 1-1. Patterns of atoms in space lattices.

the various physical and chemical phenomena. It is definitely understood, however, that both the chemical composition and the physical arrangement of the particles in a material influence its properties. The assumption is usually made that materials are composed of atoms, each consisting of a nucleus with a positive charge of electricity, with negatively charged electrons revolving about this nucleus. Chemical properties of a material are fixed by the number of electrons in each atom. The physical properties, on the other hand, are determined by the nature and arrangement of each atom. The geometric pattern produced in a crystal of a metal by the atoms is called a *space lattice*. The determination of the space lattice configuration is accomplished by using X-ray examinations. It is known that each metal, when allowed to cool, forms its own type of space lattice. There are fourteen known lattice configurations for metals but most of them crystallize according to only three types. They are the body-centered cubic, face-centered cubic, and the hexagonal lattice as shown in Fig. 1-1. For example, the atoms of chromium are arranged as a body-centered cubic lattice as shown in Fig. 1-1(a), the atoms being located at the corners of a cube about 3×10^{-8} cm. on a side with one atom in the center. A single crystal is made up of a number of space lattice patterns as indicated in Fig. 1-1(b).

Based on assumptions regarding the forces acting between atoms, physicists have determined the values of the cohesive strength in specific materials. These theoretical strengths, however, have been found to greatly exceed the actual strengths based on test specimens. This discrepancy may be due to the presence of various types of flaws and cracks in materials. It appears, however, that a thorough understanding of the properties of materials will ultimately require a complete study by the physicist of the atomic structure of matter.

Testing and Applications. The mechanical properties of materials are most commonly determined under static tension or static compression. Tension and compression tests are the most common because for most materials they are the simplest tests to make. The results obtained from tension and compression tests serve in determining the quality of the material even though members of machines or structures are rarely subjected to simple tension or simple compression.

The tension test is most commonly used with both ferrous and nonferrous metals, whereas for many non-metallic materials such as concrete, mortar, timber, and brick the compression test is ordinarily used. The materials most often tested under compression are those having a low tensile strength compared to the compressive strength and are the materials that are usually employed to resist compressive loadings.

Tension or compression tests are not only made to determine the properties of the material but are also used for tests of the fabricated member or manufactured product. For example, tests of wire, rods, tubing, reinforcing bars, fabrics, fibers, anchor chains, crane hooks, and eyebars are made in tension. In compression, tests are made for tile, masonry blocks, brick, building blocks, cast iron and concrete pipe, pedestals, wall sections, columns, and for concrete constructions of various kinds using concrete cylinders.

1-2. MECHANICAL PROPERTIES IN SIMPLE TENSION

Many machine and structural members are subjected to axial tensile loads as, for example, bridge members, guy wires, and bolts. The member AD in the truss shown in Fig. 1-2(a) is subjected to simple

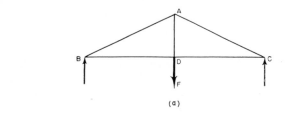

(a)

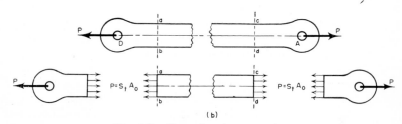

(b)

Fig. 1-2.   Stress in a truss member.

tension.   The load P produces an internal force or stress P on the member AD [Fig. 1-2(b)].   When the load is axially applied, the intensity of stress is uniformly distributed over the intermediate cross section of the member between A and D.   Then the internal force per initial unit area A_0, called the *stress* or unit stress is[1]

$$S_t = \frac{P}{A_0} \tag{1-1}$$

The stress S_t is usually measured in pounds per square inch since the load P is usually measured in pounds and the area A_0 in square inches.

[1] The word *stress* will be used in this book to denote *unit stress* or *stress intensity*.   In cases where the entire internal force is referred to, the term *total stress* will be used.

The tensile force P also produces a stretching or elongation of the member AD. For an intermediate length L_0 of the member AD, each section will be assumed to have a uniform stress distribution. It will also be assumed that a uniform stress distribution will produce a uniform elongation e_t. Actually, this uniform deformation or strain will be produced only if the material is assumed to have uniform resisting properties throughout. Then for intermediate sections of a tension specimen and for uniform elongation, the deformation may be expressed by the elongation per unit length, namely,

$$\epsilon_t = \frac{e_t}{L_0} \tag{1-2}$$

The deformation ϵ_t is usually expressed in inches per inch and is called the *unit strain* or *strain*.[2]

The determination of stress and strain for tension members in structures and machines is considered in courses on Strength of Materials and Stress Analysis, and hence in this book our chief concern will be with the mechanical properties of materials. In general, it is not economical to make tests on full-sized structural and machine members. Instead, samples or specimens of the material are tested. Common types of tension specimens are shown in Fig. 1-3.

A tension test is usually made in a Universal testing machine[3] which applies a tensile strain and load to the specimen by means of an electrically driven gear mechanism or by a hydraulic pump unit. Machines with either type of mechanism are provided with a means for measuring the applied load by the use of a lever weighing mechanism, a pendulum, or a hydraulic gage. In one of the standard tension tests, total strains are measured by means of a strain gage[3] for desired increments of load. Readings are not taken up to the rupture of the specimen since this information usually is not needed. The total strain is measured for an intermediate length L_0 of the specimen, called the gage length. Then if e_t is the total strain for any particular load, $\epsilon_t = e_t/L_0$ (eq. 1-2) can be used to define the average strain. From the original cross-sectional dimensions, the initial cross-sectional area A_0 is known, and for a particular load P

---

[2] The word *strain* will be used in this book to denote *unit strain*. In cases where the entire strain for the length L_0 is referred to, the term *total strain* will be used.

[3] Testing machines and strain gages are discussed in Part III.

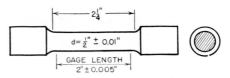

ROUND SPECIMEN WITH 2 IN. GAGE LENGTH
FOR DUCTILE METALS

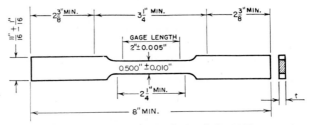

RECTANGULAR SPECIMEN WITH 2 IN. GAGE
LENGTH FOR PLATES AND SHEETS WITH
t=0.01 TO 0.50 IN. FOR DUCTILE METALS

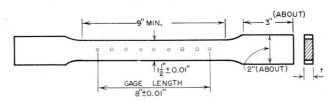

RECTANGULAR SPECIMEN WITH 8 IN. GAGE
LENGTH FOR PLATES AND SHEETS WITH
$t > \frac{3}{16}$ IN. FOR DUCTILE METALS

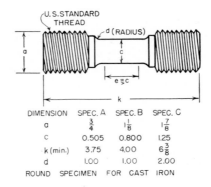

DIMENSION	SPEC. A	SPEC. B	SPEC. C
a	$\frac{3}{4}$	$1\frac{1}{8}$	$1\frac{7}{8}$
c	0.505	0.800	1.25
k (min.)	3.75	4.00	$6\frac{3}{8}$
d	1.00	1.00	2.00

ROUND SPECIMEN FOR CAST IRON

(a) SPECIMENS FOR METALS

Fig. 1-3. Common types of standard tension specimens.

10

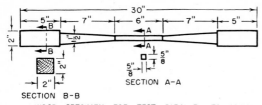

SECTION B-B

WOOD SPECIMEN FOR TEST PARALLEL TO GRAIN

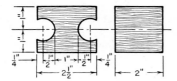

WOOD SPECIMEN FOR TEST PERPENDICULAR TO GRAIN

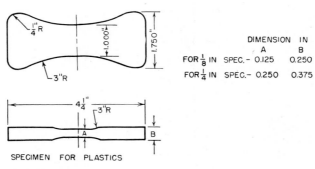

SPECIMEN FOR CEMENT MORTAR AND GYPSUM PRODUCTS

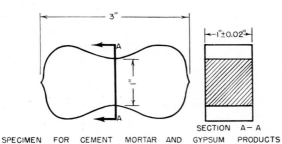

	DIMENSION	IN
	A	B
FOR $\frac{1}{8}$ IN SPEC.-	0.125	0.250
FOR $\frac{1}{4}$ IN SPEC.-	0.250	0.375

SPECIMEN FOR PLASTICS

(b) SPECIMENS FOR NON-METALS

Fig. 1-3 (Cont'd). Common types of standard tension specimens.

11

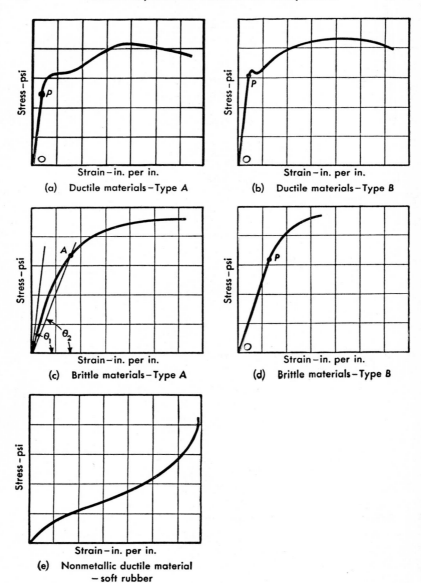

(a)   Ductile materials – Type A

(b)   Ductile materials – Type B

(c)   Brittle materials – Type A

(d)   Brittle materials – Type B

(e)   Nonmetallic ductile material
– soft rubber

Fig. 1-4.   Stress-strain diagrams in tension.

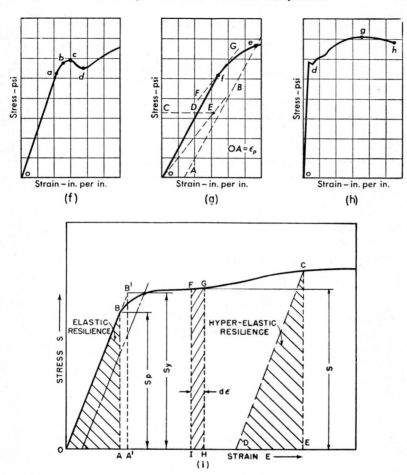

Fig. 1-4 (Cont'd).   Stress-strain diagrams in tension.

the stress $S_t = P/A_0$, as defined by eq. (1-1).   With the values of
the stress S_t and strain ϵ_t known for various loads, a diagram showing the relation between the stress and strain, called the *stress-strain
diagram,* can be plotted.   The values of the stress based on the original area A_0, and the strain based on the original gage length are
called the nominal stress and nominal strain or the *conventional* stress
and strain.   In the plastic range where the strains are large, the

actual or *true* stress and strain are not accurately indicated by using the original cross-sectional area and the original gage length.   The determination of true stress-strain relations is discussed in Article 1-6.   For most purposes, however, the nominal stress and strain as considered in this article are satisfactory.

Some common types of stress-strain diagrams for engineering materials are shown in Fig. 1-4.   A stress-strain diagram for a ductile material as, for example, a steel or aluminum alloy, is shown in Fig. 1-4(a).   A *ductile material* is one that has a large tensile strain before rupture, whereas a *brittle material* is one with a relatively small strain before rupture.   For metals, a tensile strain of 0.05 in. per in. at rupture has been used as the dividing value for strain to distinguish ductile and brittle materials.   For some steels, in place of the tensile stress-strain diagram of Fig. 1-4(a), one similar to Fig. 1-4(b) is obtained.   For brittle materials such as concrete and malleable cast iron, stress-strain relations as shown in Fig. 1-4(c) are representative.   However, for some non-metallic brittle materials as, for example, laminated plastics, a stress-strain diagram like the one shown in Fig. 1-4(d) is common.   Rubber is a highly ductile material and has a stress-strain diagram different from those for other materials.   For soft rubber, stress-strain relations as shown in Fig. 1-4(e) are obtained.

The stress-strain diagrams may be considerably changed, depending on the rate of application of the load and strain used.   With increase in rate of loading or strain, a raising of the stress-strain curve is produced.   The influence of strain rate on the stress-strain curve and the strength of the material is discussed in Chapter 5.

An examination of the stress-strain diagrams in Figs. 1-4 shows that there is considerable variation in the shape and character of the stress-strain relations for engineering materials.   However, for many materials such as those shown in Figs. 1-4(a), (b), and (d), an inspection of the initial stage of loading shows that the test data fall approximately on a straight line.   That is, for the straight-line part of the stress-strain diagram the stress is approximately proportional to the strain, or,

$$S_t = E_t \epsilon_t \quad \text{or} \quad E_t = S_t / \epsilon_t \qquad (1\text{-}3)$$

In eq. (1-3), E_t is the slope of the straight line OP and is the constant of proportionality or stress-strain ratio.   This value E_t is usu-

ally called the *modulus of elasticity* or *Young's modulus* in tension.
It is an experimental constant that varies in magnitude depending
on the material.   Since S_t is measured usually in psi and ϵ_t in in. per
in., the modulus E is measured in psi.   For example, approximate
values of the modulus for some of the common materials are: steel
alloys, 30×10^6 psi; aluminum alloys, 10.6×10^6 psi; magnesium
alloys, 6.5×10^6 psi; timber, 0.5×10^6 to 2.5×10^6 psi; and plastics,
0.02×10^6 to 3.5×10^6 psi.   Other values of E for a number of
engineering materials are given in Part II.

The stress-strain relation defined by eq. (1-3) was first recorded by
the English scientist Sir Robert Hooke in 1678, and is referred to as
Hooke's law.   For the analysis of stresses and strains in machine
and structural parts, Hooke's law represents a basic relationship
upon which much of the stress analysis theory has been based.

Figures 1-4(a), (b), and (d) show that the straight-line relation
between stress and strain as defined by eq. (1-3) is applicable only
up to certain values of stress represented by the point P.   The
stress corresponding to the point P is called the *proportional limit*.
Beyond the proportional limit the strain increases more rapidly.
For some materials as, for example, concrete and cast iron [Fig.
1-4(c)] or rubber [Fig. 1-4(e)], there is no proportional limit and the
stress-strain diagram is curved for the entire range of stress.   For
the relatively small stress values used in design, however, the stress-
strain relation up to the design stress value may be assumed to be
linear without serious error.

In place of the stress-strain relation of eq. (1-3), it is sometimes
convenient to express eq. (1-3) in terms of the measured quantities.
That is, placing the values of the stress S_t and strain ϵ_t from eqs.
(1-1) and (1-2) in eq. (1-3), the modulus of elasticity is

$$E_t = \frac{S_t}{\epsilon_t} = \frac{(P/A_0)}{(e_t/L_0)} = \frac{PL_0}{A_0 e_t} \tag{1-4}$$

Equation (1-4) defines the modulus of elasticity in tension in
terms of the axial tensile load P, the original gage length L_0, the
original cross-sectional area A_0, and the total tensile strain e_t.   In
using eq. (1-4) it should be realized that this relation is not valid for
P/A_0 values exceeding the range of proportionality between stress
and strain.

In addition to giving the relation between stress and strain, the

stress-strain diagram is useful in defining certain mechanical properties of the material. These properties, called strength, stiffness,
ductility, resilience, and toughness are defined in the following.

Strength. The ability of a material to resist loads without
yielding or fracturing is called strength. In the stress-strain diagrams of Figs. 1-4(a) and (b), two ranges of loading can be distinguished. First, an *elastic range* covering the region extending
from small strains to strain values slightly beyond the proportional
limit. Second, a *plastic range* beyond the proportional limit where,
for a given change in stress, the change in strain is much greater
than in the elastic range.

A simple physical explanation can be made for the transition from
a linear stress-strain region where the strains are small to a curved
stress-strain range. This can be done if a material is considered to
be made up of a number of crystals with planes of weakness oriented
in different directions. As the tensile load is applied to a specimen
the crystals most favorably oriented with respect to the slip direction will be the first ones to move along the slip planes of weakness.
As the load is increased, a larger percentage of the crystals will slip
for equal increments of load until the deformation due to slip is
sufficiently large to produce a measurable increase in increment of
strain for equal increments of loads. That is, the rate of strain to
stress increases and the curved stress-strain part of the stress-strain
curve is reached. With further increase in stress the strain increases
and becomes larger, or the slope of the stress-strain curve becomes
smaller.

Stress values at the transition from the elastic range to the plastic
range define the *elastic strength*, as distinguished from the stress
points in the plastic range which define *plastic strength*. *Elastic
strength* points are shown in Figs. 1-4(f) and (g). The *proportional
limit*, point a in Fig. 1-4(f), is an elastic strength point and is defined
as the stress value beyond which the stress is no longer proportional to the strain. An exact determination of the proportional
limit is difficult because of the gradual change from a straight line
to a curve at point a. Furthermore, the value obtained for the
proportional limit is influenced by the sensitivity of the strain gage
and by the scale used in plotting. Another elastic strength value
is the *elastic limit* represented by point b in Fig. 1-4(f). The elastic
limit is defined as the maximum stress that can be applied to a

material without producing a permanent set or deformation when the load is reduced. That is, if the specimen is stressed slightly above point b and then the load is removed, the gage length will not return to its original value and a permanent deformation will be produced. Although in some cases the proportional limit and the elastic limit coincide, the elastic limit may be on the curved portion of the stress-strain diagram slightly beyond the proportional limit, as shown in Fig. 1-4(f). The exact determination of the elastic limit is difficult and inconvenient. In view of the fact that neither the elastic limit nor the proportional limit can be used satisfactorily for defining the elastic strength, there have been a number of practical elastic strengths that have been used.

For materials with stress-strain relations as shown in Fig. 1-4(f), an upper yield point c and a lower yield point d can be used to give easily selected values that define the transition from the elastic to the plastic range. The upper and lower yield points represent stress values at which the material deforms appreciably with little change in stress. The reason for the existence of an upper and lower yield point is that when the upper yield point is reached, the number of crystals in which slip occurs is greatly increased and the movement of the head of the testing machine or the straining of the specimen is not sufficiently rapid to overcome the deformation of the specimen produced by slip. This explanation is confirmed by the fact that in impact loading conditions where the strain and load are rapidly applied, upper and lower yield points do not exist and the stress-strain curve is smooth. Tests have shown that the magnitude of the lower yield point is less influenced by test variables than is the upper yield point. For this reason the lower yield point is used to define the elastic strength for materials with stress-strain curves as shown in Fig. 1-4(f).

For materials having no upper or lower yield point, the beginning of yielding is defined as the stress at which the permanent set reaches a specified value. To determine the value of this stress, an offset strain $OA = \epsilon_p$ is measured from the origin O, as shown in Fig. 1-4(g), and a line AB is drawn through point A parallel to the straight-line part of the stress-strain diagram. The intersection of this line and the stress-strain curve defines a point e, and the stress corresponding to point e is called the *yield strength*, as determined by the offset method. The yield strength determined in the foregoing manner is that specified by the American Society for Testing Materials.[4] Commonly used values of ϵ_p are 0.002 and 0.0035 in. per in. Although the offset yield strength method gives a stress value that only approximately determines the beginning of yielding, it does give a means of accurately defining a point on the stress-strain curve. In this way a satisfactory basis for comparing yield strengths of materials is provided.

Sometimes for stress-strain curves such as in Fig. 1-4(g) the elastic strength is defined by *Johnson's Apparent Elastic Limit*. Point f in Fig. 1-4(g) represents Johnson's apparent elastic limit. It is a stress value for which the rate of change of strain with respect to stress is 50 per cent greater than at the initial straight part of the curve. In determining Johnson's apparent elastic limit, a horizontal line CE is drawn and a distance $DE = 0.5\ CD$ is measured to define point E. A line FG is then drawn parallel to OE and tangent to the stress-strain curve. The stress value corresponding to the point of tangency f is then the yield stress as determined by Johnson's apparent elastic limit. In place of $DE = 0.5\ CD$ a value of $DE = CD$ has sometimes been used. The elastic strength determined in this way is called the *useful limit point*. Both Johnson's apparent elastic limit and the useful limit point are undesirable because it is difficult to select accurately the exact point of tangency of the tangent to the stress-strain curve. For this reason the offset method is almost universally used for finding the elastic strength in tension. For some materials and tests, however, Johnson's apparent elastic limit is required by specification. Stresses such as the Johnson's apparent elastic limit or the useful limit point afford a means of defining approximately the limits of application of Hooke's law.

The strength of ductile materials in the plastic range in tension is usually defined by the *ultimate strength*. The ultimate strength represents the maximum stress reached as indicated by point g in Fig. 1-4(h). The maximum stress is then the maximum load divided by the original cross-sectional area. The ultimate strength in tension is often called the *tensile strength*. Occasionally the plastic strength is defined by the *breaking strength*. The breaking strength is represented by point h in Fig. 1-4(h) and has a value equal to the load at rupture divided by the original cross-sectional area. One reason

---

[4] The description of the method is given under *Determination of Yield Strength*, Standards of the American Society for Testing Materials.

that the breaking strength is infrequently used is that its determination may be subject to considerable error. For brittle materials like cast iron and concrete, with stress-strain curves as shown in Fig. 1-4(c), there is no choice in the procedure for defining strength—the shape of the curve makes it necessary to define strength by the ultimate stress.

In summarizing the various definitions of strength it is found that the customary standard practice in the case of ductile materials is to define elastic strength by the lower yield point if one exists, or to use the *A.S.T.M. offset yield strength* in cases where there is no yield point. For both brittle and ductile materials the standard practice is to define the plastic strength by the ultimate or tensile strength.

Although strength is the most commonly used mechanical property for the determination of dimensions in structural and machine design, other mechanical properties are also important. Those properties that measure the ability of materials to deform or to absorb energy are discussed below.

Stiffness. The mechanical property that defines the resistance of a material to deformation in the elastic range is called *stiffness*. Stiffness of a ductile material is measured by the modulus of elasticity E_t as defined by eq. (1-3). From this expression, a high value of $E_t = S_t/\epsilon_t$ means a small value of the strain ϵ_t for a given value of stress S_t. That is, a large value of the modulus of elasticity means that the relative deformation of the material is small. For example, steel alloys have modulus-of-elasticity values of 30×10^6 psi and aluminum alloys about 10×10^6 psi. Then, since $E_t = S_t/\epsilon_t$ for a given value of the stress, the deformation of a tension member made of an aluminum alloy would be three times that of a tension member made of a steel alloy. In other words the steel alloy is three times as stiff as the aluminum alloy.

In the design of some machine elements the property of stiffness is very important. For example, in some machine tools a slight deflection resulting from lack of stiffness in the loaded tool could result in inaccurate work.

For materials with non-linear stress-strain curves, as in Fig. 1-4(c), the modulus of elasticity is sometimes taken as the slope of the tangent to the stress-strain curve at zero stress. This modulus E_1 is called the *initial tangent modulus* and is equal to tan θ_1 where θ_1 is the angle shown in Fig. 1-4(c). For curved stress-strain diagrams, another method of measuring the stiffness is by using the *secant modulus* E_2. The secant modulus is obtained by joining the point of zero stress O and a specified stress value A. Then the secant modulus is E_2 = slope of OA = $\tan \theta_2$. The specified stress value is sometimes taken as the design stress. The slope of the stress-strain curve at some prescribed point is sometimes taken as the modulus. This latter value is called the *tangent modulus*.

Another material constant that is related to stiffness is *Poisson's ratio*. Poisson's ratio is defined as the ratio of the lateral strain to the axial strain in simple tension. Most metals have a value of this ratio between 0.25 and 0.35. A value of 0.30 is generally used for steel. Values of Poisson's ratio for rubber compounds approach 0.25 while concrete has a ratio of about 0.20.

NUMERICAL EXAMPLE. A solid steel cylinder of circular cross section has a diameter of 4 in. and a length of 20 in. It is subjected to a tensile load of 120,000 lb. If $E = 30 \times 10^6$ psi and Poisson's ratio $\mu = 0.30$, determine (a) the increase in length, (b) the decrease in diameter, and (c) the decrease in volume.

SOLUTION. The increase in the length e = the strain times the length = $\epsilon L = \dfrac{S}{E} L = (P/A_0)(L_0/E)$. Since the area

$$A_0 = \pi d^2/4 = \pi \times 4^2/4 = 4\pi,$$

$$e = \left(\frac{P}{A_0}\right)\left(\frac{L_0}{E}\right) = \left(\frac{120,000}{4\pi}\right)\left(\frac{20}{30 \times 10^6}\right) = 0.00637 \text{ in.}$$

The decrease in diameter is equal to the lateral strain times the diameter, or

$$\Delta d = (\mu\epsilon)d = \mu\left(\frac{S}{E}\right)d$$

$$= \mu\left(\frac{P}{A_0}\right)\left(\frac{d}{E}\right) = \frac{0.3 \times 120,000 \times 4}{4\pi \times 30 \times 10^6}$$

$$= 0.000383 \text{ in.}$$

For a unit volume of the cylinder 1 in. $\times$ 1 in. $\times$ 1 in., the change in volume is equal to the increase in volume in the direction of the load less the volume decrease produced by the lateral contraction. That is, the change in volume per unit volume is

$$\Delta v = \epsilon - 2\mu\epsilon = \epsilon(1 - 2\mu)$$
$$= (0.000318)(0.4) = 0.0001272 \text{ cu. in.}$$

The total change in volume equals the total volume times the unit volume change, or

$$V \, \Delta v = AL \, \Delta v = 4\pi \times 20 \times 0.0001272$$
$$= 0.032 \text{ cu. in.}$$

Ductility. The mechanical property that measures the deformation characteristics of a material in the plastic range is called the *ductility*. Ductility is usually measured by the *percentage elongation* of a tensile specimen at fracture, for a specified gage length. This does not give an accurate value of the deformation, since at and near fracture the unit strains at different points along the gage length differ. The percentage elongation, however, is an adequate measure of ductility for the purpose of comparing ductilities of various engineering materials. The ductility in tension is measured by the percentage elongation in a tensile specimen for a specified gage length, or

$$D_e = \left(\frac{L_b - L_0}{L_0}\right) 100 \tag{1-5}$$

In eq. (1-5), L_0 is the original gage length and L_b is the gage length after fracture. In Figs. 1-4(a), (b), (c), and (d) the strain corresponding to the end point multiplied by 100 is the percentage elongation. It should be noted that the percentage elongation is based on the original gage length and not the final gage length. In reporting ductility values it is important to specify the gage length used. This is necessary because a large part of the strain occurs in the "necked down" part of the gage length and the longer the gage length used the smaller will be the percentage elongation.

Ductility measurement by the percentage elongation is the standard method. For example, in the Standards of the American Society for Testing Materials, minimum requirements for ultimate strength, yield strength, and percentage elongation in tension are specified for many materials.

Ductility is sometimes measured by the *percentage reduction in cross-sectional area*, for the cross section where the specimen breaks. The percentage reduction in area is then defined by

$$D_a = \left(\frac{A_0 - A_b}{A_0}\right) 100 \tag{1-6}$$

In eq. (1-6), A_0 is the original cross-sectional area and A_b is the cross-sectional area where rupture occurred.

Ductility is an important property of materials. When ductility is high it is an insurance factor against excessive loads not considered in the design. In other words, high ductility permits considerable deformation before fracture in the event that unforeseen loads greater than the yield load occur. On the other hand, if ductility is small, a small overload may produce fracture.

Ductility is also an important property in various metal-processing operations such as drawing, rolling, die casting, and forging. For example, in forming a sheet by cold bending, the required curvature may not be achieved if the ductility is low. In such cases the sheet would fracture before it could be bent to the desired shape.

Resilience. The capacity of a material to absorb energy in the elastic range is designated as its *resilience*. Resilience is measured by the *modulus of resilience*, or the strain energy per unit volume required to stress the material in tension from zero stress to the proportional limit. For a unit volume, the work done in applying the stress to the proportional limit is the average force times the deformation, or

$$u_p = \left(\frac{S_p}{2}\right)(\epsilon_p) = \left(\frac{S_p}{2}\right)\left(\frac{S_p}{E_t}\right)$$

or
$$U_p = \frac{S_p{}^2}{2E_t} \tag{1-7a}$$

The units of the modulus u_p are in psi or in. lb. per cu. in.

In terms of the stress-strain diagram, the modulus of resilience u_p is designated by the area OAB in Fig. 1-4(i). The area OAB represents the modulus u_p since it is equal to

$$\frac{AB \times OA}{2} = \left(\frac{S_p}{2}\right)(\epsilon_p) = \frac{S_p{}^2}{2E_t},$$

or equal to the value of u_p as given by eq. (1-7a).

In many cases the proportional limit cannot be determined accurately and its approximate value as given by the yield stress is used. That is,

$$u_y = \frac{S_{yp}{}^2}{2E_t} \tag{1-7b}$$

Then the area $OA'B'$ is selected in place of OAB and the error is represented by the ratio of the area $ABB'A'$ to the area OAB.

The modulus of resilience also may be considered as the amount of energy that can be recovered when the stress is released from the proportional limit. If the load is released from the point C in the plastic range, the recovery diagram is approximately a straight line CD parallel to OB and the energy released is designated by the area CDE. This energy per unit volume of the material has been called the *hyperelastic resilience*.

High resilience is desired in members such as springs and in various automobile parts where it is necessary to resist high stresses and at the same time to deform appreciably. Since the modulus of resilience $u_p = S_p \epsilon_p / 2$, a material has a high resilience when both the proportional limit S_p and the strain ϵ_p are high. Or, from eqs. (1-7a) and (1-7b), the modulus of resilience is high when the proportional limit or yield stress is high and the modulus of elasticity is low.

Toughness. Toughness is the mechanical property that indicates the ability of a material to absorb energy in the plastic range. Toughness is sometimes measured by the *modulus of toughness*, which is the amount of strain energy per unit volume absorbed up to rupture. In Fig. 1-4(i) the work done per unit volume in going from F to G is $S\,d\epsilon$. The total strain energy to rupture is $\int_0^{\epsilon_b} S\,d\epsilon$; or since $S\,d\epsilon$ is the shaded area $FGHI$, then $\int_0^{\epsilon_b} S\,d\epsilon$ is the area under the stress-strain diagram to rupture. An approximate but more convenient measure of toughness for ductile materials is called the *toughness index number*, or *merit number*, and is equal to the ultimate stress times the strain at rupture, or

$$T_0 = S_u \epsilon_b \quad \text{or} \quad T_0 = \frac{P_u e_b}{A_0 L_0} \tag{1-8}$$

The area defined by eq. (1-8) is approximately the area under the stress-strain diagram to rupture and is always somewhat larger than this area.

Sometimes toughness is determined by multiplying the average of the yield stress and ultimate stress by the strain at failure. In other words, the area of the stress-strain diagram is assumed to be the same as the area of a rectangle with a base equal to the unit strain at failure and with an altitude equal to the average of the yield stress and ultimate stress.

Whether the actual area under the stress-strain diagram is used or the foregoing approximate areas are assumed as measures of the toughness, the main consideration is that the same procedure should be used in comparing the toughness of ductile materials. Also, the exact value of the toughness is not correctly represented by the area under the stress-strain curve since, in the plastic range, the changes in dimensions during loading introduce errors, and the stress and strain as calculated by eqs. (1-1) and (1-2) are incorrect. In other words, the true stress and strain based on the actual dimensions of the specimens, rather than the original dimensions, should be used. For brittle materials such as cast iron, the modulus of toughness is some-

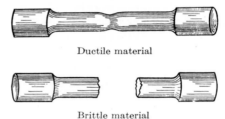

Ductile material

Brittle material

Fig. 1-5(a).   Failure of materials in tension.

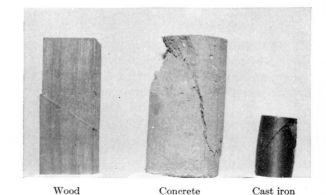

| | Wood | Concrete | Cast iron |

Ductile material   Brittle materials

Fig. 1-5(b).   Failure of materials in compression.   (Courtesy P. B. Kapp, Pennsylvania State College.)

times determined by assuming that the area under the stress-strain curve is equal to the area of a parabola. That is, the area is taken as two-thirds the ultimate stress times the strain at rupture. Since the toughness is equal to a stress times a strain as given in eq. (1-8), the units for toughness are in psi or in. lb. per cu. in.

Toughness is desirable in parts subjected to shock or impact as, for example, axles, gears, and automobile frames. As indicated by eq. (1-8), a high value of toughness occurs in materials with large values of the ultimate strength and large values of the strain at fracture or percentage elongation. That is, toughness depends upon both the ultimate strength and ductility of the material.

The localized necking of a tensile specimen near fracture in ductile materials means that the strain at fracture varies considerably with the gage length over which it is measured. This is indicated in Fig. 1-5(a), which shows fractured tensile specimens. That is, the strain at fracture or percentage elongation becomes greater with shorter gage lengths. It is important, therefore, to specify the gage length used when reporting a toughness value.

An examination of the mode of fracture in specimens subjected to tensile loads is of significance in identifying the type and kind of material. For example, materials that are weaker in shear than in tension are ductile materials; whereas those that are relatively weak in tension are brittle materials. Figure 1-5(a) shows fractured specimens of ductile and brittle metals subjected to tension. The fracture of the ductile specimens is characterized by the "cone-and-cup" type fracture in which the fractured surface makes an angle of approximately 45° with the axis of the specimen, indicating the influence of the shear stresses on the failure and fracture of the material. The brittle type of fracture in tension, as in Fig. 1-5(a), shows failure occurring on a plane perpendicular to the direction of the applied load or on the plane of maximum tensile stress.

Sometimes impact tests are made in which the work required to rupture a specimen is determined from the energy of a falling weight or pendulum. It should be noted that these tests do not give measurements of toughness as defined in the foregoing. The tests are of value in indicating the effects of variations in materials or in measuring the sensitivity of the material to notches. Mechanical properties of materials for impact loadings are discussed in Chapter 5.

A comparison of the mechanical properties of materials is facilitated by a comparison of the stress-strain diagrams in tension. Figure 1-6 shows tension stress-strain diagrams for a number of important engineering materials. These diagrams show the variations in the strength, stiffness, and ductility in graphical form. Figure 1-6

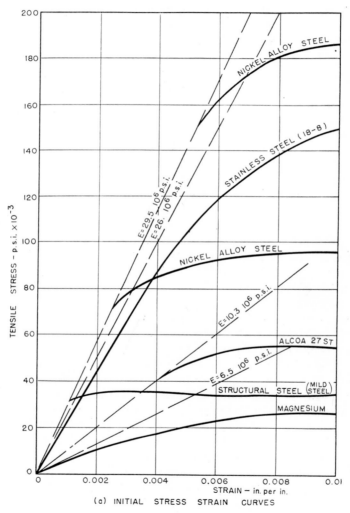

Fig. 1-6.   Stress-strain curves in tension.

shows that there is a wide range in values for the ultimate and yield strengths and the ductility, but fewer possible values for the modulus of elasticity. For example, although the strengths of steel vary over a wide range, the modulus of elasticity of all steels is about 30×10^6 psi. For aluminum alloys also, the strengths vary considerably, but the modulus of elasticity remains about 10.6×10^6 psi. In Part II, tables of values for mechanical properties of common engineering materials are given.

NUMERICAL EXAMPLE. *Determination of Elastic Mechanical Properties for Simple Tension.* In a standard tension test of steel, on a specimen with a gage length of 2 in. and a diameter of 0.505 in., the load at the proportional limit was 8000 lb. and the load at the lower yield point was 8200 lb. The total strain for the 2-in. gage

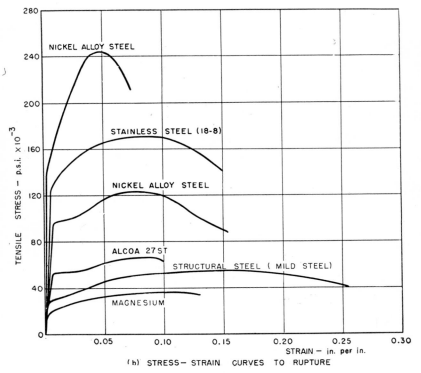

Fig. 1-6 (Cont'd).   Stress-strain curves in tension.

length at a load of 4000 lb. was 0.00135 in.   The straight-line (elastic) part of the stress-strain curve passed through the point of zero stress and strain.   Determine:

(a) the proportional limit,
(b) the yield stress,
(c) the modulus of elasticity,
(d) the modulus of resilience based on the proportional limit,
(e) the percentage error in the modulus of elastic resilience, using the yield stress.

SOLUTION.   The original cross-sectional area of a specimen 0.505 in. in diameter is

$$A_0 = \frac{\pi(0.505)^2}{4} = 0.20 \text{ sq. in.}$$

Then the proportional limit $S_p = P/A_0 = 8000/0.20 = 40,000$ psi. The yield stress $S_{yp} = P/A_0 = 8200/0.20 = 41,000$ psi.   By eq. (1-4) the modulus of elasticity in tension is

$$E_t = \frac{S_t}{\epsilon_t} = \frac{P/A_0}{e_t/L_0} = \frac{4000/0.20}{0.00135/2} = 29.6 \times 10^6 \text{ psi}$$

The modulus of resilience based on the proportional limit is, by eq. (1-7a),

$$u_p = \frac{S_p{}^2}{2E_t} = \frac{(40,000)^2}{2 \times 29.6 \times 10^6} = 27.0 \text{ in. lb. per cu. in.}$$

The modulus of resilience based on the yield stress is

$$u_y = \frac{S_{yp}{}^2}{2E_t} = \frac{(41,000)^2}{2 \times 29.6 \times 10^6} = 28.4 \text{ in. lb. per cu. in.}$$

Then the percentage error in the value of the modulus of resilience, using the yield stress, is

$$\frac{28.4 - 27.0}{27.0} \times 100 = 5.2\%$$

NUMERICAL EXAMPLE. *Determination of Plastic Mechanical Properties for Simple Tension.*   A steel tension specimen with an original diameter of 0.505 in. and gage length of 8 in. was found to have an ultimate tensile load of 14,200 lb. and a breaking load of 10,000 lb.   The gage length at rupture was 10.3 in. and the diameter at the ruptured cross section was 0.38 in.   Determine:

(a) the ultimate stress,
(b) the breaking stress,
(c) the percentage elongation in 8 in.,
(d) the percentage reduction in area, ∽
(e) the toughness index number.

SOLUTION. The ultimate stress is

$$S_u = P/A_0 = 14{,}200/0.20 = 71{,}000 \text{ psi}$$

The breaking stress is

$$S_b = P/A_0 = 10{,}000/0.20 = 50{,}000 \text{ psi.}$$

To determine the percentage elongation, eq. (1-5) is used, or

$$D_e = \left(\frac{L_b - L_0}{L_0}\right) 100 = \frac{10.3 - 8.0}{8.0} \times 100 = 28.8\%$$

The percentage reduction in area is calculated by using eq. (1-6) or, since the final area $A_b = \pi \times (0.38)^2/4 = 0.114$ sq. in., the percentage reduction in area is

$$D_a = \left(\frac{A_0 - A_b}{A_0}\right) 100 = \frac{0.20 - 0.114}{0.20} \times 100 = 43\%$$

The toughness index number is determined by eq. (1-8), or

$$T_0 = S_u \epsilon_b = 71{,}000 \times \frac{10.3 - 8.0}{8.0} = 20{,}400 \text{ in. lb. per cu. in.}$$

NUMERICAL EXAMPLE. *Mechanical Properties of a Brittle Material in Simple Tension.* In a tension test for cast iron using a specimen with a 2-in. gage length and a diameter of 0.505 in., the ultimate and fracture load was 5400 lb. The elongation at rupture was 0.005 in. Determine:

(a) the ultimate stress,
(b) the per cent elongation,
(c) the modulus of toughness, assuming the stress-strain curve to be a parabola,
(d) the secant modulus based on a stress of 5000 psi. The strain at this stress was 0.0002 in. per in.

SOLUTION. The ultimate stress is

$$S_u = P/A_0 = 5400/0.20 = 27{,}000 \text{ psi.}$$

Since the change in length is 0.005 in. for a gage length of 2 in., the percentage elongation is

$$\left(\frac{L_b - L_0}{L_0}\right) 100 = \frac{0.005}{2} \times 100 = 0.25\%$$

The modulus of toughness, assuming the stress-strain curve to be a parabola, equals $\frac{2}{3}(S_u \epsilon_b) = \frac{2}{3}(27,000)(0.0025) = 45.0$ in. lb. per cu. in.   The secant modulus for a stress of 5000 psi and strain of 0.002 in. per in. is $E = S/\epsilon = 5000/0.0002 = 25 \times 10^6$ psi.

NUMERICAL EXAMPLE.   *Comparison of Mechanical Properties in Simple Tension.*   Three tension members made of a steel alloy, an aluminum alloy, and a plastic are each 5 ft. long and 2 sq. in. in area. *Given:*

Proportional limits—40,000, 46,000, and 35,000 psi respectively.
Ultimate stresses—70,000, 68,000, and 40,000 psi respectively.
Moduli of elasticity—30 × 10⁶, 10.6 × 10⁶, and 1.5 × 10⁶ psi respectively.
Strain at fracture—0.25, 0.18, and 0.04 in. per in. respectively.

Compare the mechanical properties of the three materials, relative to the steel alloy, by obtaining the ratio of appropriate values for each property.
Also determine the total strains at the proportional limits and the ultimate loads.

SOLUTION.   Ratios of proportional limits are

$$R_a = \frac{46,000}{40,000} = 1.15 \quad \text{and} \quad R_p = \frac{35,000}{40,000} = 0.88$$

Similarly, the ratios of the ultimate stresses are

$$R_a = \frac{68,000}{70,000} = 0.97 \quad \text{and} \quad R_p = \frac{40,000}{70,000} = 0.57$$

The stiffness ratios are

$$R_a = \frac{10.6}{30} = 0.35 \quad \text{and} \quad R_p = \frac{1.5}{30} = 0.05$$

The ratios of the resiliences are

$$R_a = \left(\frac{S_a}{S_o}\right)^2 \left(\frac{E_s}{E_a}\right) = 3.79$$

and
$$R_p = \left(\frac{S_p}{S_s}\right)^2 \left(\frac{E_s}{E_p}\right) = 15.5.$$

The toughness index ratios are

$$R_a = \frac{S_a' \epsilon_a}{S_s' \epsilon_s} = \frac{68,000}{70,000} \times \frac{0.18}{0.25} = 0.70$$

and
$$R_p = \frac{S_p' \epsilon_b}{S_s' \epsilon_s} = \frac{40,000}{70,000} \times \frac{0.04}{0.25} = 0.09$$

The strains at the proportional limit for each of the steel, aluminum, and plastic members are, respectively,

$$e_s = \epsilon L_0 = \frac{S}{E} L_0 = \frac{40,000}{30 \times 10^6} \times 60 = 0.080 \text{ in.}$$

$$e_a = \epsilon L_0 = \frac{S}{E} L_0 = \frac{46,000}{10.6 \times 10^6} \times 60 = 0.26 \text{ in.}$$

$$e_p = \epsilon L_0 = \frac{S}{E} L_0 = \frac{35,000}{1.5 \times 10^6} \times 60 = 1.40 \text{ in.}$$

The ultimate loads for each material are, respectively,
$$P_s = S_u A_0 = 70,000 \times 2 = 140,000 \text{ lb.}$$
$$P_a = S_u A_0 = 68,000 \times 2 = 136,000 \text{ lb.}$$
$$P_p = S_u A_0 = 40,000 \times 2 = 80,000 \text{ lb.}$$

1-3. MECHANICAL PROPERTIES IN SIMPLE COMPRESSION

Simple compression stresses are similar to tensile stresses except that the direction of the stresses is reversed. There are many examples of members subjected to compressive stresses in structures made of concrete, building brick, and stone. Cast iron is commonly used for members subjected to essentially compressive stresses such as bearing plates for machines. Because of their application to members subjected mainly to compressive stresses, wood, concrete, and cast iron are the main materials tested in compression. The results of compression tests are plotted in a manner similar to tension tests. Most of the remarks made regarding the tension test and mechanical properties in tension apply to compression. The main exception is that for ductile materials such as steel, the ultimate compressive strength cannot be determined, since the increase in load in the plastic range increases the cross-sectional area and reduces the true stress. It becomes difficult, therefore, to fracture specimens of ductile material since the lateral expansion ultimately produces a flat disk. In cases where the specimen of ductile material can be fractured, the results are meaningless because the area has been greatly changed. A deformed specimen of a ductile material in compression is shown in Fig. 1-5(b).

For failure of brittle materials under compression, lateral spreading out as for ductile materials does not result, but failure occurs by shear and sliding on an inclined plane [Fig. 1-5(b)]. A shear-type failure takes place since a brittle material is weaker in shear than in compression. Figure 1-5(b) shows typical compression fractures for various engineering materials.

The modulus of elasticity and yield strengths for many structural materials are approximately equal in tension and compression, although there are several exceptions. For brittle materials, where the ultimate strength in compression can be determined, the strengths in tension and compression may differ greatly. For example, the ultimate strength in compression for concrete is about ten times the ultimate strength in tension.

There are certain limitations in the compression test that affect the accuracy of the results obtained. These are:

1. The difficulty of obtaining uniformly distributed stresses due to the fact that the axial load is not truly axial.

2. The unstable character of the loading compared to tensile loading tends to produce bending stresses. Accidental irregularities in alignment within the specimen are accentuated as the loading proceeds.

3. As a result of the lateral expansion of the specimen, friction is produced between the bearing plates of the testing machine and the ends of the specimen. This results in lateral stresses and a uniformly stressed simple compression specimen no longer exists.

4. To obtain the correct degree of stability, a relatively short specimen is required in some cases. With short specimens, end restraints produce inaccuracies. If, on the other hand, the specimen becomes too long, there is danger of failure by buckling. Compression tests of ductile materials show that the shape of the stress-strain diagram in compression depends considerably on the relative dimensions of the specimen. It is found, for example, that the effect of friction at the ends becomes more pronounced as the height of the specimen decreases.

Compression Specimens. In order to produce a uniform stress in a compression test a specimen of circular cross section is preferred. Square or rectangular specimens are sometimes used, since for some materials such as tile it is not feasible to cut out round specimens. The selected ratio of the length to diameter in a compression specimen is a compromise between several undesirable conditions. With increased length of specimen there is a tendency toward bending and, hence, nonuniform stress distribution. A height-diameter ratio of ten has been suggested as a practical upper limit. As the length of the specimen is decreased, the frictional restraint at the ends becomes relatively important. Furthermore, for specimen lengths less than about 1.5 times the diameter, the diagonal planes of failure intersect the end planes and thereby increase the apparent strength. A length-to-diameter ratio of 2 is commonly used. To obtain the desired precision, a compressometer

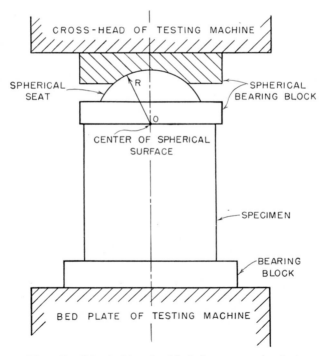

Fig. 1-7. Spherical bearing block for compression test.

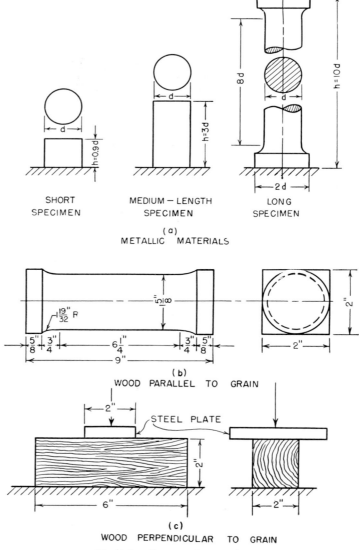

Fig. 1-8.   Compression specimens.

with a long gage length is sometimes necessary. The size of specimen selected depends upon the type of material, the type of measurements to be made, and the testing apparatus available. For tests in which only the ultimate strength is desired, a relatively short specimen can be used. For tests in which strains are measured, the gage length should be shorter than the specimen length—preferably by at least the diameter of the specimen. The ends of the specimen should be flat and perpendicular to the axis of the specimen so that the compressive stress is uniformly distributed. Adjustable bearing devices are used to insure uniformly distributed stresses by overcoming lack of parallelism between the head of the machine and the end of the specimen. Figure 1-7 shows such a device consisting of a spherical bearing block. The detailed requirements for this bearing block are given in the A.S.T.M. Standards, designation C-109. In using spherical bearing blocks it is essential that the specimen be carefully centered with respect to the center of the bearing block, thereby eliminating eccentric loading.

Standard Test Specimens. For compression tests of metallic materials the A.S.T.M. Standards, designation E-9, recommends the specimens shown in Fig. 1-8(a). The short specimens are intended to be used with bearing metals, the medium-length specimens for general use, and the long specimens for tests to determine the modulus of elasticity.

Standard specimens for concrete are cylinders of height equal to twice the diameter. Depending upon the size of the aggregate, the cylinders are made from 3 to 18 in. in diameter. In England and Europe, 6-in. cubes are commonly used for tests of concrete. For mortars, the A.S.T.M. Standards specify 2-in. cubes.

For compression tests of wood parallel to the grain, either a $2 \times 2 \times 8$-in. rectangular prism or a specimen of cylindrical form is used, as shown in Fig. 1-8(b). Compression tests perpendicular to the grain are made as shown in Fig. 1-8(c), with the load applied through a metal bearing plate.

The A.S.T.M. Standards also give types of compression specimens for materials such as drain tile, structural clay tile, sewer pipe, refractory brick, vulcanized rubber, molded insulating materials, timber for structural sizes, and building stone.

A stress-strain curve for compression of a cast-iron specimen is shown in Fig. 1-9.

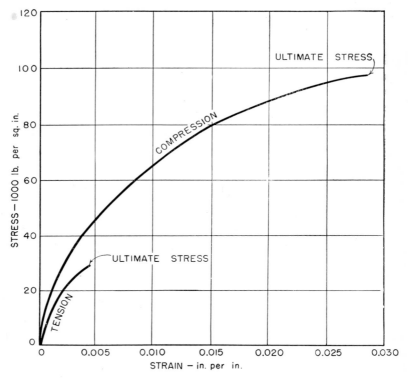

Fig. 1-9.   Stress-strain curve for a cast iron in tension and compression.

NUMERICAL EXAMPLE.   A concrete cylinder 8 in. in diameter and with a gage length of 10 in. is used in a compression test to obtain the stress-strain diagram in compression.   The specimen failed at a load of 58,000 lb. and a total strain of 0.0186 in.   Assume that the ultimate and fracture loads are equal.   Determine:

(a) the ultimate compression strength,
(b) the average percentage contraction at fracture,
(c) the modulus of toughness, assuming a parabolic stress-strain curve,
(d) the secant modulus for a stress of 650 psi if the total strain for this stress is 0.036 in.

SOLUTION. The cross-sectional area of the specimen is

$$A_0 = \frac{\pi d^2}{4} = \frac{\pi \times 64}{4} = 50.3 \text{ sq. in.}$$

Then the compressive ultimate strength is

$$S_c = \frac{P}{A_0} = \frac{58,000}{50.3} = 1150 \text{ psi}$$

The percentage contraction at fracture is

$$C = \left(\frac{e_c}{L_0}\right)(100) = \frac{0.0186}{10} \times 100 = 0.19\%$$

The modulus of toughness equals the area under the stress-strain diagram and is, approximately,

$$T = \tfrac{2}{3}S_c\epsilon_c = \tfrac{2}{3} \times 1150 \times 0.00186 = 1.43 \text{ in. lb. per cu. in.}$$

For a stress of 650 psi the secant modulus is

$$E = \frac{S_c}{\epsilon_c} = \frac{650}{(0.036/10)} = 1.81 \times 10^5 \text{ psi}$$

NUMERICAL EXAMPLE. A cast-iron bearing plate 10 in. by 10 in. by 2.5 in. thick is subjected to a uniformly distributed compressive load. Determine the load to produce fracture and the contraction of the plate at fracture if the compressive strength of the cast iron is 35,000 psi and the strain at fracture is 0.002 in. per in. What is the total strain energy corresponding to fracture if the stress-strain diagram is assumed to be parabolic?

SOLUTION. The compressive load to produce fracture of the bearing plate is

$$P = S_c A_0 = 35,000(10 \times 10) = 3.5 \times 10^6 \text{ lb.}$$

The total contraction of the plate at fracture would be

$$e_c = \epsilon_c L_0 = 0.002 \times 2.5 = 0.005 \text{ in.}$$

The total strain energy corresponding to fracture is equal to

$$\tfrac{2}{3}S_c\epsilon_c \times \text{(volume of the plate)} = \tfrac{2}{3}S_c\epsilon_c(A_0 L_0)$$

$$= \tfrac{2}{3} \times 35,000 \times 0.002 \times 100 \times 2.5 = 11,670 \text{ in. lb.}$$

1-4. DESIGN OR WORKING STRESSES

Design specifications for structural and machine parts specify, among other values, the design or working stress values in simple tension and compression. The values of these design stresses are based on either the ultimate or the yield strength of the material. In most design specifications for ductile materials the design stress is selected so that it is less than the yield stress. The design stress is equal to the yield stress or ultimate stress in tension or compression divided by a number called the *factor of safety*. That is, the design or working stress is

$$S_w = \frac{S_{yp}}{N_y} \quad \text{or} \quad S_w = \frac{S_u}{N_u} \tag{1-9}$$

where N_y and N_u are the factors of safety, S_{yp} is the yield stress, and S_u is the ultimate stress.

The design stress for ductile materials is usually based on the yield stress as given by the first of eqs. (1-9). For brittle materials there is no choice, and the ultimate stress is the basis for the design stress as given by the second of eqs. (1-9). The determination of the values of the factor of safety is an important matter, for it is desirable that the value be neither too high nor too low. If the value of the factor of safety is too high, the design stress is too low and the structural or machine part is larger than necessary and, hence, uneconomical. If, on the other hand, the value of the factor of safety is selected too low, the design stress is too high and the member becomes unsafe. In selecting the value of the factor of safety it is desirable to separate the effects of the various factors that influence it.

Selection of Factor of Safety. Selection of the factor of safety N involves many considerations. Past performance of a material or machine part must still play an important part in selection. It is important, however, to make as rational a determination of N as possible. For this purpose a separation of the various factors influencing N is desirable. If N_1, N_2, N_3, $\cdots N_n$ denote the quantitative value of each factor. then the over-all factor of safety can be expressed by

$$N = N_1 \times N_2 \times N_3 \times \cdots N_n \tag{1-10}$$

A rational estimate, leading to a more accurate value of N, involves a consideration of the following factors:

(1) *Material Factors* N_1, N_2, *and* N_3. These consider the possible variation in the strength S as well as the differences between the laboratory test on which S is based and the service conditions. The possible variation in the strength depends upon the process of manufacture, the thoroughness of testing and inspection, and the character of the material itself. This possible nonuniformity can, however, be approximately predicted and a rational allowance for the factor of safety estimated. If the expected variation in strength is $k_v S$, the material factor N_1 is

$$N_1 = \frac{S + k_v S}{S} = 1 + k_v \tag{a}$$

As considered later, the strength S may have various possible values depending upon the combinations of stress present and the type of loading applied. For fatigue stress conditions where flaws might be present, a large value of k_v should be used because of the progressive nature of fatigue failures.

The material factor N_2, which allows for the difference in behavior between the laboratory strength and the strength in the prototype, is a difficult one to estimate. If the strength S considers the type of load and the "combined stress effect," the factor N_2 may be modified. In machine design the weakest point in the member is considered and adjacent parts are not stressed to their maximum possible values. With ductile materials and static loads this condition prevents failure in many cases. For example, the yielding at a rivet hole under static conditions is not serious since a redistribution of stress with increase in stress values at the lower stressed points, and decrease in stress at the higher stressed points, is produced. If stress concentration is not considered in determining the strength, an allowance must be made for this. This allowance can sometimes be based on laboratory tests. If the foregoing considerations are provided for by the factor k_c, the material factor N_2 is

$$N_2 = \frac{S + k_c S}{S} = 1 + k_c \tag{b}$$

A third material factor N_3 is applicable to static loads and ductile materials only. This value attempts to provide for the variation in the ratio of the yield tensile strength S_{yp} to the ultimate tensile strength S_u of ductile materials. An approximate method that allows for this is to introduce the factor N_3 as given by the equation

$$N_3 = \frac{S_{yp} - (S_u - S_{yp})}{S_{yp}} = 2 - k_u \tag{c}$$

where $k_u = S_u / S_{yp}$.

(2) *Load Factor* N_4. The actual load on a machine or structural member will not be that assumed in a design since the magnitude, distribution, and

type of loading can usually be only roughly approximated. In many problems, however, an estimate can be made of the possible load variation from that assumed. In cases where impact loads are present, an equivalent static load can be determined. Influences of possible variations in load distributions from those assumed can also be estimated. Stress variations corresponding to these possible load variations can then be found. If, for the critical point, this stress variation is $k_l S_w$, the factor N_4 is

$$N_4 = \frac{S_w + k_l S_w}{S_w} = 1 + k_l \qquad (d)$$

where k_l is the stress variation due to the possible load changes divided by the working stress.

(3) *Stress Analysis Factor N_5.* Many problems arise in design for which the stress analysis is inadequate or, at best, approximate. Methods used for stress determination are based on assumptions regarding the material behavior and load effects. Even under conditions where static loads and Hooke's law can be assumed, the theory of elasticity has its limitations and an approximate stress value is determined. When conditions of vibration or instability occur, with possible failure by buckling, the designer must either analyze these effects or provide for them in the factor of safety. In many problems the stress analysis factor of safety N_5 can be obtained accurately by improving the method of stress analysis used. This is done either by using a more accurate theory such as the theory of elasticity or an experimental method of stress analysis. The photoelastic, strain rosette, and stress-coat methods have been of great help in this respect. In a particular design, if the percentage error in stress based on an experimental or improved theoretical method is $100\,k_a$, the stress analysis factor becomes

$$N_5 = \frac{S + k_a S}{S} = 1 + k_a \qquad (e)$$

(4) *Fabrication Factor N_6.* For machine parts in which tolerances in dimensions are provided for—and also where this is not the case—the resulting dimensions are not those assumed in determining the stress. The error can be taken care of by selecting an appropriate fabrication factor. More important than these variations in dimensions are the changes in the properties of the material and the initial stresses sometimes produced by the method of fabrication adopted. Operations such as punching of plates for rivets or the bending and hammering of parts into a required shape weaken the material and introduce initial stresses. Sometimes the heat treatment applied to the test specimen has a different effect from what it would have if applied to the larger machine part. In large welded constructions, as in ships where stress-relieving cannot be applied, high shrinkage stresses occur.

In some instances the effects of fabrication methods can be controlled and the influences estimated with reasonable accuracy. If the fabrication factor is k_f, the fabrication factor of safety N_6 becomes

$$N_6 = \frac{S_w + k_f S_w}{S_w} = 1 + k_f \tag{f}$$

The value of N_6 is based on the working stress S_w since the value of k_f can best be determined if based on this stress.

(5) *Time Factor* N_7. This factor includes the influence of external conditions in modifying the material properties. Deterioration of a material with time as, for example, the corrosion of steel or decay of wood by moisture will modify the factor of safety used. In this respect the estimated life of the machine and provision for maintenance will greatly influence the value of the time factor N_7. Another time factor, sometimes provided for in the determination of S, is the influence of creep at both normal and elevated temperatures. Creep, which is a continued plastic deformation with time, occurs in lead and other alloys at normal temperatures. At elevated temperatures, as found in equipment used in the oil refining, turbine, and automotive industries, creep has an important influence in the selection of working stresses. Some data to evaluate the time factor N_7 can be obtained, based on service conditions and mechanical tests made on parts that have been in operation for a number of years. Laboratory tests have been useful in some problems in estimating the influence of time effects on strength. Many such studies have been made as, for example, the influence of corrosion on the fatigue strength of steel. Based on the foregoing considerations, a time factor N_7 will be selected in terms of the correction factor k_t, where

$$N_7 = \frac{S + k_t S}{S} = 1 + k_t \tag{g}$$

(6) *Failure Factor* N_8. In determining the factor of safety, the consequences in the event of failure are an extremely important consideration. If failure would result in loss of life, a higher factor of safety should naturally be used. When failure would result in loss of valuable property or serious interruption of production processes, an ample factor of safety should be provided. If, on the other hand, only the operation of an inexpensive machine part is temporarily interrupted, the failure factor k_e can be small. Sometimes certain precautions can be taken to eliminate serious consequences if failure occurs. Spiral-steel reinforcement in concrete columns is an example of this kind of insurance against a disastrous type of failure. For ductile materials and static loads, yielding accompanied by redistribution of stresses also gives an insurance against serious failure.

In many machines it will be necessary to determine the failure factor of safety N_8 largely from the information available on previous failures and from experience with similar constructions. In any event, the factor becomes

$$N_8 = \frac{S_w + k_e S_w}{S_w} = 1 + k_e \tag{h}$$

Other factors may be encountered in special cases—factors not included in the above discussion. For these situations the factor N_8 can be modified to provide for unusual conditions.

An inspection of the foregoing discussion shows that the resultant factor of safety N becomes

$$N = N_1 \times N_2 \times N_3 \times N_4 \times N_5 \times N_6 \times N_7 \times N_8 \tag{1-10a}$$

Substituting values of N_1 to N_8 from eqs. (a) to (h) in eq. (1-10a),

$$N = (1 + k_v)(1 + k_c)(2 - k_u)(1 + k_l)(1 + k_a)$$
$$\times (1 + k_f)(1 + k_t)(1 + k_e) \tag{1-10b}$$

where k_v = material variation factor
$\quad k_c$ = material stress factor
$\quad k_u$ = ratio of ultimate strength to yield strength in static tension
$\quad k_l$ = load variation factor
$\quad k_a$ = stress analysis factor
$\quad k_f$ = fabrication factor
$\quad k_t$ = time factor
and $\quad k_e$ = failure factor

There will, of course, still be a number of uncertainties in determining the factor of safety by using an equation similar to eq. (1-10b). A rational method has been outlined, however, which should lead to a more accurate value. Separation of the many considerations influencing the factor of safety has been made in a simple manner so that a more intelligent estimate of each can be provided. However, the designer must still rely on past experience and the past performance of a similar design when estimating the factor of safety to use in the present design. Magnitudes of factors of safety vary greatly. For example, 2.5 is commonly used for structural steel under static loads, while 15 or 20 is sometimes used for timber subjected to dynamic loads.

Sometimes the selection of the factor of safety is out of the hands of the designer. Individual companies or national organizations, including engineering societies, formulate values of design stresses in their design specifications. For the design of buildings, the larger cities in the United States have set up their own building codes giving values of design stresses and load values to use in specific cases. For design of machine parts, working stress values have not been standardized to the same extent as in structural design. This is due to the greater number of materials, loading conditions, and types of members encountered in machine design.

1-5. UTILIZATION OF TENSION AND COMPRESSION PROPERTIES

The foregoing articles have defined mechanical properties in tension and compression and have shown how these properties are determined. The manner in which these properties can be used is an important aspect of machine, structural, and aircraft design. This article attempts to give an introduction to the subject of how mechanical properties of materials are utilized in design.

Usually the cross-sectional dimensions of a tension or compression member are based on the design stress as determined from the yield or ultimate strength of the material. Sometimes, however, an allowable deformation or resilience is a controlling factor. The following examples illustrate the design of some simple tension and compression members.

NUMERICAL EXAMPLE. *Truss Member.* For the simple truss in Fig. 1-2(a), determine the required cross-sectional area of the member CD if the design stress is 20,000 psi, $F = 200,000$ lb., $CD = 20$ ft., and $AD = 10$ ft. If the truss members are steel with $E = 30 \times 10^6$ psi, determine the elongation at CD.

SOLUTION. For equilibrium of the total stresses for joint C,

$$\Sigma F_y = 0, \quad \text{or} \quad -P_{CA} \sin \underline{|ACD} + 100,000 = 0$$

or
$$P_{CA} = 100,000 \times \frac{\sqrt{20^2 + 10^2}}{10} = 224,000 \text{ lb.}$$

To determine P_{CD},

$$\Sigma F_x = 0, \quad \text{or} \quad P_{CD} - P_{CA} \cos \underline{|ACD} = 0$$

and
$$P_{CD} = 224,000 \times \frac{20}{\sqrt{20^2 + 10^2}} = 200,000 \text{ lb.}$$

For a design stress of 20,000 psi, the required area for the member CD is

$$A_0 = \frac{P_{CD}}{S_w} = \frac{200,000}{20,000} = 10 \text{ sq. in.}$$

The elongation of the member CD is, by Hooke's law,

$$e = \epsilon L_0 = \frac{S}{E} L_0 = \frac{20,000 \times 20 \times 12}{30 \times 10^6} = 0.16 \text{ in.}$$

NUMERICAL EXAMPLE.   A structural tension member 10 ft. long is subjected to a load of 120,000 lb.   There is a choice between two materials, (1) an aluminum alloy at fifteen cents per lb., and (2) a structural steel at seven cents per lb.   Select the most economical material based on

(a) ultimate strengths with a factor of safety of 5 if

$$S_{\text{al}}' = 45,000 \text{ psi} \quad \text{and} \quad S_{\text{st}}' = 90,000 \text{ psi}$$

(b) a limiting elongation of 0.20 in.   Use values of

$$E_{\text{al}} = 10.5 \times 10^6 \text{ psi} \quad \text{and} \quad E_{\text{st}} = 30 \times 10^6 \text{ psi}$$

(c) an allowable elastic resilience of 2.5 in. lb. per cu. in.   The densities of the steel and the aluminum alloy are

$$w_{\text{al}} = 0.102 \quad \text{and} \quad w_{\text{st}} = 0.284 \text{ lb. per cu. in.}$$

SOLUTION.   The cost C for each member is the unit cost per unit weight c times the weight, or $C = c(wA_0L_0)$.   Since the area $A = P/S$, then $C = c(wPL_0/S)$.   Using the foregoing equation, the costs based on each requirement are:

(a) *Based on Ultimate Strength:*

$$S_{\text{al}} = \frac{S_{\text{al}}'}{N} = \frac{45,000}{5} = 9,000 \text{ psi}$$

$$S_{\text{st}} = \frac{S_{\text{st}}'}{N} = \frac{90,000}{5} = 18,000 \text{ psi}$$

Then

$$C_{\text{al}} = c\left(\frac{wPL_0}{S}\right) = 0.15\left(\frac{0.102 \times 120,000 \times 120}{9,000}\right) = \$24.50$$

and

$$C_{\text{st}} = c\left(\frac{wPL_0}{S}\right) = 0.07\left(\frac{0.284 \times 120,000 \times 120}{18,000}\right) = \$15.90$$

Based on the ultimate strength, a comparison of the costs for each member shows the aluminum alloy member to be considerably more expensive than the steel member.

(b) *Based on Elongation.* The design stresses based on an allowable elongation of 0.20 in. are

$$S_{al} = \epsilon E_{al} = \frac{e}{L_0} E_{al} = \frac{0.20}{120} \times 10.5 \times 10^6 = 17{,}500 \text{ psi}$$

$$S_{st} = \epsilon E_{st} = \frac{e}{L_0} E_{st} = \frac{0.20}{120} \times 30 \times 10^6 = 50{,}000 \text{ psi}$$

Then the corresponding costs are

$$C_{al} = c\left(\frac{wPL_0}{S}\right) = 0.15\left(\frac{0.102 \times 120{,}000 \times 120}{17{,}500}\right) = \$12.60$$

$$C_{st} = c\left(\frac{wPL_0}{S}\right) = 0.07\left(\frac{0.284 \times 120{,}000 \times 120}{50{,}000}\right) = \$\ 5.70$$

A comparison of the foregoing shows that the cost of the steel member is less than half that of the aluminum alloy member.

(c) *Based on Resilience.* The allowable resilience as indicated by eq. (1-7b) is $u = S^2/2E$. Then the design stresses based on an allowable resilience of 2.5 in. lb. per cu. in. are

$$S_{al} = \sqrt{2E_{al}u} = \sqrt{2 \times 10.5 \times 10^6 \times 2.5} = 7250 \text{ psi}$$

$$S_{st} = \sqrt{2E_{st}u} = \sqrt{2 \times 30 \times 10^6 \times 2.5} = 12{,}250 \text{ psi}$$

The corresponding costs are

$$C_{al} = c\left(\frac{wPL_0}{S}\right) = 0.15\left(\frac{0.102 \times 120{,}000 \times 120}{7250}\right) = \$30.20$$

$$C_{st} = c\left(\frac{wPL_0}{S}\right) = 0.07\left(\frac{0.284 \times 120{,}000 \times 120}{12{,}250}\right) = \$23.40$$

In this case also the steel is less expensive than the aluminum alloy. It should be noted, however, that there may be other factors than the above-mentioned mechanical properties to consider in selecting a particular material.

NUMERICAL EXAMPLE. A square cast-iron bearing plate is subjected to a compressive load of 180,000 lb. The cast iron has an ultimate compressive strength of 40,000 psi and a contraction at fracture of 0.01 in. per in. Determine the cross-sectional area required based on

(a) the ultimate strength with a factor of safety of 8,

(b) the toughness, assuming the stress-strain curve to be parabolic and using an allowable strain energy of $\frac{1}{8}$ the toughness.

SOLUTION.   Based on the ultimate strength, since the design stress is $S_u/N = 40{,}000/8 = 5000$ psi, the area required is

$$A_0 = \frac{P}{S_w} = \frac{180{,}000}{5000} = 36 \text{ sq. in.}$$

The toughness is

$$T = \tfrac{2}{3}S_u\epsilon_b = \tfrac{2}{3}(40{,}000)(0.01) = 266.7 \text{ in. lb. per cu. in.}$$

The allowable strain energy is

$$T_w = \frac{T}{8} = \frac{266.7}{8} = 33.3 \text{ in. lb. per cu. in.}$$

The stress-strain curve is parabolic so that $S^2 = k\epsilon$. Since $S_w = 40{,}000$ when $\epsilon_b = 0.01$ in. per in., then

$$k = \frac{S_w{}^2}{\epsilon_b} = \frac{(40{,}000)^2}{0.01} = 16 \times 10^{10}$$

and
$$S_w{}^2 = k\epsilon_w = 16 \times 10^{10}\epsilon_w$$

But since the allowable strain energy is $T_w = \tfrac{2}{3}S_w\epsilon_w$, and since $S_w{}^2 = 16 \times 10^{10}\epsilon_w$, then

$$T_w = \frac{2}{3} S_w \left(\frac{S_w{}^2}{16 \times 10^{10}} \right) = \frac{2S_w{}^3}{48 \times 10^{10}}$$

But the allowable strain energy $T_w = 33.3$ in. lb. per cu. in., so that

$$S_w = \sqrt[3]{24 \times 10^{10} \times 33.3} = 20{,}000 \text{ psi}$$

Then the required area based on the allowable strain energy is

$$A_0 = \frac{P}{S_w} = 180{,}000/20{,}000 = 9 \text{ sq. in.}$$

Strength-Weight Ratio.   The development of light-weight alloys for use in many applications, particularly aircraft parts, has led to the concept of design based on the strength-weight ratio.[5] For simple tension or compression the strength P is the design stress times the area, or $P = S_w A_0$. The weight of the member W, for

[5] See L. B. Tuckerman, "Aircraft: Materials and Testing," *Proc. A.S.T.M.*, 1935, Vol. 35, p. 3.

members with constant cross-sectional areas, is equal to the weight per unit volume γ times the volume A_0L_0, or

$$W = \gamma A_0 L_0$$

The strength-weight ratio is then equal to $P/W = S_w A_0/(\gamma A_0 L_0)$, or

$$\frac{P}{W} = \frac{S_w}{\gamma L_0} \tag{1-11}$$

Since a high strength P for a low weight W is desired, the strength-weight ratio P/W should be high. By eq. (1-11) a high value of P/W occurs with a high value of the working stress S_w and low values of the density and length of member. That is, in selecting a material it is desirable to select one with a high design stress or high strength and a low density. The foregoing result is common sense and a result that need not have been expressed in terms of an equation. It will be seen in Chapter 2, however, that for more complicated stresses such as torsion and bending it is desirable to express the strength-weight ratio in terms of an equation.

NUMERICAL EXAMPLE. Compare the strength-weight ratios of four tension members 5 ft. long if the materials are an aluminum alloy, a magnesium alloy, a steel alloy, and a glass-laminated plastic. The design stresses are, respectively, 15,000, 8000, 20,000, and 5000 psi. The densities are, respectively, 0.101, 0.065, 0.284, and 0.050 lb. per cu. in.

SOLUTION. By eq. (1-11) the strength-weight ratios for the four materials are, respectively,

$$\left(\frac{P}{W}\right)_{al} = \frac{15,000}{0.101 \times 60} = 2470$$

$$\left(\frac{P}{W}\right)_{mg} = \frac{8000}{0.065 \times 60} = 2050$$

$$\left(\frac{P}{W}\right)_{st} = \frac{20,000}{0.284 \times 60} = 1170$$

$$\left(\frac{P}{W}\right)_{pl} = \frac{5000}{0.050 \times 60} = 1670$$

Although the steel has the lowest strength-weight ratio, there are other considerations than strength in selecting the most adequate material. The cost may greatly influence the selection of the most suitable material for a given construction.

1-6. TRUE STRESS-STRAIN RELATIONS IN SIMPLE TENSION

In previous articles the stress and strain in the plastic range were determined based on the original cross-sectional dimensions and gage length before loading. In the plastic range there is considerable change in the cross-sectional area and gage length, and the values of the stress and strain based on the original values may be greatly in error. The stress and strain, as usually determined, are sometimes called the *nominal stress* and *nominal strain*, as distinguished from the *true stress* and *true strain* based on the changing area and changing gage length.

The *true stress* in simple tension is equal to the axial load P divided by the instantaneous area A. That is, the true stress S' is

$$S' = \frac{P}{A} \qquad (1\text{-}12)$$

To define the *true strain* in simple tension consider a specimen stressed in the plastic range and let the gage length which was originally L_0 be L_i. Now let the load be changed a small amount ΔP so that the change in gage length is ΔL_i and the new gage length is L_i. Then the change in strain is $\Delta L_i/L_i$. For the entire range of loading from zero load to a load P, or for a change in gage length from L_0 to L, the true strain becomes

$$\delta = \text{limit} \sum \frac{\Delta L_i}{L_i} = \int_{L_0}^{L} \frac{dL_i}{L_i}$$

Designating *log* as the logarithm of a number to the Napierian or natural base, the foregoing equation can be written as

$$\delta = \log \frac{L}{L_0} \qquad (1\text{-}13a)$$

Equation (1-13a) can also be expressed in terms of the nominal strain by noting that $L = (L_0 + \Delta L_0)$ or

$$\delta = \log \frac{L}{L_0} = \log \left(\frac{L_0 + \Delta L_0}{L_0} \right)$$

or $$\delta = \log (1 + \epsilon) \qquad (1\text{-}13b)$$

That is, the true strain equals the logarithm of one plus the nominal strain. The true strain as defined by eqs. (1-13a) and (1-13b) was first proposed by Ludwik.[6]

---

[6] P. Ludwik, *Elemente der technologischen Mechanik*, Verlag Julius Springer, Berlin, 1909.

In a manner similar to Ludwik's definition of true strain, Mac-Gregor[7] has suggested a more rational definition of *true reduction in area* in simple tension. The true reduction in area may be defined as

$$q' = -\int_{A_0}^{A} \frac{dA_i}{A_i} = -\log \frac{A}{A_0}$$

or

$$q' = \log \frac{A_0}{A} \tag{1-14}$$

where A = the final cross-sectional area and A_0 = the original cross-sectional area.

The true stress can be expressed in terms of the true strain in place of the cross-sectional area by using eqs. (1-13b) and (1-14) and the plasticity condition of constancy of volume. That is, in the plastic range, tests show that the volume of the specimen remains approximately constant. Thus,

$$A_0 L_0 = AL \quad \text{or} \quad \frac{L}{L_0} = \frac{A_0}{A} \tag{a}$$

Placing the value of L/L_0 from eq. (a) in eq. (1-13a),

$$\delta = \log \frac{A_0}{A} \tag{b}$$

Comparing eqs. (1-13b) and (b), since the left-hand sides of these equations are the same, the right-hand sides must be equal, or

$$\frac{A_0}{A} = 1 + \epsilon \quad \text{or} \quad A = \frac{A_0}{1 + \epsilon} \tag{c}$$

Then if the value of A as given by eq. (c) is placed in eq. (1-12), the true stress in terms of the true strain becomes

$$S' = \frac{P}{A_0} (1 + \epsilon) \tag{1-15}$$

That is, the true stress equals the nominal stress (P/A_0) times one plus the nominal strain.

---

[7] C. W. MacGregor, "Relation Between Stress and Reduction in Area for Tensile Tests of Metals," *Metals Technology*, April, 1937; "The Tension Test," *Proc. A.S.T.M.*, 1940, Vol. 40, pp. 506-534; "The True Stress-Strain Tension Test—Its Role in Modern Materials Testing," *Journal Franklin Institute*, August and September, 1944, Vol. 239, Nos. 2 and 3.

A comparison of eqs. (b) and (1-14) shows that the *true strain* and *true reduction in area* are equal. That is,

$$\delta = q' \tag{1-15a}$$

This relation will be shown to be very helpful in obtaining true stress-strain relations experimentally.

Test Methods for Determining True Stress-Strain Diagrams. Various test procedures have been developed for the determination of the true stress-strain curve. These are:

(1) *Method Using Lateral Dimensions.* This method is especially simple for specimens of circular cross section. When this procedure is applied to such cross sections the diameter of the specimen is measured for various increments of load to rupture. A micrometer or dial gage is used in measuring this diameter and care is exercised to select the minimum diameter by moving the gage over the entire gage length of the specimen. One advantage of this procedure is that the readings can be extended into the necked-down region.

For a circular cross section the true stress and strain can be determined from the load and diameter measurements and by use of eqs. (1-12) and (b). In using eqs. (1-12) and (b), values of $A_0 = \pi d_0^2/4$ and $A = \pi d^2/4$ are selected, where d_0 and d are the initial diameter and diameter at any load P, respectively. Then the true stress and true strain in terms of the diameter readings are

$$S' = \frac{P}{(\pi d^2/4)} \tag{1-16}$$

and

$$\delta = \log\left(\frac{d_0^2}{d^2}\right) = 2\log\left(\frac{d_0}{d}\right) \tag{1-17}$$

For specimens of rectangular cross section a good approximation for the area A can be obtained by calculating the area from the width, thickness at the edges, and thickness at mid-width. With these measurements the area can be calculated approximately by assuming that the top and bottom edges of the specimen are parabolic and that the sides remain straight. With the area calculated in this way the true stress and true strain can then be determined by eqs. (1-12) and (b). Figure 1-10 shows a true stress-strain curve obtained by using diameter values. For purpose of comparison, the nominal stress-strain curve is also shown in Fig. 1-10.

(2) *Method Using Axial Strains.* The determination of axial

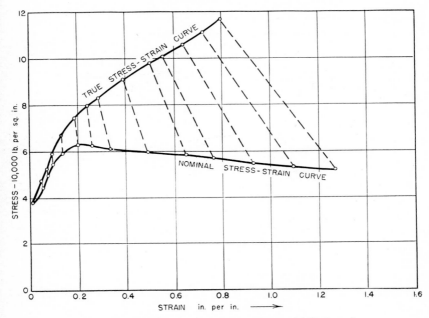

Fig. 1-10.   True stress-strain curve for semi-killed steel.

strains at various load increments is sometimes employed as a procedure for the determination of the true stress-strain diagram in
tension.   With the nominal axial tensile strain ϵ known, eqs. (1-15)
and (1-13b) can be used to determine the true stress and true strain.
In this method the assumption is made that the axial strain is uniform over the entire gage length.   The values calculated in this way
are satisfactory for strains below the point of necking, since the
strain up to necking is approximately uniform over the gage length.
Beyond necking, however, the strain at the location of necking is
much greater than at other parts of the gage length.   Furthermore,
the necked section may occur entirely outside the gage length in
some cases.

(3) *Two-Load Method.*   The two-load method for obtaining the true
stress-strain diagram was devised by MacGregor.[8]   In this method a

[8] C. W. MacGregor, "A Two-Load Method of Determining the Average True
Stress-Strain Curve in Tension," *Jour. App. Mech.*, Dec. 1939, Vol. 6 (4), pp.
A156-158.

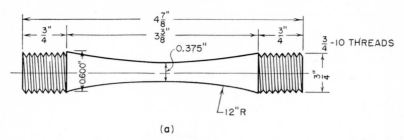

(a)

Fig. 1-11(a).   Tapered tension specimen.

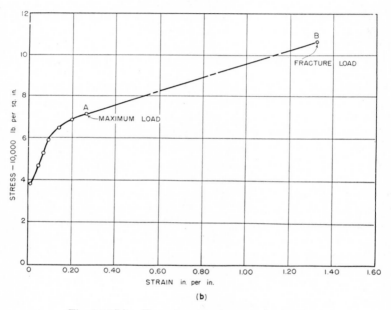

(b)

Fig. 1-11(b).   True stress-strain curve for tension.

specimen of circular cross section, tapered from the ends to the center, is used, as shown in Fig. 1-11(a).   The diameters at a number of cross sections before loading and after fracture are measured with a micrometer, dial gage, or a comparator.   During the test the maximum load reached ($P_{\max}$) and the load at fracture (P_f) are recorded.   The true stress-strain values up to the maximum load can be obtained from the maximum load and the final diameters at various cross sections, since beyond the maximum load all the plastic strain is essentially localized in the section of constant diameter.

That is, if D_{i0} is the original diameter on some cross section of the taper and D_i is the final diameter at this section, then the true stress and true strain for a point on the stress-strain curve are, by eqs. (1-12) and (b),

$$S' = \frac{P_{max}}{A_i} = \frac{P_{max}}{(\pi D_i^2/4)} \tag{1-18}$$

and
$$\delta = \log\left(\frac{A_{i0}}{A_i}\right) = 2\log\left(\frac{D_{i0}}{D_i}\right) \tag{1-19}$$

Points on the true stress-strain curve approximately up to the maximum load [point A, Fig. 1-11(b)] can be obtained by applying eqs. (1-18) and (1-19) to various cross sections of the tapered part of the specimen. The end point of the true stress-strain curve (point B, Fig. 1-11(b)) corresponding to the fracture load, can be located by using the fracture load P_f and the diameter of the minimum cross section at fracture. Between points A and B in Fig. 1-11(b) a straight line is assumed, since many metals show a linear relation between the true stress and true strain from the maximum to the fracture loads.

The advantage of this method is that it is a rapid test in which no measurements on the specimen need be made during the loading of the specimen. Furthermore, it is a test that is well adapted to high-speed and high-temperature tests, since measurements need not be made during the test. A disadvantage of the test is that the strain rate varies over the specimen length. This is a particularly important consideration in high-temperature tests because the varying strain rate will modify the plastic stress-strain relation. Another disadvantage of the test is that, because of the change in cross section of the specimen, the stress is no longer uniformly distributed simple tension. The latter objection is not important, however, since the departure from a uniformly distributed tensile stress is slight for the specimen used.

Relation Between True Stress and True Strain. True stress-strain tension data for many metals and alloys show that from the maximum load to the fracture load there is a linear relation between stress and strain. Many attempts have been made to express an empirical relation between the true stress and true strain to cover the entire range of the stress-strain relation. In recent years, a relation that was proposed several years ago has been shown to represent approximately the true-stress true-strain relation. Considerable test data show that the true stress and true strain are related by the equation

$$S' = k\delta^n \tag{1-20}$$

where k and n are constants of the material.

The constant k is called the *strength coefficient* and n is called the *strain-hardening exponent.* By taking the logarithm of both sides of eq. (1-20), $\log_{10} S' = \log_{10} k + n \log_{10} \delta$. Thus, on log-log paper eq. (1-20) would plot as a straight line. Figure 1-12 shows data obtained by Low,[9] plotted in terms of $\log S'$ versus $\log \delta$. Values of k and n from reference (9) are listed in Table 1-1.

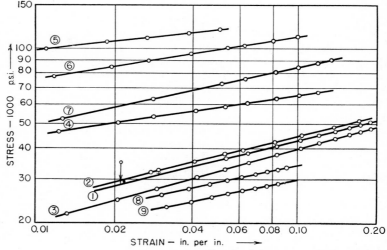

Tests by J. R. Low and F. Garofalo.
Courtesy Addison-Wesley Press.

Fig. 1-12.   Logarithmic stress-strain curves for various metals.
(*Note:* Numbers on graph refer to materials listed in Table 2.)

Hollomon[10] shows that for plain carbon steels with carbon contents from 0.78% to 0.2% there is very little change in the value of n, the value varying from about 0.94 to 1.00. Tension stress-strain data plotted as in Fig. 1-12 usually depart from a straight line at both low and high stress values. Various corrections have been proposed to make the test data fall closer to a straight line. For the low stress values it has been proposed to decrease the true strain values and, hence, make the test points fall closer to the straight line

[9] J. Low and F. Garafalo, "Precision Determination of Stress-Strain Curves in the Plastic Range," *Proc. S.E.S.A.*, 1947, Vol. 4, No. 2, pp. 16-25.
[10] J. H. Hollomon, "Tensile Deformation," *Metals Technology*, June, 1946.

Table 1-1

Material Constants n and k for Different Sheet Materials

Material	Treatment	n	k (psi)	Thickness (inches)
1. 0.05% Carbon rimmed steel	Annealed	0.261	77,100	0.037
2. 0.05% Carbon killed steel	Annealed and temper-rolled	0.234	73,100	0.037
3. Same as #2, completely decarburized	Annealed in wet hydrogen	0.284	75,500	0.037
4. 0.05/0.07% Phosphorus low-carbon steel	Annealed	0.156	93,330	0.037
5. SAE 4130 Steel	Annealed	0.118	169,400	0.037
6. SAE 4130 Steel	Normalized and temper-rolled	0.156	154,500	0.037
7. Type-430 stainless steel (17% Cr.)	Annealed	0.229	143,000	0.050
8. Alcoa 24-S aluminum	Annealed	0.211	55,900	0.040
9. Reynolds R-301 aluminum	Annealed	0.211	48,450	0.040

Tests by J. R. Low and F. Garafalo

by plotting only the plastic strains and subtracting the elastic strain from the total strain. That is, the true plastic strain is $\delta_p = \delta_t - S'/E$, where δ_t is the elastic plus the plastic true strain. This correction is made only for the small strain values since, for most of the range of strain, the elastic part of the total strain is negligible. The correction is made up to about 5% strain for steels.

Another correction has been proposed for bringing the test data into agreement with the straight line for stress values near fracture. This correction attempts to introduce the influence of the combined state of stress present in the necked-down part of the tensile specimen near fracture.

Apart from the fact that the true stress and true strain represent the correct values of the stress and strain in simple tension, these quantities are of importance in understanding plastic behavior of materials and members under combined states of stress. True stress and true strain are also necessary in specifying formability limits in the bending of sheet metals to various shapes.

Criterion Defining the Beginning of Necking. Beyond the maximum load the specimen necks down and reaches a condition referred to as *instability.* It is of interest to define the beginning of necking of the point of maximum load in terms of the true stress and true strain values. To do this, note that the maximum load or load at the beginning of necking is defined when the change in load $dP = 0$. Since $P = S'A$ and $\delta = \log A_0/A$ or $A = A_0/$antilog δ, then

$$P = S'A = \frac{S'A_0}{\text{antilog } \delta}$$

or

$$dP = - \left(\frac{S'A_0}{\text{antilog } \delta}\right) d\delta + \left(\frac{A_0}{\text{antilog } \delta}\right) dS' \tag{d}$$

At the maximum load $dP = 0$ or, by eq. (d),

$$\frac{dS'}{d\delta} = S' \tag{1-21}$$

Equation (1-21) states that the point of maximum load occurs at the point on the true stress-true strain curve where the slope of the curve equals the stress value for the point. That is, the maximum load is at a point A in Fig. 1-13, where $\overline{CB} = 1.0$ in. per in. true strain. This result can be proved by noting that

$$\frac{dS'}{d\delta} = \tan \lfloor ABC = \frac{\overline{AC}}{\overline{CB}}.$$

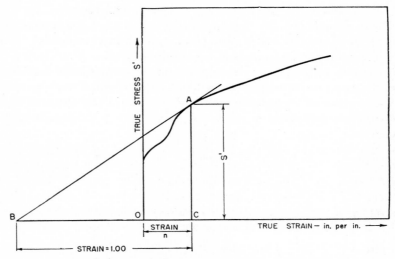

Fig. 1-13. Determination of theoretical maximum load.

And since $dS'/d\delta = S' = \overline{AC}$ by eq. (1-21), then $\overline{AC}/\overline{CB} = \overline{AC}$, or $\overline{CB} = 1.0$.

The point of instability cannot be located directly by the foregoing method. A more convenient method of locating the point of maximum load or instability is possible if the true stress-true strain relation is expressed empirically. Assuming that eq. (1-20) represents the true stress-true strain relation, then from eq. (1-20) for the point of maximum load, if δ_m is the strain at the maximum load,

$$\frac{dS'}{d\delta_m} = nk\delta_m^{n-1} \tag{e}$$

But by eq. (1-21) for the point of maximum load,

$$\frac{dS'}{d\delta_m} = S' = k\delta_m^n \tag{f}$$

Comparing eqs. (e) and (f), since the left-hand sides are the same, the right-hand sides are equal, or

$$k\delta_m^n = nk\delta_m^{n-1}$$

or

$$\delta_m = n \tag{1-22}$$

That is, by eq. (1-22) the maximum load or the beginning of necking occurs at a true strain value equal to the strain-hardening exponent. The point of maximum load can be obtained by locating a point A on the true-stress true-strain curve in Fig. 1-13 where the true strain equals n, as defined by eq. (1-22).

The point of maximum load is important in defining limits for forming operations. Materials with high values of n are the best for forming into various shapes, since eq. (1-20) shows that, for n less than one, the higher the value of n, the smaller is the strain δ for a given stress.

True-stress true-strain diagrams as related to the tension test have been discussed in the foregoing. It is also possible to determine true-stress true-strain diagrams for simple compression. In obtaining pure compression free from end effects and bending stresses, however, there are a number of difficulties encountered.

NUMERICAL EXAMPLE. In a tension test of steel using a round specimen, the diameters for two loads (4900 and 6400 lb.) were 0.342 and 0.328 in. respectively. If the original diameter of the specimen was 0.360 in., determine

(1) the true stress and true strain for the two loads given,
(2) the strength coefficient k and strain-hardening exponent n, assuming the log-log stress-strain relation,
(3) the theoretical maximum load, using eq. (1-22).

SOLUTION. By eqs. (1-16) and (1-17) the true stress and true strain corresponding to a load of 4900 lb. are, respectively,

$$S' = \frac{P}{(\pi d^2/4)} = \frac{4900}{(\pi \times 0.342^2/4)} = 53,400 \text{ psi}$$

and $\delta = 2 \log \left(\dfrac{d_0}{d}\right) = 2 \log \left(\dfrac{0.360}{0.342}\right) = 0.103$ in. per in.

The true stress and true strain for the load of 6400 lb. are, respectively,

$$S' = \frac{P}{(\pi d^2/4)} = \frac{6400}{(\pi \times 0.328^2/4)} = 75,800 \text{ psi}$$

and $\delta = 2 \log \left(\dfrac{d_0}{d}\right) = 2 \log \left(\dfrac{0.360}{0.328}\right) = 0.185$ in. per in.

Since the foregoing stress values are assumed to be points in the stress-strain relation $S' = k\delta^n$, then

$$53,400 = k\,(0.103)^n$$

and $$75,800 = k\,(0.185)^n$$

or $$n \log_{10} 0.103 = \log_{10} 53,400 - \log_{10} k$$

and $$n \log_{10} 0.185 = \log_{10} 75,800 - \log_{10} k$$

Solving the foregoing equations simultaneously for k and n,

$$k = 207,800 \text{ psi} \quad \text{and} \quad n = 0.598$$

To determine the theoretical maximum load using eq. (1-22), note that by eq. (1-22) the maximum load occurs for a strain value $\delta_m = n = 0.598$ in. per in. For a value of $\delta_m = 0.598$ using eq. (1-20), the stress is

$$S_m' = k\delta_m{}^n = 207,800\,(0.598)^{0.598} = 152,900 \text{ psi}$$

From eq. (b), since $\delta_m = \log_e A_0/A$, $A_0/A = $ antilog δ_m or

$$A = A_0/\text{antilog } \delta_m = 0.0559 \text{ sq. in.}$$

With the true stress S_m' at the maximum load and the actual area A known, the maximum load is

$$P_m = S_m'A = 152,900 \times 0.0559 = 8550 \text{ lb.}$$

NUMERICAL EXAMPLE. In a tension test with a specimen 0.505 in. in diameter, a true-stress true-strain diagram was obtained by measuring the axial strain for a 1-in. gage length. For a load of

11,000 lb. the strain reading was 0.10 in.   For a load of 12,000 lb. the strain was 0.51 in.   Determine:

  (a) The true stress and true strain corresponding to the two loads given.
  (b) The k and n values, assuming that the true stress-true strain relation is defined by $S' = k\delta^n$.
  (c) The value of the maximum load based on eq. (1-22).

SOLUTION.   The true stress and true strain are defined by eqs. (1-15) and (1-13b) respectively.   Then for the 11,000-lb. load the true stress and true strain are

$$S' = \frac{P}{A_0} (1 + \epsilon) = \frac{11,000}{(\pi \times 0.505^2/4)} (1 + 0.10) = 60,600 \text{ psi}$$

and

$$\delta = \log (1 + \epsilon) = \log (1 + 0.10) = 0.0953 \text{ in. per in.}$$

For the 12,000-lb. load the true stress and true strain are

$$S' = \left(\frac{P}{A_0}\right) (1 + \epsilon) = \frac{12,000}{(\pi \times 0.505^2/4)} (1 + 0.51) = 90,700 \text{ psi}$$

and

$$\delta = \log (1 + \epsilon) = \log (1 + 0.51) = 0.4121 \text{ in. per in.}$$

The foregoing true stress-true strain values are assumed to be points on the log-log true stress-strain relation $S' = k\delta^n$, so that

$$60,600 = k (0.0953)^n$$

and
$$90,700 = k (0.4121)^n$$

or
$$n \log_{10} 0.0953 = \log_{10} 60,600 - \log_{10} k$$

and
$$n \log_{10} 0.4121 = \log_{10} 90,700 - \log_{10} k$$

Solving the foregoing equations simultaneously for k and n,

$$k = 115,700 \text{ psi} \quad \text{and} \quad n = 0.275$$

To determine the theoretical value of the maximum load the value of the true strain corresponding to the maximum load is calculated first.   By eq. (1-22) this strain is $\delta_m = n = 0.275$ in. per in.   Then by eq. (1-20) the true stress at the maximum load is

$$S_m' = k\delta_m^n = 115,700 (0.275)^{0.275} = 81,200 \text{ psi}$$

Using eq. (b), since $\delta = \log A_0/A$,

$$A = \frac{A_0}{\text{antilog } \delta_m} = 0.152 \text{ sq. in.}$$

The maximum load then equals

$$P_m = S_m' A = 81,200 \times 0.152 = 12,350 \text{ lb.}$$

NUMERICAL EXAMPLE. A tension member of a 24S-O aluminum alloy has an original cross-sectional area of 4 sq. in. If $k = 56,000$ psi and $n = 0.21$, determine the maximum load and the change in length of the member at this maximum load if the original length is 4 ft.

SOLUTION. By eq. (1-22) the true strain at the maximum load is $\delta_m = n = 0.21$ in. per in. Then the true stress at the maximum load is

$$S_m' = k\delta_m{}^n = 56,000 \ (0.21)^{0.21} = 40,300 \text{ psi}$$

The reduced cross-sectional area at the maximum load is determined from eq. (b). That is,

$$\delta_m = \log\left(\frac{A_0}{A}\right) \quad \text{or} \quad A = \frac{A_0}{\text{antilog } \delta_m}$$

or

$$A = \frac{4}{\text{antilog } 0.21} = 3.24 \text{ sq. in.}$$

The maximum load is

$$P_m = S_m' A = 40,300 \times 3.24 = 131,000 \text{ lb.}$$

By eq. (1-13), the nominal strain at the maximum load is

$$\epsilon_m = \text{antilog } \delta_m - 1 = 1.234 - 1 = 0.234 \text{ in. per in.}$$

The total change in length at the maximum load is

$$e = 0.234 \times 48 = 11.2 \text{ in.}$$

1-7. FACTORS THAT MODIFY STRESS-STRAIN RELATIONS

Either the nominal or the true stress-strain diagrams for tension and compression can be modified in various ways by changes in the specimen, by the manner of loading, or by external conditions. With reference to the specimen, it has been found that the shape, the relative value of the cross-sectional dimensions to the gage length, the types of ends, and the surface conditions all modify the stress-strain relations in simple tension. Templin[11] showed that,

[11] R. L. Templin, "Some Factors Affecting Strain Measurements in Tests of Metals," *Proc. A.S.T.M.*, 1934, Vol. 34, p. 182.

particularly in the determination of the modulus of elasticity, it is necessary to maintain an axial load in order to obtain reliable data. For this purpose, and to show the influence of the stress-strain relation, tension tests were made with various eccentricities of loading. Templin also determined the influence of shape of cross section on the stress-strain relations by testing I-beam, channel, angle, and tubular members.

Many investigations have shown the influence of the *speed of loading*[12] on the stress-strain relation. The yield strength in tension has been found to increase with increase in speed of loading. In rapid tensile-impact tests the yield point has been found to be 10 to 20 per cent higher than at slow speeds. Ludwik[13] was probably the first investigator to study the effect of speed on the yield strengths of metals. He proposed the following empirical logarithmic speed relation for simple tension:

$$S_{yp} = S_a + S_b \log \left(\frac{v}{v_1} \right) \tag{1-23}$$

where S_{yp} equals the yield stress for a strain rate v, and S_a, S_b, and v_1 are experimental constants. Although the speed of testing influences the yield strength considerably, it is found usually to have much less effect on the ultimate strength.

The stress-strain relation is modified by the manner of loading. That is, the stress-strain relations will be changed depending upon whether the load or strain is applied at a constant rate or whether some intermediate condition prevails. The usual test is more or less of the *constant-strain type* rather than the *constant-load type*. Davis[12] devised a special testing machine for applying loads at a constant load rate to tensile specimens. By varying the rates of loading, Davis found differences in yield strengths of as much as 30 per cent. In the constant load-rate type of test the load cannot decrease, so that a lower yield point can never be recorded in this type of test.

The influence of *strain-hardening*, or initial stretching beyond the yield stress, modifies the subsequent stress-strain relation. That is,

[12] For a bibliography on effect of loading speed see E. A. Davis, "The Effect of the Speed of Stretching and the Rate of Loading on the Yielding of Mild Steel," *Trans. A.S.M.E.*, 1939, Vol. 61, p. A-137.

[13] See A. Nadai and C. W. MacGregor, "On Laws of Similitude in Materials Testing," *Proc. A.S.T.M.*, 1934, Vol. 34, p. 216.

if a tensile specimen is stressed beyond the yield stress value to a point B, as shown in Fig. 1-14(a), then unloaded to C and reloaded, the yield strength is raised from a value at A to that at D. Subsequent unloadings and reloadings increase the yield strength further. In loading to B, unloading to C, and reloading to D, a certain amount of strain energy is dissipated in the form of heat produced by internal friction. This lost energy is represented by the shaded area in Fig. 1-14(a). The loss in strain energy is called mechanical *hysteresis*, and the shaded diagram in Fig. 1-14(a) is called the *hysteresis loop*. In unloading to C there is a recoverable elastic strain ϵ_e' represented

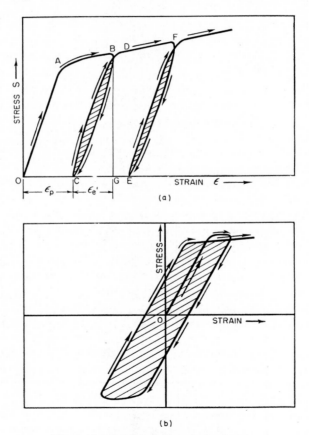

Fig. 1-14.   Influence of strain hardening.

by CG and a permanent plastic strain $\epsilon_p = OC$. That is, for any point on the stress-strain diagram in the plastic range the strain can be considered to be made up of two parts, an elastic and a plastic strain. In the case of steels, the elastic strain is negligible for total strains beyond 5 per cent elongation. Continued stressing in tension is found to have much less effect upon the ultimate strength. The toughness and ductility of the material, however, are found to be decreased.

If, in place of reloading in tension, a tension specimen is unloaded after stressing beyond the yield stress and then loaded in compression, there is found to be a subsequent reduction in the yield stress when the specimen is again loaded in tension. This change in yield strength is illustrated in Fig. 1-14(b). Figure 1-14(b) also shows that there is considerably more mechanical hysteresis or loss in strain energy per cycle of stressing as compared to stressing in the same direction. The foregoing influence on the yield stress value is known as the *Bauschinger effect,* named after Johann Bauschinger who first noted the above experimental results of unloading and reloading a tensile specimen.

It should be noted that although stretching beyond the yield stress with subsequent stretching or strain-hardening improves the yield strength, the strain-hardening benefits disappear when the metal is subjected to annealing temperatures.

Strain-hardening is encountered in many manufacturing processes such as rolling of bars, drawing of tubes, and punching of holes in plates. In cases where strain-hardening reduces ductility and increases hardness to undesirable extents, annealing can be used to reestablish the initial hardness and ductility. Strain-hardening sometimes finds practical application in manufacturing. For example, undesirable stretching of chains and cables used for hoisting machines during service is eliminated by initial stretching and overstrain. Cylinders of hydraulic presses are sometimes submitted to an initial internal pressure in order to introduce a permanent deformation in the walls. The strain-hardening and residual stresses produced in this way eliminate permanent set in service. The overstraining of metals is sometimes used in manufacturing of guns by introducing initial stresses which, combined with the subsequent stresses produced by the internal explosion, give a more favorable resultant stress distribution than would have occurred without the

initial stressing.   A treatment similar to that given guns is sometimes applied to turbine disks and rotors.   By running such parts
at overspeeds a permanent set is produced, which raises the subsequent yield stress and produces initial stresses of favorable sign during later service use.   Results similar to the above are obtained in
pressing hubs of locomotive wheels on their axles.

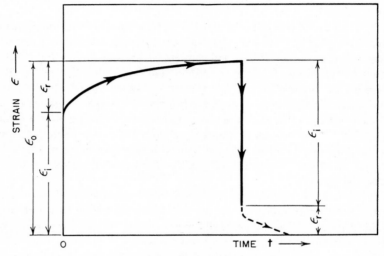

Fig. 1-15.   Elastic after-effect.

There are certain elastic after-effects that modify the stress-strain
relations.   That is, in the elastic range, if a load is suddenly applied,
an instantaneous strain ϵ_i is produced (Fig. 1-15).   Then with a
constant load, a residual strain ϵ_r results during a time t.   If the load
is removed suddenly, the strain is reduced an amount ϵ_i.   The residual strain ϵ_r is eventually released with time, as shown in Fig.
1-15.   The strain ϵ_r is found to vary as the logarithm of the time.
Furthermore, the strain ϵ_r equals a constant times the total strain
ϵ_0, where $\epsilon_0 = \epsilon_r + \epsilon_i$.   It is also found that cold-working greatly
increases ϵ_r.   There are other elastic after-effects such as drop in
temperature during sudden loading in tension, and increase in temperature during sudden loading in compression.[14]

---

[14] For a further discussion of elastic after-effects see C. Zener, *Elasticity and
Anelasticity of Metals*, University of Chicago Press, 1948.

1-8. SPECIAL PROPERTIES

The mechanical properties considered in the foregoing articles are the main ones used in design and for the selection of materials. Sometimes other properties than those considered are employed in the selection of materials. These properties include malleability, machinability or adaptability to fabrication or construction, durability, hardness, and thermal, acoustical, electrical, and chemical properties.

Durability denotes the ability of a material to resist destruction over long periods of time.   There are various types of destructive forces so that there is no single measure for durability.   Durability may involve resistance to weathering, resistance to freezing and thawing action, resistance to change in properties, and resistance to decay.   The durability of a structure may be modified by range of temperature, range of humidity, or the amount of smoke in an atmosphere.

Malleability signifies the capacity of a material to withstand plastic deformation in compression without fracture.   It is related to ductility in tension but no general method has been devised for measuring malleability.   It is an important property in the rolling, pressing, or hammering of materials to required shapes.

Workability and *machinability* represent the ability of a material to be formed into a required shape.   Workability is an important property of materials, since in some cases it is not economical to form the material to the desired shape because of difficulties encountered in forming.   For example, the ability of certain materials to be die cast has led to great improvement in the design of many products.   Forming by casting, cutting, grinding, rolling, hammering, and forging is dependent upon the properties of the materials considered.   Ductility, malleability, and hardness of materials are related to workability and are properties that must be considered in selecting the most desirable method of forming.   The property of workability may often considerably affect the cost of the finished part.

Electrical Properties.   Two important electrical properties of materials are their *conductivity* and *resistance*.   Electrical conductivity designates the ability of a material to transmit electric current.   Electrical resistance is the reciprocal of conductivity and represents the capacity to prevent the flow of an electric current.

The resistance of a wire of homogeneous composition varies directly with its length and inversely with its cross-sectional area.

Thermal Properties. The quantity of heat required to raise the temperature of a unit mass of material one degree varies with the material. This quantity is called the *specific heat*. The rate of transfer of heat by conduction is also dependent upon the material. The *thermal conductivity* of a material is the rate of transfer of heat per unit time, through a unit thickness, across a unit area, for a unit difference in temperature.

Acoustical Properties. Some materials, when subjected to sound waves, absorb more of the sound waves than other materials, leaving only a small amount of the sound waves to be reflected. Reflection of sound from walls, ceilings, and floors may be too great and reverberations of sound may result. The percentage of the original sound wave that is absorbed is called the *coefficient of absorption*, while the percentage of the sound wave reflected from a surface is called the *coefficient of reflection*. Porous materials such as fiber board have a high absorption coefficient while wood, concrete, plaster, and the nonporous materials have a low absorption coefficient.

Chemical Properties. An important general chemical property of a material is the degree and ease with which it may enter into chemical composition with other materials. The possible chemical combinations between materials are naturally of significance in various manufacturing processes. Chemical properties, as related to corrosion of metals and the destructive effects of boiler feed water in disintegrating the walls of a boiler, are important considerations.

Hardness Tests. *Hardness* is measured in various ways and indicates different properties depending upon the way in which it is measured. That is, hardness may represent the ability of a material to resist scratching, abrasion, cutting, or penetration.[15] The type of hardness to be tested in a material depends upon its service requirements. For example, many structural and machine parts such as rails, gears, and axles require a high resistance to indentation. Sometimes the hardness of a material is measured by its ability to absorb energy under impact loads. Hardness, as measured by re-

---

[15] See Hugh O'Neill, *The Hardness of Metals and Its Measurement*, The Sherwood Press, Cleveland, 1935; S. R. Williams, *Hardness and Hardness Measurements*, American Society for Metals, 1942; and V. E. Lysaght, *Indentation Hardness Testing*, Reinhold Publishing Corp., New York, 1949.

sistance to abrasion, is also a measure of the wearing quality of a material.   Hardness, as measured by resistance to cutting, is an indication of the machinability qualities of a material.

The indentation hardness test is the most common, and a variety of instruments are used to measure this type of hardness.   The indenter, which is either a ball, cone, or pyramid, is usually made of hard steel or diamond and is most commonly used under static loads. The load to produce a given depth of indentation or the indentation produced by a given load is used to measure hardness.   In the *Brinell hardness test*, a spherical ball in contact with a flat specimen of the material is subjected to a given compressive load as illustrated in Fig. 1-16.   The diameter of the indentation is measured by an optical micrometer and the hardness is defined by the Brinell hardness number, which equals the applied load divided by the area of the surface of indentation.   The Brinell hardness number is expressed by the equation

$$B = \frac{2P}{\pi D(D - \sqrt{D^2 - d^2})} \tag{1-24}$$

where P = the applied load in kilograms, D = the diameter of the steel ball in millimeters (usually 10 mm.), and d = the diameter of the indentation in millimeters.   Brinell hardness numbers as calculated by eq. (1-24) are listed in tables as given by A.S.T.M. Specification E-10 for various diameters of the indentation.

The *Rockwell test* is also an indentation hardness test, but differs from the Brinell test in the use of smaller indenters and smaller loads. In the Rockwell test the depth of indentation is measured and a dial indicator records an arbitrary number related inversely to the depth of indentation.   There are other indentation-type hardness testing machines including the Vickers, Monotron, and Herbert machines. The Brinell and Rockwell machines, however, are the most common ones used in this country.

The *scleroscope* is a dynamic-type machine used for measuring hardness by determining the rebound height of a small indenter dropped from a fixed height onto the surface to be measured.

The *Vickers hardness tester* is not as commonly used in this country as the Rockwell and Brinell testers, although in recent years it is found in many American testing laboratories.   It is of particular value for hard or thin materials where a spot hardness is required.

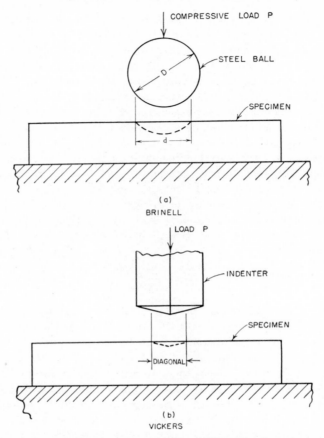

Fig. 1-16.   Indentations by Brinell and Vickers hardness testers.

It is similar to the Brinell tester in that an indentation is made and the hardness is determined from the ratio P/A where P is the load in kilograms and A is the surface area of the indentation in square millimeters.   The indenter is a four-sided inverted pyramid with an apex angle of 136°.   The Vickers hardness number, or load divided by surface area of contact, is

$$V = \frac{1.854P}{D} \tag{1-25}$$

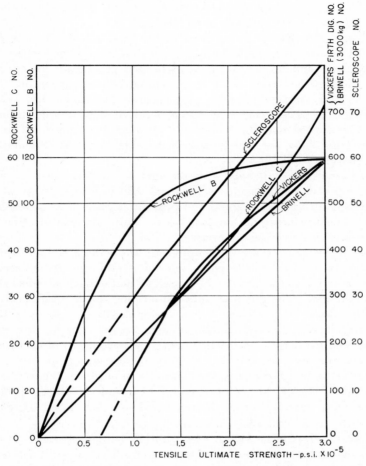

Fig. 1-17.   Approximate relation between hardness numbers and tensile
ultimate strengths of structural steels.

where P = the load in kilograms and D = the average length of the
two diagonals of the impression in the plane of the surface of the
metal measured in millimeters (Fig. 1-16b).

Different values of the load can be applied in the Vickers test by
adding weights to a scale pan.   The diagonal of the square is meas-

ured by a microscope and charts are used for finding the Vickers hardness number V as given in eq. (1-25).

Figure 1-17 gives a comparison of the hardness numbers as obtained by the Rockwell, Brinell, Vickers, and scleroscope testers.

Abrasion and *wear* tests have been used principally for paving materials. Such tests have been employed experimentally for metals and concrete surfaces. For concrete aggregates and brick, a number of pieces comprising a sample are tumbled in a drum for a specified period and the percentage of wear determined. This is called the *rattler test* and is described in the A.S.T.M. Standards, designations C-131 and C-7.

Machinability of metals is determined by various special tests. The depth of a hole made by a special drill in a given time while operating at a constant speed and pressure is selected as a measure of cutting hardness and machinability. This test, named after its originator, is known as the *Bauer drill test*.

Resistance to scratching is measured by the scratch test, in which an arbitrary scale is employed in terms of several common materials. Each material in this group will scratch all materials of a lower hardness number. The group of minerals forming this minerologists' or Mohs's scale are, in order of increasing hardness, talc, gypsum, calcite, fluorite, apatite, feldspar, quartz, topaz, sapphire or corundum, and diamond. In recent years the development of extremely hard abrasives has made it necessary to devise a more adequate hardness scale. For this reason the range of hardness between feldspar and diamond has been extended to include in order, vitreous pure silica, quartz, topaz, garnet, fused zirconia, fused alumina, silicon carbide, and boron carbide.

Use of Hardness Tests. In addition to determining the degree of hardness of materials relative to each other, hardness tests are employed to determine the uniformity of samples of a metal or the uniformity of results of some treatment such as heat treatment or case-hardening. Furthermore, correlations between hardness and strength have made it possible to determine approximately the tensile strength of steels from hardness test results. In Fig. 1-17 the variation in tensile strength values is shown for structural steels, with the hardness numbers determined using four methods.

PROBLEMS

1-1. (a). The following data were obtained from a tension test of an aluminum alloy:

Load (pounds)	Elongation (inches)	Load (pounds)	Elongation (inches)
0	0	7200	0.0070
1000	0.0010	8000	0.0080
2100	0.0020	8300	0.0090
3200	0.0030	8600	0.0100
4200	0.0040	8700	0.0120
5200	0.0050	8750	0.0140
6200	0.0060	8800	0.0180
		(fracture load)	

The specimen was of circular cross section with 0.50-in. diameter and 2-in. gage length. Plot the stress-strain diagram, using the above results.

(b). From the stress-strain diagram of Prob. 1-1(a) determine the following strength values: (1) proportional limit; (2) Johnson's apparent elastic limit; (3) yield strength, using the A.S.T.M. offset method with an offset of 0.2%.

1-2. Using the stress-strain diagram of Prob. 1-1(a), find: (a) the modulus of elasticity; (b) the modulus of elastic resilience based on the A.S.T.M. offset yield strength.

1-3. In a tension test of steel the ultimate load is 13,100 lb. and the extension 0.52 in. The diameter of the specimen is 0.50 in. and the gage length 2.0 in. Determine: (a) the ultimate strength; (b) the ductility; (c) the toughness index number.

Ans. $S_u = 66,900$ psi, $D_e = 26\%$, $T_0 = 17,400$ in. lb./cu. in.

1-4. The following load-elongation data results from an axial tension test on an SAE 1020 steel specimen. The initial gage length is 2 in., the initial diameter is 0.505 in., and the final diameter is 0.391 in. Calculate the stresses and strains from the data given, and plot two stress-strain diagrams on the same sheet showing: (a) all the data; (b) the data from $e = 0$ to $e = 0.0098$ in.

Load (pounds)	Elongation (inches)	Load (pounds)	Elongation (inches)
600	0	8,500	0.0058
1200	0.0002	8,500	.0068
1800	.0004	8,400	.0080
2400	.0006	8,200	.0098
3000	.0008	8,200	.020
3600	.0010	8,400	.030
4200	.0012	9,400	.050
4800	.0014	10,600	.075
5400	.0016	11,400	.100
6000	.0018	12,300	.150
6500	.0020	12,800	.200
7000	.0023	13,500	.300
7400	.0026	13,700	.380
8000	.0032	13,100	.450
8300	.0038	11,500	.500 (fracture)

From the curves drawn, calculate the following mechanical properties:

(a) proportional limit
(b) upper yield point
(c) lower yield point
(d) yield stress at 0.2% offset (A.S.T.M. offset yield strength)
(e) Johnson's apparent elastic limit
(f) tangent modulus of elasticity at 65,000 psi
(g) secant modulus of elasticity at 65,000 psi
(h) modulus of elastic resilience
(i) total elastic resilience for the 2-in. gage length
(j) ultimate stress
(k) nominal fracture stress
(l) true fracture stress
(m) percentage elongation in 2-in. gage length
(n) final gage length
(o) percentage reduction in area
(p) modulus of toughness
(q) toughness index number
(r) total toughness for the 2-in. gage length.

1-5.   For a tension test of cast iron the following stress and strain values were determined:

Stress (psi)	Strain (in./in.)	Stress (psi)	Strain (in./in.)
0	0	13,000	0.00075
2500	0.00010	16,000	0.0010
5000	0.00022	20,000	0.0014
8000	0.00040	23,000	0.0017
9500	0.00050	24,500	0.0020
		27,000	0.0025

Plot the stress-strain diagram and determine: (a) the initial tangent modulus; (b) the secant modulus based on a stress of 20,000 psi.

1-6. For a concrete test cylinder 8 in. in diameter and with a gage length of 10 in., the compressive loads and corresponding deformations are:

Load (pounds)	Deformation (inches)	Load (pounds)	Deformation (inches)
0	0	36,000	0.00421
4,000	0.00026	40,000	0.00609
8,000	0.00053	44,000	0.00692
12,000	0.00081	48,000	0.00922
16,000	0.00113	52,000	0.01177
20,000	0.00158	56,000	0.01575
24,000	0.00206	58,000	0.01847
28,000	0.00260	60,000	Failed
32,000	0.00327		

Plot the stress-strain diagram using these data and determine: (a) the secant modulus based on a stress of 650 psi; (b) the initial tangent modulus; (c) the average modulus of toughness using the area under the stress-strain diagram.

1-7. (a) A tension member in a construction is required to resist a load of 200,000 lb. The length of the member is 10 ft. If the material to be used is steel with an ultimate strength of 95,000 psi, a modulus $E = 30 \times 10^6$ psi and the factor of safety is 5, determine the cross-sectional area required.

(b) If the member in Prob. 1-7(a) is to have a maximum allowable elongation of 0.10 in., what is the required area?

(c) What area should be selected to meet both requirements of strength and deformation?

Ans. (a) $A = 10.5$ sq. in.; (b) $A = 8.0$ sq. in.; (c) $A = 10.5$ sq. in.

1-8. (a) What is the allowable resilience in in. lb. per unit volume in Prob. 1-7 based on the area selected? (b) How does the resilience computed in Prob. 1-8(a) compare with the modulus of elastic resilience using a yield stress of 55,000 psi?   *Ans.* $u_a = 6.01$ in. lb. per cu. in.

$$u_y = 50.4 \text{ in. lb. per cu. in.}$$

1-9.   (a) A tension test specimen is 0.5 in. in diameter and has a gage length of 2 in.   The yield-point load is 21,000 lb. and the total strain at the yield load is 0.0070 in.   Determine the possible percentage error in yield stress if the yield load is in error by $+200$ lb. and the diameter is in error by -0.01 in.

(b) What is the percentage error in the modulus E in Prob. 1-9(a) if the error in the strain at yield is 0.0002 in.?   Use $P = 21,000$ lb. and a diameter of 0.50 in. as the correct values.

(c) What is the percentage error in the modulus of elastic resilience considering possible errors in stress and strain as determined in Probs. 1-9(a) and (b)?

1-10.   A tension member in a structure is 10 ft. long and is subjected to a load of 200,000 lb.   There is a choice between two materials, (a) a structural nickel steel at 7 cents per lb., and (b) an aluminum alloy at 15 cents per lb.   Select the most economical material if the ultimate strength of the structural nickel steel is 95,000 psi and the aluminum alloy 51,200 psi.   The densities of the steel and aluminum alloy are, respectively, 0.284 and 0.102 lb. per cu. in.   Use a factor of safety of 5.

Ans. $C_{st} = \$25.10$ and $C_{al} = \$35.80$.

1-11.   Solve Prob. 1-10 based on yield strengths of 55,000 and 18,500 psi respectively for the structural nickel steel and aluminum alloy.   Use a factor of safety of 2.

1-12.   Determine the required cross-sectional areas of the members in Prob. 1-10 and compare the costs if the members are designed on the basis of a limiting elongation of 0.10 in.   Use values of $E_{st} = 30 \times 10^6$ psi and $E_{al} = 10.5 \times 10$ psi.   *Ans.* $C_{st} = \$19.00$ and $C_{al} = \$41.90$.

1-13.   For the tension member in Prob. 1-10 determine the working stresses for each material based on an allowable elastic resilience of 2.5 in. lb. per cu. in.   Using these working stresses, determine the cross-sectional areas required and compare costs of the two members.   The moduli of elasticity for the steel and aluminum alloy are 30×10^6 and 10.5×10^6 psi respectively.   *Ans.* $C_{st} = \$39.00$ and $C_{al} = \$50.70$.

1-14.   A $\frac{1}{2}$-inch-diameter rod of a magnesium alloy is 10 ft. long.   It has a modulus of elasticity of 6.5×10^6 psi, a yield strength of 29,000 psi, and an ultimate strength of 44,000 psi.   Determine: (a) the load required to produce an extension of $\frac{1}{8}$ in.; (b) the load to produce yielding; (c) the maximum load that can be resisted.

Ans.   (a) $P = 1330$ lb.;   (b) $P = 5690$ lb.;   (c) $P = 8610$ lb.

1-15. A round rod of structural steel 2 in. in diameter and 10 ft. long is used for a balcony hanger to support a static axial tensile load of 80,000 lb. If the ultimate stress is 65,000 psi and the yield stress is 35,000 psi, what are the factors of safety (a) with respect to yielding, and (b) with respect to the ultimate strength?

1-16. A 24S-T aluminum alloy tube has an outside diameter of 2 in. and a wall thickness of 0.065 in. It supports a tensile load of 15,000 lb. What is the factor of safety with respect to yield if the yield strength is 45,000 psi?

Ans. $F = 1.2$.

1-17. Two structural steel plates 2 in. wide by $\frac{1}{2}$ in. thick are connected by a single rivet 1 in. in diameter using a lap joint. An axial ultimate tensile load of 20,000 lb. is applied to the connection. If the ultimate shear strength of the rivet is 44,000 psi, the ultimate tensile strength of the plate is 55,000 psi, and the bearing strength is 95,000 psi, determine the factors of safety with respect to the three types of stress.

Ans. $F_t = 1.37$, $F_c = 2.38$, $F_s = 1.73$.

1-18. A single rivet is used to connect two plates 3 in. wide and $\frac{1}{2}$ in. thick. Determine the diameter of the rivet if the factors of safety for tension and shear are equal and if the ultimate strengths in tension and shear are, respectively, 55,000 and 44,000 psi. *Ans.* $d = 1.20$ in.

1-19. Solve Prob. 1-18 if the factors of safety in bearing and tension are to be equal and if the bearing strength is 95,000 psi.

1-20. The piston of a steam engine is 18 in. in diameter and is subjected to a steam pressure of 300 psi. If the diameter of the piston rod is 3 in., what was the design stress for this rod? What factor of safety was used if the ultimate stress was 90,000 psi?

1-21. Determine the strength-weight ratios of the steel and aluminum alloys in Prob. 1-10. *Ans.* 558 and 840.

1-22. Compare the strength-weight ratios of four tension members each 4 ft. long and 2 sq. in. in cross-sectional area. They are made of a steel alloy, an aluminum alloy, a magnesium alloy, and a laminated glass plastic. The ultimate stresses are, respectively, 70,000, 68,000, 44,000, and 40,000 psi. The moduli of elasticity are, respectively, 30×10^6, 10.6×10^6, 6.5×10^6, and 1.5×10^6 psi. The densities of the materials are, respectively, 0.284, 0.100, 0.065, and 0.060 lb. per cu. in. Determine the strength-weight ratio based on (a) the ultimate strengths of the materials, and (b) an allowable elongation of 0.05 in. *Ans.* (a) 5150, 14,200, 14,100, and 13,900; (b) 2290, 2300, 2170, and 540.

1-23. Solve Prob. 1-22 based on the yield strengths in compression if the values of the yield stresses for the four materials are, respectively, 35,000, 46,000, 18,000, and 35,000 psi.

1-24. For a factor of safety of 5 based on the ultimate strengths in tension, determine the allowable load for each of the four materials in Prob. 1-22.

$Ans.$ $P_s = 28,000$ lb., $P_a = 27,200$ lb.,
$P_m = 17,600$ lb., $P_p = 16,000$ lb.

1-25. A true stress-strain diagram for a 1020 semi-killed steel was obtained in tension, using a specimen of circular cross section. For the plastic range the readings of load and diameter were:

Load (pounds)	Diameter (inches)	Load (pounds)	Diameter (inches)
3500	0.352	5800	0.316
4300	0.350	5700	0.302
4800	0.347	5600	0.290
5175	0.344	5300	0.270
5400	0.340	5050	0.260
5650	0.334	4950	0.255
5775	0.324	4650 (rupture)	0.235

The original diameter of the specimen was 0.364 in. Determine the true stress and true strain values and plot the true stress-strain diagram.

1-26. Plot the data for Prob. 1-25 on log-log graph paper and determine the strength coefficient k and the strain-hardening exponent n.

$Ans.$ $n = 0.29$, $k = 106,000$ psi.

1-27. For the steel in Prob. 1-25, what are the true ultimate stress (true stress at maximum load), true rupture stress, and the true ductility as defined by the true fracture strain? Compare the foregoing true values with their nominal values.

$Ans.$ *True values:* $S_u' = 74,000$ psi; $S_f' = 107,300$ psi; $D_e' = 88\%$.
Nominal values: $S_u = 55,600$ psi, $S_f = 44,500$ psi, $D_e = 140\%$.

1-28. Indicate on the stress-strain diagram in Prob. 1-25 the theoretical maximum load or point of instability. Compare this load with the actual maximum load.

1-29. Based on the calculated data of Prob. 1-25, determine the nominal stress and strain values and plot the nominal stress-strain results on the same diagram as the true stress-strain curve for purpose of comparison.

1-30. In a tension test of copper-zinc alloy using a 0.505 in. diameter specimen with a 2-in. gage length, the following data were recorded for the plastic range:

Load (pounds)	Strain (inches)	Load (pounds)	Strain (inches)
4000	0.016	10,000	0.50
6000	0.080	10,400	0.60
8000	0.180	10,600	0.70
9000	0.30	10,800	0.80
9600	0.40	10,600	0.90
		9,200	1.96

The last readings of load and strain given above are for fracture. Plot the nominal and true stress-strain diagrams, using the same origin.

1-31. Plot the true stress-strain data of Prob. 1-30 on log-log graph paper and determine the strength coefficient k and strain-hardening exponent n. *Ans.* $n = 0.37$, $k = 106,000$ psi.

1-32. For the alloy in Prob. 1-30, what are the true ultimate stress (true stress at maximum load), the true fracture stress, and the true ductility? Compare the true values obtained with the nominal values.

Ans. True values: $S_u' = 78,000$ psi; $S_f' = 91,000$ psi; $D_e' = 68\%$.

Nominal values: $S_u = 54,000$ psi; $S_f = 46,000$ psi; $D_e = 98\%$.

1-33. Determine the theoretical maximum load for Prob. 1-30 and compare with the actual value.

1-34. Plot the true stress versus the logarithm of the true strain, using the results obtained in Prob. 1-31. Draw the best straight line through the test points and obtain the equation of the line.

1-35. Using the tension stress-strain diagrams obtained in Prob. 1-30 compare the true and nominal toughness of the material based on the areas under the stress-strain diagrams.

BIBLIOGRAPHY

Batson, R. G., and Hyde, J. H., "Mechanical Testing," Vol. 1, *Testing of Materials of Construction*, Chapman and Hall, London (Dutton, New York), 1922.

Davis, H. E., Troxell, G. E., and Wiskocil, C. T., *The Testing and Inspection of Engineering Materials*, McGraw-Hill Book Co., Inc., New York, 1941.

Gilkey, H. J., Murphy, G., and Bergman, E. O., *A Manual of Materials Testing*, McGraw-Hill Book Co., Inc., New York, 1941.

Moore, H. F., *Materials of Engineering*, McGraw-Hill Book Co., Inc., New York, 1941, 6th Ed.

Murphy, G., *Properties of Engineering Materials*, International Textbook Co., Scranton, Pa., 1947.

Timoshenko, S., *Strength of Materials*, D. Van Nostrand Co., Inc., New York, 1941, Vol. 2, Chap. VII.

Timoshenko, S., and Lessels, J. M., *Applied Elasticity*, Westinghouse Technical Night School Press, East Pittsburgh, 1925, Part II.

Withey, M. O., and Aston, J., *Johnson's Materials of Construction*, John Wiley & Sons, Inc., New York, 1939, 8th Ed.

Young, J. F., *Materials and Processes*, John Wiley & Sons, Inc., New York, 1944.

Metals Handbook, American Society for Metals, Cleveland, Ohio, 1948 Edition.

Chapter 2

Static Properties in Shear and Bending

A. SHEAR PROPERTIES

Many structural and machine members are subjected to loads that produce shear stresses. It is desirable, therefore, to study the behavior of materials subjected to such stresses. Two main types of shear stresses are studied in the laboratory; namely, direct or transverse shear stresses as found in rivets, bolts, and beams, and torsional shear stresses produced in crankshafts, line shafts, and springs.

2-1. MECHANICAL PROPERTIES IN DIRECT SHEAR

In the direct shear test the procedure is usually to clamp a prismatic specimen of the material as shown in Fig. 2-1(a) so that bending stresses are minimized across the section along which the shear load is applied. This method of testing is used to give an indication of the ultimate shear strength in rivets, wooden blocks, crank pins, bolts, and other members that resist direct shear loads. However, because of bending, non-uniform shear stress distribution, and errors due to friction between parts of the tool, the strength values obtained are only approximations of the true shear strength. The accuracy of the direct shear test is partly dependent upon the sharpness of the edges of the hardened plates that bear on the specimen. The direct shear test, furthermore, gives limited information, since it cannot be used to determine the yield strength and modulus of elasticity, as it is impossible in this test to measure strains adequately. The punching shear test is also a form of the direct shear test. Its use is limited to tests of flat stock, usually made of metal.

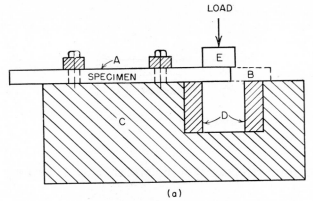

JOHNSON'S SHEAR TOOL FOR SHEAR TEST
OF METALS IN ROUND OR RECTANGULAR STOCK

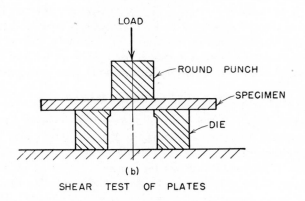

(b)

SHEAR TEST OF PLATES

LOAD ← ————— 45° ————— → LOAD
                        45°

(c)

SLOTTED SPECIMEN FOR SHEAR TEST OF FLAT PLATES

Fig. 2-1.

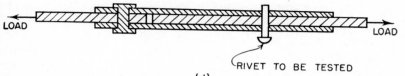

(d)

SHEAR TEST DEVICE FOR RIVETS

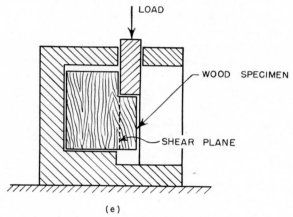

(e)

SHEAR DEVICE FOR TESTS OF WOOD

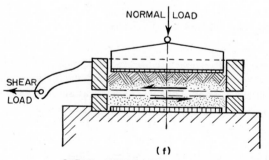

(f)

SHEAR DEVICE FOR TESTS OF SOILS

Fig. 2-1 (Cont'd).

Several types of tests have been devised for the direct shear test of materials, as illustrated in Figs. 2-1. In the Johnson shear tool, a bar of rectangular cross section, 1 by 2 in., or a cylindrical rod about 1 in. in diameter is used for the specimen. The specimen A is clamped to a base C, as indicated in Fig. 2-1(a). The compressive load applied to the tool E ruptures the specimen in single shear. If the specimen is extended to B and the gap between the dies D is bridged, the specimen will fail in double shear. In either case the ultimate shear strength is taken as the maximum load divided by the shear area. In the case of single shear, the shear area is the cross-sectional area of the specimen, while in double shear it is twice the cross-sectional area of the specimen.

A round punching device, as illustrated in Fig. 2-1(b), is sometimes used for metal plates to determine the direct shear strength. Another type of direct shear test for metals is illustrated in Fig. 2-1(c). In this test a slotted specimen is used. The device shown in Fig. 2-1(d) has been used for shear tests of rivets. A special tool and specimen (Fig. 2-1e), developed by the Forest Products Laboratory, is generally used for direct shear tests of wood. A direct shear test of soils is made as illustrated in Fig. 2-1(f). Most of the foregoing direct shear tests are performed in a Universal testing machine.

In the direct shear test the only quantity that is observed during the test is the maximum load resisted, equal to P. The average shearing strength of the material is then equal to P/A, where A is the shear area. The shear strength in single shear for rivets has been found to be greater than the double shear value, by as much as twenty per cent.

2-2. MECHANICAL PROPERTIES IN TORSION

Torsion tests are usually made on solid specimens of circular cross section.[1] They are made in special testing machines provided with a pendulum or hydraulic method of torque measurement. Various instruments are used to measure the strain or angle of twist of the specimen for a given gage length as the torque load is applied. In a torsion test, measurements are made of the twisting moments T and angles of twist θ for a gage length L as the torque is gradually applied. From these readings a torque-twist diagram is obtained,

---

[1] For a complete discussion of torsion tests see "The Torsion Test," by Albert Sauveur, *Proc. A.S.T.M.*, 1938, Vol. 38, p. 3.

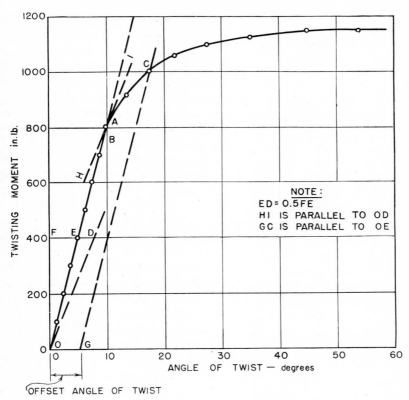

Fig. 2-2.   Torque-twist diagram for brass.

as shown in Fig. 2-2.   The information given in a torque-twist diagram can be used to determine the mechanical properties in torsion.

The *elastic strength* is obtained by using the elastic torque as determined by Johnson's apparent elastic limit (point *A*, Fig. 2-2) or by using the torque at the proportional limit (point *B*, Fig. 2-2).   If T_p is the value of either of these torques, then the elastic torsional strength is measured by the shear stress

$$S_{sp} = \frac{T_p r}{J} \tag{2-1}$$

where r = the radius and J = the polar moment of inertia of the circular cross section = $\pi r^4/2$ for a solid circular cross section.

For a hollow circular specimen the polar moment of inertia equals the polar moment of inertia of the outside circle (J_o) minus that of the inside (J_i), or

$$S_{sp} = \frac{T_p r}{J_o - J_i} \qquad (2\text{-}1a)$$

The yield strength in torsion is sometimes measured by using an offset angle of twist to determine the yield torque as indicated by point C in Fig. 2-2. If the torque corresponding to point C is T_y, then the yield strengths for solid and hollow sections become

$$S_{sy} = \frac{T_y r}{J} \qquad (2\text{-}2)$$

and

$$S_{sy} = \frac{T_y r}{J_o - J_i} \qquad (2\text{-}2a)$$

The *apparent maximum strength in torsion* is usually calculated by using eq. (2-1) or (2-1a) but replacing the torque T_p by the maximum or ultimate torque T_u. The value of the stress calculated in this way is called the *modulus of rupture*. Then for solid and hollow circular sections, respectively,

$$S_{su} = \frac{T_u r}{J} \qquad (2\text{-}3)$$

and

$$S_{su} = \frac{T_u r}{J_o - J_i} \qquad (2\text{-}3a)$$

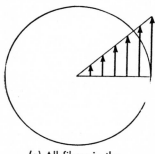

(a) All fibers in the elastic range

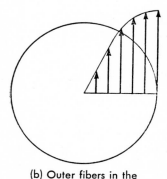

(b) Outer fibers in the plastic range

Fig. 2-3. Shear stress distribution in torsion.

It should be noted that, since eqs. (2-3) and (2-3a) are based on Hooke's law, the stresses determined are not the actual maximum shear stresses on the outer fibers of the maximum torque. In the plastic range the shear stress distribution is non-linear, as indicated in Fig. 2-3(b), and not linear as shown in Fig. 2-3(a) for the elastic case. The strengths obtained using the elastic equations, although not the exact values, give an index of the ultimate strength in torsion.   For comparing and selecting materials, the shear strengths calculated using the foregoing equations are sufficiently accurate.

For special determinations of maximum torsional strength, where greater accuracy is required, thin-walled tubes of circular cross section are used.   For such specimens the shear stresses are uniform.

A more accurate measurement of the maximum strength in torsion for solid specimens than is given by eqs. (2-3) and (2-3a) has been obtained by the theory of plasticity, using the torque-twist diagram. It is shown by this theory that the shear stress on the outer fiber, corresponding to the torque T, is

$$S_s = \left(\frac{1}{2\pi r^3}\right)\left(3T + \theta\frac{dT}{d\theta}\right) \tag{2-3b}$$

In applying this equation to find the stress S_s, the value in the bracket can be obtained from the torque-twist diagram, as shown in Fig. 2-4, by noting that it is equal to $[3\overline{AC} + \overline{DB}(\overline{AB}/\overline{DB})] = (3\overline{AC} + \overline{AB})$. For brittle materials such as cast iron, eq. (2-3b) gives an accurate value of the shear stresses in a solid circular shaft.   For ductile

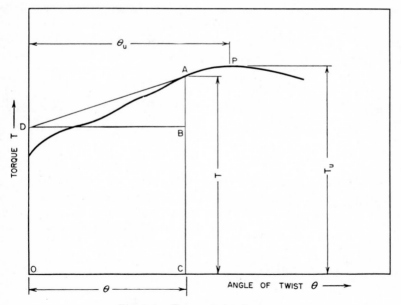

Fig. 2-4.   Torque-twist diagram.

materials the large deformations produced make the application of eq. (2-3b) somewhat inaccurate, yet more accurate than the elastic theory.

Referring to the torque-twist diagram of Fig. 2-4, the shear stress on the outer fiber corresponding to the maximum torque (point P) can be obtained by eq. (2-3b), since by Fig. 2-4 the maximum torque occurs where the slope of the curve $dT/d\theta = 0$. Then placing $T = T_u$ (the maximum or ultimate torque) and $dT/d\theta = 0$ in eq. (2-3b),

$$S_{su} = \frac{3T_u}{2\pi r^3} \tag{2-3c}$$

A comparison of eqs. (2-3) and (2-3c) shows that the modulus of rupture given by eq. (2-3) is $33\frac{1}{3}$ per cent higher than the more correct value given by eq. (2-3c).

The type of specimen fracture in shear differs from that for both tension and compression since there is essentially no reduction in area or elongation. For materials that fail in shear in a torsion test of a solid bar, the fractured surface is a plane normal to the axis of the specimen, as shown in Fig. 2-5(a). For ductile materials, such as steel, the fracture is commonly silky in texture. For materials in which the tensile strength is less than the shear strength, as in the case of cast iron or concrete, failure occurs by separation in tension along a helicoidal surface, as shown in Fig. 2-5(b). The heli-

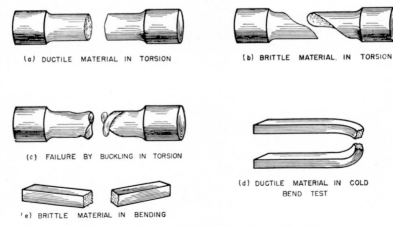

(a) DUCTILE MATERIAL IN TORSION   (b) BRITTLE MATERIAL IN TORSION

(c) FAILURE BY BUCKLING IN TORSION

(d) DUCTILE MATERIAL IN COLD
BEND TEST

(e) BRITTLE MATERIAL IN BENDING

Fig. 2-5.   Types of failure in torsion and bending.

coidal type of fracture can be reproduced by applying torsion manually to a piece of chalk.

Thin-walled tubular specimens of ductile materials with a reduced section greater in length than the diameter will fail by buckling if the wall is too thin (Fig. 2-5c).

Stiffness in torsion is measured by the modulus of elasticity in shear E_s, as determined from the equation $\theta = \dfrac{TL}{E_sJ}$. That is,

$$E_s = \frac{TL}{\theta J} \tag{2-4}$$

where L = the gage length of the specimen and J = the polar moment of inertia = $\pi r^4/2$ for a solid circular section, and $(J_o - J_i)$ = the polar moment of inertia for a hollow section, T = the torque in in. lb. for some point on the elastic straight-line portion of the torque-twist diagram, and θ = the angle of twist in radians, corresponding to the torque T. The modulus of elasticity in shear, as defined by eq. (2-4), is often called the *modulus of rigidity*.

Ductility in torsion indicates, as for tension, the ability of a material to deform in the plastic range. Ductility in torsion is sometimes measured by the percentage elongation of the outer fiber which is equal to

$$D_t = \left(\frac{L' - L}{L}\right) 100 \tag{2-5}$$

where L = the original length of the outer fiber, and L' = the final length of the outer fiber. The value of L' is computed from L and $r\theta$.

The value of ductility as defined by eq. (2-5) is not the one commonly used. It is the usual practice to specify the angle of twist at fracture for a given gage length and specimen diameter.

Resilience in torsion is measured by the modulus of resilience, which represents the average energy per unit volume required to stress a material to the proportional limit. The value of the modulus of resilience can be obtained by dividing the total work or strain energy produced in loading to the proportional limit by the volume of the specimen included within the gage length L. That is,

$$u_s = \frac{T_p \theta_p}{2}\left(\frac{1}{AL}\right) \tag{2-6}$$

where T_p = the torque at the proportional limit, θ_p = the angle of twist in radians for a gage length L at the proportional limit load, A = the cross-sectional area, and L = the gage length.

For a *solid circular specimen*, since $\theta_p = \dfrac{T_p L}{E_s J}$, and noting that $S_{sp} = \dfrac{T_p r}{J}$ or $T_p = \dfrac{S_{sp} J}{r}$, then by eq. (2-6),

$$
\begin{aligned}
u_s &= \frac{T_p \, \theta_p}{2AL} = \frac{T_p^2 L}{(E_s J)(2AL)} \\
&= \left(\frac{S_{sp}J}{r}\right)^2 \frac{L}{(E_s J)(2AL)} \\
&= \frac{S_{sp}^2}{2E_s}\left(\frac{J}{Ar^2}\right)
\end{aligned}
$$

or
$$
u_s = \frac{S_{sp}^2}{4E_s} \tag{2-7a}
$$

If the proportional limit S_{sp} is replaced by the shear yield stress S_{sy}, the modulus of elastic resilience for a solid circular cross section is approximately determined by the equation

$$
u_s = \frac{S_{sy}^2}{4E_s} \tag{2-7b}
$$

The modulus of resilience in torsion, as defined by eq. (2-7b), is measured in in. lb. per cu. in. since S_{sy} and E_s are in psi, and thus $S_{sy}/(4E_s)$ is in psi or in. lb. per cu. in.

A comparison of the value u_s, as given by eq. (2-7b), with the value as given for tension [equal to $S_{yp}^2/(2E)$], shows that the value in shear is $\frac{1}{2}$ the value in tension. This is true because the strain energy per unit volume obtained for torsion represents the average value for a specimen of circular cross section in which the shear stress varies throughout the cross section and does not remain uniform as in simple tension. In torsion the variation in stress is linear, with a maximum value on the outer fiber and zero at the center.

Although torsion tests are usually made on solid specimens of circular cross section, as considered in the foregoing discussion, thin-walled tubular specimens are used for more accurate results. A thin-walled specimen should be used because, with such a specimen, a uniform shear stress distribution is obtained and the "strengthening effect" of the inner fibers in the solid specimen is eliminated.

For ultimate shear strength determination, tubular specimens should have short reduced sections with a ratio of length of reduced section to diameter (L/d) of about 0.5, and a diameter-to-thickness ratio (d/t) of about 10 to 12.   For yield strength and modulus of elasticity determinations, a tubular specimen with a length of at least 10 diameters and a d/t ratio of about 8 to 10 are recommended.   For larger ratios of d/t there is a tendency to failure by buckling.   In torsion tests with thin-walled circular specimens, the ends should be plugged so that the pressure from the jaws of the testing machine will not collapse the specimen.

For a thin-walled tubular specimen of circular cross section of inside diameter d and wall thickness t subjected to a torque T, the shear stress is obtained by noting that the total shear force is equal to the shear stress S_s times the area $t\pi d$.   Then the resisting torque, equal to the applied torque, is $(S_s t\pi d)(d/2 + t) = T$, or

$$S_s = \frac{2T}{t\pi d(d + 2t)} \qquad (2\text{-}8a)$$

The *elastic torsional strength* for a thin-walled tubular specimen is obtained from the foregoing equation by replacing T with the torque at the proportional limit, T_p.   Then the elastic torsional strength is

$$S_{sp} = \frac{2T_p}{t\pi d(d + 2t)} \qquad (2\text{-}8b)$$

Some of the properties in torsion can be compared to those in tension.   For example, tests on thin-walled tubular specimens in torsion show that the yield strength in torsion for ductile metals is about 0.6 the yield strength in tension.

The *angle of twist* can be obtained by noting that the shear strain is $\epsilon_s = S_s/E_s$, where E_s is the modulus of elasticity in shear or the modulus of rigidity.   For a gage length L, the total circumferential movement is $\epsilon_s L = S_s L/E_s$.   Then the angle of twist θ for a length L is the strain $\epsilon_s L$ divided by the radius $(d/2 + t)$, or

$$\theta = \frac{\epsilon_s L}{(d/2 + t)} = \frac{2S_s L}{E_s(d + 2t)} = \frac{4TL}{\pi E_s \, td(d + 2t)^2} \qquad (2\text{-}9)$$

The *stiffness in torsion* can be obtained from eq. (2-9) by solving for E_s.   Then

$$E_s = \frac{4TL}{\pi\theta \, td(d + 2t)^2} \qquad (2\text{-}10)$$

The *modulus of elastic resilience* for a thin-walled tubular specimen is the work done per unit volume in stressing the specimen to the proportional limit. Since this stress is assumed to be uniform and equal to S_{sp}, the modulus of resilience in torsion is

$$u_s = \frac{(S_{sp})(\epsilon_s)}{2} = \frac{S_{sp}{}^2}{2E_s} \tag{2-11}$$

Toughness in torsion is sometimes measured by the strain energy, or work done per unit volume required to rupture the specimen. That is, the toughness is the area under the torque-twist diagram up to fracture divided by the volume of the specimen AL for the gage length L. An approximate value of the toughness for ductile materials is obtained by using $T_u\theta_f$ as the approximate value of the area under the torque-twist diagram, where T_u is the maximum torque and θ_f is the angle of twist at fracture in radians. Then the approximate value of the average strain energy per unit volume required to fracture the specimen, or the toughness, is equal to

$$u_f = \frac{T_u\theta_f}{AL} \tag{2-12}$$

The toughness value u_f is measured in in. lb. per cu. in., since T_u is measured in in. lb., θ_f is measured in radians, A is measured in in.², and L is measured in in.

In the study of Strength of Materials it is shown that the modulus of rigidity is theoretically related to the modulus of elasticity in tension by the equation

$$E_s = \frac{E}{2(1 + \mu)} \tag{2-13}$$

where μ = Poisson's ratio.

The value of the modulus of rigidity E_s, as given by eq. (2-13), does not agree with values obtained in torsion tests. For example, 'or steel with values of $E = 30 \times 10^6$ psi and $\mu = 0.29$, the modulus $E_s = 11.6 \times 10^6$ psi. The experimental values of E_s for steel are usually over 12×10^6 psi. This discrepancy is partly explained by the theoretical assumptions made in eqs. (2-4) and (2-13) for E_s. Equation (2-13) can be used, however, to obtain an approximate value of Poisson's ratio when E_s and E are known.

NUMERICAL EXAMPLE. *Determination of Mechanical Properties in Torsion Using a Solid Round Specimen.* In a torsion test of a brass specimen 0.50 in. in diameter with a gage length of 8 in., the torque at yield was found to be 950 in. lb. The maximum torque was 1400 in. lb. and the angle of twist at rupture was 515°. On the straight-line part of the torque-twist diagram a torque of 850 in. lb. corresponded to an angle of twist of 10 degrees. Determine the values of the following shear properties:

(a) the yield strength,
(b) the modulus of rupture,
(c) the modulus of rigidity,
(d) the approximate value of the modulus of resilience,
(e) the approximate value of the modulus of toughness,
(f) Poisson's ratio, if the modulus of elasticity in tension of the brass is 15.9×10^6 psi.

SOLUTION.   The yield strength in torsion is, by eq. (2-2),

$$S_{sy} = \frac{T_y r}{(\pi r^4/2)} = \frac{2 \times 950}{\pi \times 0.25^3} = 38{,}700 \text{ psi}$$

By eq. (2-3) the modulus of rupture is

$$S_{su} = \frac{T_u r}{J} = \frac{2T_u}{\pi r^3} = \frac{2 \times 1400}{\pi \times 0.25^3} = 57{,}100 \text{ psi}$$

The modulus of elasticity in shear, or modulus of rigidity, is defined by eq. (2-4) and is equal to

$$E_s = \frac{TL}{\theta J} = \frac{TL}{\theta(\pi r^4/2)}$$

or $\qquad E_s = \dfrac{2 \times 850 \times 8}{(10 \times \pi/180) \times \pi \times 0.25^4} = 6.35 \times 10^6 \text{ psi}$

The approximate value of the modulus of elastic resilience is, by eq. (2-7b),

$$u_s = \frac{S_{sy}^2}{4E_s} = \frac{(38{,}700)^2}{4 \times 6.32 \times 10^6} = 59.3 \text{ in. lb. per cu. in.}$$

By eq. (2-12) the approximate value of the modulus of toughness is

$$u_f = \frac{T_u \theta_f}{AL} = \frac{1400 \times 515 \times (\pi/180)}{\pi \times (0.25)^2 \times 8} = 8030 \text{ in. lb. per cu. in.}$$

The value of Poisson's ratio as determined by the moduli of elasticity in shear and tension is, by eq. (2-13),

$$\mu = \frac{E}{2E_s} - 1 = \frac{15.9}{2 \times 6.32} - 1 = 0.25$$

NUMERICAL EXAMPLE. *Determination of Mechanical Properties in Torsion of a Hollow Tubular Specimen.* In a torsion test of a fully heat-treated aluminum alloy, a tubular specimen with an internal diameter of 1 in. and a wall thickness of 0.10 in. was used. For a gage length of 2 in. the angle of twist was 0.2 degrees for a torque of 730 in. lb. The offset yield torque T_y was found to be 2460 in. lb. The angle of twist at fracture was 62 degrees and the torque at fracture was 4500 in. lb. Determine the following shear properties:

(a) the yield strength,
(b) the modulus of rupture,
(c) the modulus of rigidity,
(d) the approximate value of the modulus of resilience,
(e) the approximate value of the modulus of toughness.

SOLUTION. For a circular cross section with 1-in. internal diameter and 0.10-in. wall thickness the value of

$$J = J_o - J_i = (\pi/2)(0.6^4 - 0.5^4) = 0.105 \text{ in.}^4$$

The yield strength, from eq. (2-2), is

$$S_{sy} = \frac{T_y r}{J} = \frac{2460 \times 0.60}{0.105} = 14{,}100 \text{ psi}$$

The modulus of rupture is given by eq. (2-3), or

$$S_{su} = \frac{T_u r}{J} = \frac{4500 \times 0.60}{0.105} = 25{,}800 \text{ psi}$$

By eq. (2-4) the modulus of rigidity is

$$E_s = \frac{TL}{\theta J} = \frac{730 \times 2}{(0.2 \times \pi/180)(0.105)} = 3.99 \times 10^6 \text{ psi}$$

The modulus of resilience for a hollow cross section will be determined by eq. (2-6), or

$$u_s = \left(\frac{T_p \theta_p}{2}\right)\left(\frac{1}{AL}\right) = \left(\frac{T_p^2 L}{2E_s J}\right)\left(\frac{1}{AL}\right) = \frac{T_p^2}{2E_s JA}$$

And, since $S_{sp} = \dfrac{T_p r}{J}$,

$$u_s = \frac{S_{sp}^2 J}{2 E_s r^2 A}$$

Replacing S_{sp} by S_{sy} and using $A = A_o - A_i$,

$$u_s = \frac{S_{sy}^2 J}{2 E_s r^2 \pi (0.6^2 - 0.5^2)} = \frac{(14,100)^2 \, (0.105)}{2 \times 3.99 \times 10^6 \times 0.36 \times \pi \times 0.11}$$

$$= 21.1 \text{ in. lb. per cu. in.}$$

By eq. (2-12) the approximate value of the modulus of toughness becomes

$$u_f = \frac{T_u \theta_f}{AL} = \frac{4500 \times 62 \times (\pi/180)}{\pi \times 0.11 \times 2}$$

$$= 7040 \text{ in. lb. per cu. in.}$$

2-3. UTILIZATION OF TORSION PROPERTIES

Strength and stiffness are the usual considerations in the design of members (such as shafting) subjected to torsion. Adequate strength and stiffness are provided for by specifying the allowable design shear stress and allowable angle of twist for a given shaft length.

If the yield strength for a ductile material is not available, an approximate value can be obtained by selecting the yield strength in torsion equal to 0.6 the yield strength in tension. For some brittle materials, such as cast iron, the ultimate static strength in torsion and tension are about the same, so that the design stresses for tension and torsion may be assumed to be equal. Torsion members such as shafts are usually subjected to stress concentration which must be considered in evaluating strength. For example, the A.S.M.E. Code for Design of Transmission Shafting provides for a reduction in strength of 25 per cent to take care of the strength reduction produced by a keyway.

NUMERICAL EXAMPLE. A steel shaft 10 ft. long is 4 in. in diameter. The yield strength of the steel in torsion is 52,000 psi and the modulus of elasticity in shear is 12×10^6 psi. Determine the torque at yield, the angle of twist at yielding, and the strain energy to produce yielding.

SOLUTION.   The yield torque, using eq. (2-2), is

$$T_y = S_{sy} \frac{J}{r} = \frac{52,000 \times (\pi/2) \times 2^4}{2} = 653,000 \text{ in. lb.}$$

The angle of twist at yielding is found approximately by eq. (2-4),

or $$\theta_y = \frac{T_y L}{E_s J} = \frac{653,000 \times 120}{12 \times 10^6 \times (\pi/2)(2)^4} = 0.261 \text{ radians} = 15°$$

The strain energy required to produce yielding is

$$U = \frac{T_y \theta_y}{2} = \frac{653,000 \times 0.261}{2} = 85,000 \text{ in. lb.}$$

NUMERICAL EXAMPLE.   A shaft 4 in. in diameter has a yield strength in torsion of 52,000 psi and an angle of twist of 15° for a length of 10 ft.   If the shaft is designed for an allowable shear stress of 13,000 psi and an allowable angle of twist of 1 degree in 20 diameters of length, what are the factors of safety based on the yield strength, stiffness, and resilience?

SOLUTION.   With respect to strength, the factor of safety is

$$F_s = \frac{S_{sy}}{S_{sw}} = \frac{52,000}{13,000} = 4.0$$

The allowable angle of twist is $(L/20d)$ or 1.5 degrees.   Since the angle of twist producing yielding is 15 degrees, the factor of safety with regard to stiffness is $15/1.5 = 10.0$.

The allowable strain energy per unit volume is

$$u_s = S_{sw}^2/(4E_s) = 13,000^2/(4 \times 12 \times 10^6) = 3.52 \text{ in. lb. per cu. in.}$$

The allowable total strain energy is

$$u_s V = 3.52 \times \pi \times 2^2 \times 120 = 5300 \text{ in. lb.}$$

The ratio of the strain energy producing yielding to the allowable strain energy is

$$85,300/5300 = 16$$

Since strain energy is proportional to the square of the stress, the factor of safety ratio based on strain energy $= \sqrt{16} = 4$.

The above calculations show that the factors of safety differ depending upon the properties considered.

NUMERICAL EXAMPLE.   A hollow circular shaft of an alloy is 5 ft. long and has an inside diameter d_i equal to one-half the outside diameter d_o. The applied twisting moment is 420,000 in. lb. and $E_s = 4.0 \times 10^6$ psi. Determine the cross-sectional dimension if (a) the yield stress in shear is 32,000 psi and the factor of safety is 2.5, and (b) the allowable angle of twist is 1 degree in 20 outside diameters of length.

SOLUTION. The outer diameter based on the shear strength is determined from eq. (2-2a), using $d_i = d_o/2$. That is,

$$S_s = (Tr)/(J_o - J_i)$$

or
$$\frac{32,000}{2.5} = \frac{420,000 \times d_o/2}{(\pi/32)(d_o{}^4 - d_i{}^4)}$$

and
$$d_o = 5.64 \text{ in.} \quad \text{and} \quad d_i = 2.82 \text{ in.}$$

Equation (2-4) defines the outer diameter d_o if an allowable angle of twist $= \pi/180$ radians is used. That is,

$$\theta = \frac{TL}{E_sJ}$$

or
$$1 \times \frac{\pi}{180} = \frac{420,000 \times 20d_o}{4 \times 10^6 \times (\pi/32)(d_o{}^4 - d_i{}^4)}$$

and
$$d_o = 10.92 \text{ in.} \quad \text{and} \quad d_i = d_o/2 = 5.46 \text{ in.}$$

Comparing these with the previous values of d_o and d_i, the required values are $d_o = 10.92$ in. and $d_i = 5.46$ in.

Strength-Weight Ratio in Torsion. For a member of circular cross section subjected to torsion the strength is $T = S_{sw}J/r$ and the weight is $m = \gamma AL$. The strength-weight ratio in torsion is therefore

$$\frac{T}{m} = \left(\frac{S_{sw}J/r}{\gamma AL}\right) = \left(\frac{S_{sw}\pi r^4/2}{r}\right)\left(\frac{1}{\gamma\pi r^2 L}\right) = \frac{S_{sw}r}{2\gamma L}$$

which shows that the strength-weight ratio of a *solid circular shaft* in torsion is increased by increasing the stress S_{sw} and the radius r, and by decreasing the density γ and the length L.

For a thin-walled circular section, if $t =$ the wall thickness,

$$J = \left(\frac{\pi}{2}\right)[r^4 - (r - t)^4]$$

Since $(r - t)^4 = r^4 - 4r^3t + 6r^2t^2 - 4rt^3 + t^4$ and t is small, then the approximate value of $(r - t)^4$ is $r^4 - 4r^3t$ and

$$J = \left(\frac{\pi}{2}\right) (r^4 - r^4 + 4r^3t) = 2\pi r^3t$$

For a thin-walled tube the approximate value of A is $2\pi rt$. Then the strength-weight ratio can be defined as

$$\frac{T}{m} = \left(\frac{S_{s.r}J}{r}\right)\left(\frac{1}{\gamma AL}\right) = \left(\frac{S_{sw}}{r\gamma L}\right)\left(\frac{2\pi r^3t}{2\pi rt}\right) = \frac{S_{sw}r}{L\gamma}$$

or

$$\frac{T}{m} = \frac{rS_{sw}\sqrt{2\pi rt}}{L\gamma\sqrt{2\pi rt}} = \left(\frac{S_{sw}}{\sqrt{2\pi}\,L\gamma}\right)\left(\frac{\sqrt{A}}{\sqrt{t/r}}\right) \tag{2-14}$$

Equation (2-14) shows that the strength-weight ratio varies directly as the square root of the cross-sectional area and indirectly as the square root of the wall thickness-radius ratio t/r. By decreasing the value of t/r, while leaving the area the same, the strength-weight ratio is increased. That is, by increasing r and reducing t, with the area A constant, the strength-weight ratio is increased. It should be noted, however, that with too small a value of t/r, failure by buckling may occur.

B. BENDING PROPERTIES

There are many structures, particularly buildings, where the members are subjected mostly to bending. The determination of flexure or bending stresses in members subjected to bending is considered in the study of Strength of Materials. The most common type of member in which bending stresses are produced is the beam. For this reason the usual laboratory test made to study bending is the flexure test of a specimen in simple bending.

2-4. MECHANICAL PROPERTIES IN BENDING

In the complete flexure or bending test, a load-deflection diagram is obtained. In most flexure tests the specimen is subjected to either "two-point" or center loading, as in Fig. 2-6. The loading is applied by a Universal testing machine or, in some cases, by a special hand-operated bending machine. A deflectometer is placed on or under

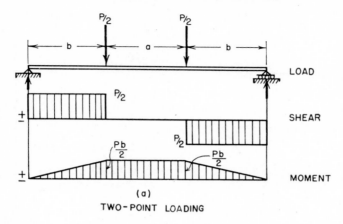

(a)
TWO-POINT LOADING

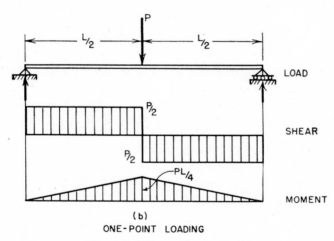

(b)
ONE-POINT LOADING

Fig. 2-6.   Flexure test loadings.

the specimen, usually at center, to determine the vertical deflection as the load is applied.   Loads and deflections are measured at predetermined increments of load or deflection and a *load-deflection diagram* is plotted using these load and deflection values, as shown in Fig. 2-7.   For ductile materials the complete load-deflection curve cannot be determined because the deflection corresponding to rupture

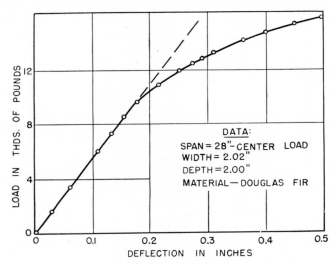

Fig. 2-7.   Load-deflection diagram.

cannot be obtained and the specimen continues to deflect.   For materials such as cast iron or wood and most plastics, however, the deflection diagram to rupture can be determined.   Mechanical properties in bending are obtained by the use of the load-deflection diagram.

   Strength.   Strength in bending is defined as the elastic strength, yield strength, apparent ultimate strength, or modulus of rupture. To determine the elastic strength in bending it is necessary first to determine the proportional limit load.   This load is sometimes measured by using Johnson's apparent elastic limit procedure as applied in the tension test.   That is, the load used is the load where the rate of change of deflection with respect to the load is 50 per cent greater than for the straight-line portion of the load-deflection diagram.   Figure 2-8 illustrates the determination of the elastic load by this method.   The yield load is found by using an offset deflection corresponding to the offset strain in simple tension, as illustrated in Fig. 2-8.   For a yield load of P_y, the maximum moment M_y, corresponding to the yield load, can be calculated for a particular type of loading.   For the two-point loading of Fig. 2-6(a), with $b = L/3$, the maximum moment at yield is $M_y = P_y L/6$, and for

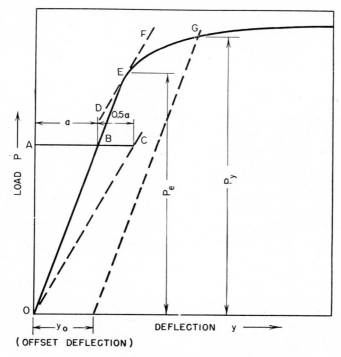

NOTE: D F IS PARALLEL TO O C AND BC = 0.5 A B
P_e = ELASTIC LOAD BY JOHNSON'S METHOD
P_y = YIELD LOAD BY OFFSET METHOD

Fig. 2-8.   Determination of elastic and yield load in bending.

Fig. 2-6(b) the maximum moment is $M_y = P_y L/4$. In either case the *yield strength* is measured by the yield stress as given by the equation

$$S_{by} = \frac{M_y c}{I} \tag{2-15}$$

where M_y is the maximum moment corresponding to the load P_y in in. lb., c is the distance from the neutral axis to the outermost fiber in in., and I is the moment of inertia of the cross section in in.[4].

The ultimate strength in bending cannot be determined from eq. (2-15), because Hooke's law does not apply in the plastic range. In order to compare the maximum strengths of materials in bending, however, an approximate measure of ultimate strength, called the *modulus of rupture* in bending, is determined by using the beam formula. That is, for a maximum moment M_u corresponding to the maximum load, the modulus of rupture is

$$S_u = \frac{M_u c}{I} \qquad (2\text{-}16)$$

It is important to realize that the value obtained by eq. (2-16) does not represent the actual ultimate stress on the outer fibers at the point of maximum load. The stress calculated by eq. (2-16) is of use, however, in giving an index of the ultimate strength for the purpose of comparing the flexure strengths of various materials. The actual and assumed stress distributions in bending are illustrated in Fig. 2-9. Figure 2-9 shows that the actual stress on the outer fiber at maximum load is less than the value calculated by eq. (2-16) which is represented by the straight-line variation shown in Fig. 2-9.

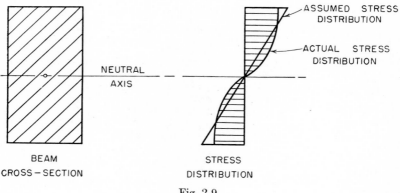

Fig. 2-9.

In addition to the bending stresses computed in the foregoing, transverse shear stresses are produced. For specimens of the usual dimensions, however, these stresses are small and may be neglected.

Stiffness. As in tension, the stiffness in bending is the property that defines the ability of a material to deform in the elastic range. Stiffness in bending is measured by the modulus of elasticity in bending. The deflection equation is used to calculate the modulus of elasticity in bending. For a specimen subjected to two-point loading with loads $P/2$ at the third point, the theoretical deflection at the center is

$$y = \frac{23PL^3}{1296EI}$$

If a point on the elastic straight-line portion of the load-deflection diagram is selected, and the values of P and y for this point are substituted in the foregoing equation, the value of E, determined from the resulting equation, is the modulus of elasticity in bending E_b. That is,

$$E_b = \frac{23PL^3}{1296Iy} \tag{2-17a}$$

For a specimen with center loading the deflection at the center is $y = PL^3/(48EI)$, and

$$E_b = \frac{PL^3}{48Iy} \tag{2-17b}$$

Theoretically the values of the modulus of elasticity in bending E_b, as calculated by eqs. (2-17), and the value of the modulus of elasticity in tension E are identical. Actually, because of errors in testing and the assumptions made in deriving the deflection equation, the values of E and E_b may differ.

Ductility. For brittle materials such as cast iron, the ductility in bending is sometimes measured by the maximum deflection or deflection at fracture. The magnitude of this deflection is dependent on the cross-sectional dimensions of the specimen, the span length, and the manner of loading. The maximum deflection, as a measure of ductility, is of value only in comparing the ductilities of materials when specimens of identical dimensions, span length, and type of loading are used.

For ductile materials the usual flexure test cannot be used to measure ductility, because the specimen continues to deflect as the load is applied and fracture cannot be produced. To produce fracture in bending of a ductile material, the *cold-bend test* is used. This test consists of bending a bar around a pin over a large angle. The angle of bending at which a crack starts is taken as a measure of ductility. Specifications define the required ductility in a material by stating the minimum angle of bend necessary for a bar and pin

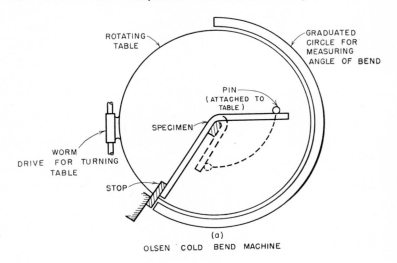

ROTATING TABLE

GRADUATED CIRCLE FOR MEASURING ANGLE OF BEND

PIN (ATTACHED TO TABLE)

SPECIMEN

WORM DRIVE FOR TURNING TABLE

STOP

(a)

OLSEN COLD BEND MACHINE

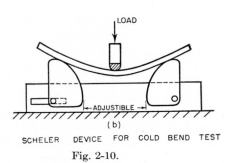

LOAD

ADJUSTIBLE

(b)

SCHELER DEVICE FOR COLD BEND TEST

Fig. 2-10.

of specified size. The main features of two types of cold-bend apparatus are shown in Fig. 2-10.

Bend tests are made not only to obtain an index of ductility but also to evaluate loss of ductility produced by certain heat treatments, to detect too high a carbon or phosphorus content in steel, or to determine improper rolling conditions of steel.

Fracture in a cold-bend test is influenced by annealing. For example, without annealing, a cast steel specimen, in the cold-bend test, bends through only a small angle before fracture, and the ruptured surface has a coarse granular appearance. After annealing, this material shows a much finer texture at fracture and bends through a larger angle before fracture.

Resilience. A measure of resilience in bending, used for comparing materials, is the average work done per unit volume in loading a specimen to the proportional limit. Sometimes the yield point is used in place of the proportional limit load. It should be emphasized that the resilience obtained in this way is of value only in comparing materials, since the strain energy per unit volume will depend upon the dimensions of the specimen and the manner of loading.

For a simply supported specimen with a center load, the work done per unit volume in loading to the proportional limit load P_p is

$$u_b = \frac{P_p y_p}{2AL} \qquad (2\text{-}18)$$

where y_p is the deflection under the load at the proportional limit, A is the cross-sectional area of the specimen, and L is the span length. For the loading considered,

$$y_p = P_p L^3/(48EI) \quad \text{and} \quad S_p = M_p c/I = P_p Lc/(4I)$$

or
$$P_p = 4IS_p/(Lc)$$

Using these values of y_p and P_p in eq. (2-18),

$$u_b = \left(\frac{S_p^2}{6E}\right)\left(\frac{I}{c^2 A}\right) \qquad (2\text{-}18\text{a})$$

Equation (2-18a) gives the average strain energy in bending per unit volume in a specimen subjected to a center load. The value of this resilience is expressed in terms of the stress S_p, modulus of elasticity E, moment of inertia I, cross-sectional area A, and distance from the neutral axis to the outer fiber c.

For a specimen of rectangular cross section of width b and depth d, $I = bd^3/12$, $c = d/2$, and $A = bd$. Then the resilience in bending is

$$u_b = \frac{S_p^2}{18E} \qquad (2\text{-}18\text{b})$$

If all the fibers were stressed to a value S_p equal to that of the outer fiber, the strain energy per unit volume would be $S_p^2/(2E)$, or nine times the average value given by eq. (2-18b).

Toughness. Toughness for unnotched specimens of brittle materials in static bending is sometimes measured by the average strain energy or work done per unit volume required to fracture the specimen. For a beam with a center load, the toughness based on the average work done per unit volume would be the area under the load-deflection curve divided by the volume of the specimen between supports.

An *impact test* on a notched specimen is sometimes used to define toughness for both ductile and brittle materials. In this test the energy required to rupture a cantilever or simply supported notched specimen under an impact load is used as a measure of toughness.

Bending tests are used as standard tests for many materials such as cast iron, concrete, brick and wood.[2] The two main methods of testing specimens in bending are illustrated in Fig. 2-6. The *two-point loading* shown in Fig. 2-6(a) is used, for example, in testing concrete beams. The *center-load type of test,* shown in Fig. 2-6(b), is used for tests of wood, brick, and cast iron. Figures 2-6(a) and 2-6(b) show the shear and moment diagrams for each type of loading. The variation in the moment values along the length of the specimens in Figs. 2-6(a) and 2-6(b) shows that the bending stress variations along the length of the specimen differ in these two cases of loading. The specimen with the two-point loading of Fig. 2-6(a) is subjected to pure bending or a constant moment over the central part of the span. This constant moment for an appreciable length of the specimen is claimed to be an advantage over other methods of loading, since variations in the material are considered by testing the weakest section between the points of loading. Furthermore, the part of the specimen tested is subjected to a pure bending moment free from shear stresses.

NUMERICAL EXAMPLE. A wood specimen 2×2 in. in cross section is tested using a span length of 20 in. and a center load. The proportional limit load is 980 lb. and the maximum load is 1120 lb. For a load of 600 lb. the deflection was 0.060 in. Determine:

(a) the proportional limit,
(b) the modulus of rupture,
(c) the modulus of elasticity in bending,
(d) the average resilience per unit volume.

---

[2] See A.S.T.M. Standards for a description of flexure or bending tests as specified for various materials.

SOLUTION. For a centrally loaded specimen the proportional limit is given by the equation

$$S_p = M_p c / I = \frac{(P_p L/4)(d/2)}{bd^3/12} = \frac{3}{2}\left(\frac{P_p L}{bd^2}\right)$$

$$= \frac{3}{2} \times \frac{(980)(20)}{2 \times 2^2}$$

$$= 3680 \text{ psi}$$

By eq. (2-16) the modulus of rupture is

$$S_u = M_u c / I = \frac{(P_u L/4)(d/2)}{bd^3/12} = \frac{3}{2}\left(\frac{P_u L}{bd^2}\right)$$

$$= \frac{3}{2} \times \frac{(1120)(20)}{2 \times 2^2}$$

$$= 4200 \text{ psi}$$

The modulus of elasticity in bending is defined by eq. (2-17b) for a specimen with center loading, or

$$E_b = \frac{PL^3}{48Iy} = \frac{PL^3}{4bd^3y} = \frac{600 \times 8000}{4 \times 16 \times 0.06} = 1.25 \times 10^6 \text{ psi}$$

The average resilience per unit volume for a beam of rectangular cross section and for a center load is determined by eq. (2-18b), or

$$u_b = \frac{S_y{}^2}{18E} = \frac{(3680)^2}{18 \times 1.25 \times 10^6} = 0.60 \text{ in. lb. per cu. in.}$$

NUMERICAL EXAMPLE. In 28-day tests of concrete, cylinders 6 in. in diameter by 12 in. in length were tested in tension and compression, and $7 \times 10 \times 36$-in. specimens were tested in bending with two-point loading at the third points. The tensile, compressive, and bending loads for rupture were, respectively, 7060 lb., 56,600 lb., and 7900 lb. Determine the tensile and compressive strengths and the modulus of rupture in bending. The bending load value given is the total load.

SOLUTION. The tensile ultimate stress is

$$S_u = P/A = \frac{7060}{\pi \times 9} = 250 \text{ psi}$$

The compressive ultimate stress is

$$S_u = P/A = \frac{56,500}{\pi \times 9} = 2010 \text{ psi}$$

The beam formula is used to determine the modulus of rupture, or

$$S_u = \frac{M_u c}{I} = \left(\frac{P_u L}{6}\right)\left(\frac{d/2}{bd^3/12}\right) = \frac{P_u L}{bd^2}$$

$$= \frac{7900 \times 36}{7 \times 100} = 406 \text{ psi}$$

Failure of beams in bending may occur in one of several ways. The beam may fail by yielding of the extreme fibers. In narrow beams of long span or beams with small ratios of width to depth, failure by sidewise buckling may occur. In thin-webbed members such as I-beams, failure may occur as a result of excessive shear stresses in the web or of buckling in the web due to the compressive stresses accompanying the shear stresses. Finally, failure in some cases may be produced by excessive bearing stresses at the load points and supports.

The yield stress in bending for ductile materials is generally found to be slightly higher than for tension or compression. This increase in stress is produced by the strengthening effect of the inner fibers, which restrain the yielding of the outer fibers of the bending specimen.

Factors Affecting the Flexure Properties. The type of loading influences the modulus of rupture values obtained. Tests of concrete show values ten to fifteen per cent greater with center loading than with two-point loading. Tests of cast iron and concrete show that the shorter the span length, the greater the modulus of rupture. The shape of the cross section changes appreciably the resistance of beams to bending. The modulus of rupture and the modulus of elasticity are found to be less for beams when a relatively larger proportion of the cross-sectional area is concentrated near the extreme fibers.

2-5. UTILIZATION OF BENDING PROPERTIES

The design stress values for static bending are often considered equal to the design stress values used in tension, for materials having yield strengths in tension and compression that are approximately equal. Bending tests show that the ratio of depth to span length influences the strength values obtained.   For practical purposes these differences produced by the relative dimensions of the beam are negligible.

The design of beams is usually based on a design bending stress and an allowable deflection.   In some cases the shear stresses must be considered, as in beams that have large cross sections compared to their lengths.   In beams of this type the maximum shear stress values are appreciable compared to the maximum bending stress.

NUMERICAL EXAMPLE.   A steel beam 4 in. by 10 in. is 10 ft. long and is loaded in bending.   The design bending stress is 18,000 psi and the allowable deflection is 1/360 of the span.   If the center span load at yield is 80,000 lb. and the modulus of elasticity is 30×10^6 psi, determine the factors of safety with respect to yield strength and stiffness.   The beam is subjected to a center load.

SOLUTION.   The yield stress is

$$S_{by} = \frac{Mc}{I} = \frac{(PL/4)(d/2)}{(bd^3/12)} = \left(\frac{3}{2}\right)\left(\frac{PL}{bd^2}\right)$$

$$= \frac{3}{2} \times \frac{80,000 \times 120}{4 \times 100} = 36,000 \text{ psi}$$

Then the factor of safety with respect to the yield stress is

$$F_s = S_{by}/S_w = 36,000/18,000 = 2.0$$

The center deflection at yield is given by the equation

$$y_y = \frac{PL^3}{48EI} = \frac{80,000 \times (10 \times 12)^3}{48 \times 30 \times 10^6 \times (4 \times 10^3/12)} = 0.288 \text{ in.}$$

The allowable center deflection is

$$y_w = \frac{1}{360}(L) = \frac{120}{360} = 0.333 \text{ in.}$$

Then the factor of safety with respect to the deflection becomes

$$F_y = y_w/y_y = \frac{0.333}{0.288} = 1.15$$

NUMERICAL EXAMPLE.   Compare the average resilience per unit volume at yield for a center span load as given in the foregoing problem with the value using the load distributed at the third points. The maximum stresses in each case are equal to the yield stress of 36,000 psi.

SOLUTION. For a load at the center, the average resilience per unit volume at yield can be determined by eq. (2-18b), or

$$u_b = \frac{S_y^2}{18E} = \frac{(36,000)^2}{18 \times 30 \times 10^6} = 2.4 \text{ in. lb. per cu. in.}$$

For third-point loading it will be necessary first to obtain an expression for the average resilience per unit volume. The total work done is $U_b = 2(P/2)(y/2)$ since there are two loads of value $P/2$ acting through a distance y. The deflection y at the load points can be shown to be $5PL^3/(324EI)$. Then the total work done is

$$U_b = \frac{Py}{2} = \frac{P}{2}\left(\frac{5PL^3}{324EI}\right) = \frac{5P^2L^3}{648EI}$$

The maximum bending stress is $S = \dfrac{M_{\max}c}{I} = (PL/6)(c/I)$ or $P = \dfrac{6IS}{Lc}$. Then

$$U_b = \frac{5P^2L^3}{648EI} = \left(\frac{6IS}{Lc}\right)^2\left(\frac{5L^3}{648EI}\right) = \frac{5S^2IL}{18Ec^2} = \frac{5S^2Lbd}{54E}$$

The work done per unit volume at yield equals U_b divided by the volume where the yield stress value is used for S. That is,

$$U_b = \frac{U_b}{AL} = \frac{5S_{by}^2Lbd}{54EbdL} = \frac{5S_{by}^2}{54E} = \frac{5(36,000)^2}{54 \times 30 \times 10^6} = 4.0 \text{ in. lb. per cu. in.}$$

Comparing this value with the value for a beam with center loading, the value for third-point loading is $\frac{5}{3}$ the value for center loading.

NUMERICAL EXAMPLE. Two materials are to be considered for the machine linkage in Fig. 2-11. Material #1 has a yield stress in tension of 20,000 psi and a yield stress in compression of 22,000 psi. Material #2 has a yield stress in tension of 24,000 psi and a yield stress in compression of 22,000 psi. Compare the yield loads and select the better material.

SOLUTION. The stresses at A and B in terms of the load are, respectively,

$$S_A = \frac{P}{A} - \frac{Mc}{I} = \frac{P}{bd} - \frac{(Pc)(d/2)}{bd^3/12} = P\left(\frac{2}{3} - 1\right) = -\frac{P}{3}$$

and

$$S_B = P\left(\frac{2}{3} + 1\right) = \frac{5}{3}P$$

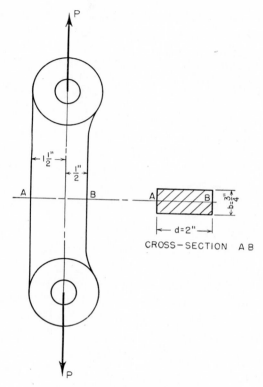

Fig. 2-11.   Machine linkage.

For material #1 the loads to produce yielding in compression and tension are obtained from the foregoing values of $S_A = -P/3$ and $S_B = \frac{5}{3}P$ by placing $S_A = 22,000$ psi and $S_B = 20,000$ psi.   That is,

$$P_c/3 = 22,000 \quad \text{or} \quad P_c = 66,000 \text{ lb.}$$

and $\qquad\quad 5P_t/3 = 20,000 \quad \text{or} \quad P_t = 12,000 \text{ lb.}$

For material #2 the yield loads in compression and tension are determined by the equations

$$P_c/3 = 22,000 \quad \text{or} \quad P_c = 66,000 \text{ lb.}$$

and $\qquad\quad 5P_t/3 = 24,000 \quad \text{or} \quad P_t = 14,400 \text{ lb.}$

A comparison of the yield loads for materials #1 and #2 shows that material #2 is preferable, as it has the higher yield load as governed by the tensile stress.

Strength-Weight Ratio in Bending. For a simply supported beam of rectangular cross section subjected to a center load P, the strength of the beam is defined by the value of P in the equation

$$S_w = \frac{Mc}{I} = \left(\frac{PL}{4}\right)\frac{(d/2)}{(bd^3/12)} = \frac{3}{2}\left(\frac{PL}{bd^2}\right)$$

or

$$P = \frac{2bd^2 S_w}{3L}$$

The weight of the beam is

$$m = \gamma L A$$

Then the strength-weight ratio becomes

$$\frac{P}{m} = \left(\frac{2bd^2 S_w}{3L}\right)\left(\frac{1}{\gamma L A}\right) = \frac{2dS_w}{3L^2 \gamma}$$

That is, the strength-weight ratio is directly proportional to the depth of the beam and inversely proportional to the length squared.

In place of a rectangular cross section, the strength for a thin-walled tube is given by the value of P in the equation

$$S_w = \frac{Mc}{I} = \left(\frac{PL}{4}\right)\left(\frac{c}{I}\right)$$

or

$$P = \frac{4IS_w}{Lc}$$

The weight of the member is

$$m = \gamma L A$$

Then the strength-weight ratio is determined by the equation

$$\frac{P}{m} = \left(\frac{4IS_w}{Lc}\right)\left(\frac{1}{\gamma L A}\right) = \frac{4IS_w}{L^2 c \gamma A}$$

The values of the moment of inertia and area can be determined approximately for a thin-walled circular tube by the equations

$$I = \frac{\pi r^4}{4} - \frac{\pi(r - t)^4}{4} \approx \pi r^3 t$$

and

$$A = \pi r^2 - \pi(r - t)^2 \approx 2\pi r t$$

where r is the outer radius and t is the wall thickness.

Using the approximate values for I and A in the equation for the strength-weight ratio,

$$\frac{P}{m} = \left(\frac{4IS_w}{Lc}\right)\left(\frac{1}{\gamma LA}\right) = \frac{4(\pi r^3 t)S_w}{L^2 r\gamma(2\pi rt)} = 2\left(\frac{S_v}{L\gamma}\right)\left(\frac{r}{L}\right)$$

The strength-weight ratio in terms of the wall thickness ratio t/r is then

$$\frac{P}{m} = \sqrt{\frac{2}{\pi}}\left(\frac{S_w}{L\gamma}\right)\left(\frac{\sqrt{A}}{L}\right)\left(\frac{1}{\sqrt{t/r}}\right) \tag{2-19}$$

For a maximum strength-weight ratio and for a constant length and cross-sectional area, the wall thickness ratio t/r in eq. (2-19) should be a minimum. That is, eq. (2-19) indicates that, by decreasing the wall thickness and increasing the radius, the strength-weight ratio can be increased indefinitely. Thus by the best selection of the dimensions, as indicated above, a more economical use of the material results and lighter-weight constructions are produced. It should be noted that there are limits to which the wall thickness can be reduced, since, for certain values, failure by buckling is possible.

PROBLEMS

2-1. In a torsion test of a steel shaft 1.50 in. in diameter the following test results were obtained: twisting moment at the proportional limit was 22,000 in. lb., angle of twist at the proportional limit was 6.66°, gage length was 30 in., and the maximum torque applied before rupture was 40,000 in. lb. Determine: (a) the proportional limit, (b) the modulus of elasticity, (c) the modulus of rupture, (d) the modulus of elastic resilience.

Ans. $S_{sp} = 33{,}100$ psi, $E_s = 11.5 \times 10^6$ psi,
$S_{su} = 60{,}500$ psi, $u_s = 24.0$ in. lb. per cu. in.

2-2. A hollow aluminum shaft of 2 in. outside diameter and 1 in. inside diameter is subjected to a twisting moment. What is the approximate value of twisting moment required to produce yielding if the yield stress in torsion is 40,000 psi? What is the angle of twist in degrees at yielding if the length of the shaft is 3 ft.? Use a value of $E_s = 3.9 \times 10^6$ psi.

2-3. Compare the torsional strength, stiffness, and weight of two steel shafts; one is circular and solid and the other is circular and hollow, with an external diameter twice the solid shaft but with the same cross-sectional area. The modulus of elasticity in shear is 12.5×10^6 psi.

Ans. $T_h/T_s = 3.5$, $\theta_h/\theta_s = 0.14$, $w_h/w_s = 1.0$.

2-4. A solid circular shaft is subjected to a twisting moment of 100,000 in. lb. The shaft is 10 ft. long. A steel with a torsional yield strength of 50,000 psi and an aluminum alloy with a torsional yield strength of 20,000 psi are to be considered. Using a factor of safety of 2, and values of cost per pound and densities as given in Prob. 1-10, determine the cost of the shaft for each material. The shafts support the same torque and are equal in length.   *Ans. C_s = \$13.95 and C_a = \$19.75.*

2-5. Solve Prob. 2-4 if the design is to be based on an allowable angle of twist of 1 degree in 20 diameters of length. Use values of modulus of elasticity $(E_s)_{st}$ = 12.5 × 10^6 psi and $(E_s)_{al}$ = 3.9 × 10^6 psi.

2-6. Solve Prob. 2-4 if the allowable modulus of resilience is 1.2 in. lb. per cu. in. $(E_s)_{st}$ = 12.5 × 10^6 psi and $(E_s)_{al}$ = 3.9 × 10^6 psi.

2-7. Derive an expression for the modulus of resilience in torsion in a circular hollow shaft with an inside diameter equal to $\frac{1}{2}$ the outside diameter.

2-8. Compare the strength-weight ratios of two circular shafts subjected to a twisting moment of 100,000 in. lb. One is steel with a torsional yield strength of 50,000 psi and the other is an aluminum alloy with a torsional yield of 20,000 psi. The densities of the steel and aluminum are, respectively, 0.284 and 0.102 lb. per cu. in. Length of each shaft = 190 in.

Ans.   503 and 760.

2-9. (a) Plot the load-deflection diagram for a rayon-base laminated plastic beam using the following data:

Load (pounds)	0	200	400	600	750	1000	1200	1400	1600
Deflection (inches)	0	0.024	0.050	0.075	0.100	0.160	0.220	0.330	0.420

(b) The specimen used in Prob. 2-9(a) was $\frac{1}{2}$ in. wide by $1\frac{1}{8}$ in. deep and the span length was 8 in. The load was applied at the mid-length of the specimen. Determine: (a) the elastic strength, using Johnson's apparent elastic limit, (b) the modulus of elasticity, (c) the modulus of rupture, (d) the average modulus of resilience per unit volume based on Johnson's apparent elastic limit.   *Ans. S_{by} = 14,300 psi, E = 1.44 × 10^6 psi,*

S_u = 30,400 psi, u_b = 8.35 in. lb. per cu. in.

2-10. A beam of rectangular cross section is simply supported at the ends and is subjected to a concentrated load at the center. Determine the ratio of the beam depth to span so that yielding will occur simultaneously in tension, compression, and shear. The yield strength of the material in shear is 0.6 the yield strength in tension or compression.   *Ans. d/L = 1.2.*

2-11. A simply supported beam of rectangular cross section is subjected to a center concentrated load P. How is the flexural strength changed by doubling each of the following: (a) depth, (b) width, and (c) span length?

2-12. A member is used as a simply supported beam with a concentrated load at the center. There is a choice between a steel and an aluminum alloy beam. The beam is to be rectangular with a width equal to $\frac{1}{4}$ the depth. The span length is 15 ft. The yield stresses for the steel and aluminum alloys are, respectively, 80,000 and 50,000 psi, and the moduli of elasticity are, respectively, 30×10^6 psi and 10.3×10^6 psi. The aluminum alloy costs twice as much as the steel alloy per pound. Compare the costs of the two beams. Determine the cost based both on the yield stresses, using a factor of safety of 2 and on an allowable deflection of $\frac{1}{360}$ of the span length. Densities of the steel and aluminum are 0.284 and 0.102 lb. per cu. in.

Ans. (a) $C_s/C_a = 1.02$; (b) $C_s/C_c = 0.82$.

2-13. Determine an expression for the average resilience per unit volume in a simply supported beam of rectangular cross section subjected to a uniformly distributed load.

2-14. For the linkage in Fig. 2-11, what should the ratio of the yield strength of the material in compression to tension be so that the member yields in tension and compression at the same load value?

Ans. $S_c/S_t = 0.20$.

2-15. Solve Prob. 2-14 if the load P is reversed in direction.

2-16. Compare the strength-weight ratios of two thin-walled tubes in

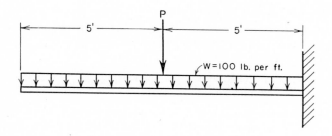

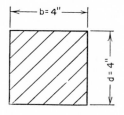

CROSS—SECTION
Fig. 2-12.

bending.   The areas of both tubes are equal but the external radius of one is twice that of the other.   Both tubes are made of the same material and are loaded in the same manner.

2-17.   (a) For the beam in Fig. 2-12 determine the load P that will produce yielding, if the yield stress in bending for the material is 4000 psi.

(b) Determine the value of the yield load P in Fig. 2-12 if the yield stress in shear is 3000 psi.

2-18.   A solid circular shaft supports loads as shown in Fig. 2-13.   The maximum deflection is not to exceed 0.05 in.   Two materials are to be considered for this beam—a steel with an allowable flexure stress of 20,000 psi and a modulus of elasticity of 30×10^6 psi, and an aluminum alloy with an allowable stress of 30,000 psi and a modulus of elasticity of 10.5×10^6 psi. Which material would result in the smallest shaft?

2-19.   For the beam in Fig. 2-12, what is the value of P for an end deflection of 0.33 in.?   Use a modulus of elasticity value of 1.5×10^6 psi.

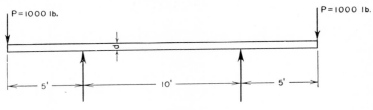

Fig. 2-13.

2-20.   What is the yield load P for the member in Fig. 2-14 if the tensile yield stress is 35,000 psi?

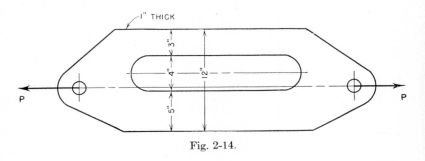

Fig. 2-14.

2-21.   The shaft in Fig. 2-15 is keyed against rotation but is simply supported at A and D.   Determine the load P that will produce yielding in

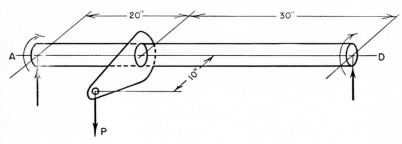

Fig. 2-15.

torsion if the yield stress in torsion is 40,000 psi. What maximum bending stress will this load produce?

BIBLIOGRAPHY

Davis, H. E., Troxell, G. E., and Wiskocil, C. T., *The Testing and Inspection of Engineering Materials*, McGraw-Hill Book Co., Inc., New York, 1941.

Gilkey, H. J., Murphy, G., and Bergman, E. O., *A Manual of Materials Testing*, McGraw-Hill Book Co., Inc., New York, 1941.

Timoshenko, S., *Strength of Materials*, D. Van Nostrand Co., Inc., New York, 1941, Vol. 2, Chap. VII.

Timoshenko, S., and Lessels, J. M., *Applied Elasticity*, Westinghouse Technical Night School Press, East Pittsburgh, 1925, Part II.

Withey, M. O., and Aston, J., *Johnson's Materials of Construction*, John Wiley & Sons, Inc., New York, 1939, 8th Ed.

Metals Handbook, American Society for Metals, Cleveland, 1948 Edition.

Chapter 3

Static Properties under Combined Stresses

In machine and structural parts the stresses often are not simple stresses represented by tension, compression, bending, or torsion, but are combined stresses acting in more than one direction. Therefore, it is important to determine the strengths of materials when subjected to various conditions of combined stresses. Various theories of failure have been proposed to define the yield and the ultimate strengths of materials subjected to combined stress. Theories have also been proposed for predicting the plastic stress-strain relations and ductility for combined states of stress. The major theories, and the utilization of these theories in design of members subjected to combined stresses, are considered in this chapter. Before discussing theories of failure for combined stresses it will be necessary first to define principal stresses, principal strains, and strain energy in terms of principal stresses. This is necessary because the theories of failure are usually expressed in terms of the principal stress and strain values.

3-1. PRINCIPAL STRESSES, STRAINS AND STRAIN ENERGY

Members subjected to combined stresses, and the determination of principal stresses in these members, are considered in the study of Strength of Materials. Shafts subjected to torsion and bending, thin-walled tubes subjected to internal pressure or axial loads and torsion, thick-walled cylinders subjected to internal pressure, and hub-and-axle shrink-fit assemblies are examples of members subjected to combined stresses.

116

Principal Stresses. The tube illustrated in Fig. 3-1(a) is subjected to torsion, and internal pressure, representing a two-dimensional state of stress. The stresses on a small element of the tube shown in Figs. 3-1(a) and 3-1(b) include a shear stress[1] S_{xy} produced by the twisting moment T, a circumferential normal stress[2] S_y produced by the internal pressure p, and a normal axial stress[2] S_x produced by the internal pressure p and axial load P.

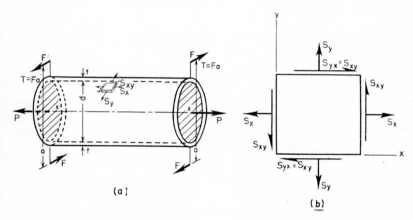

Fig. 3-1.   Thin-walled tube subjected to torsion and axial tension.

The stress value S_x in the axial direction of the tube is made up of the stress S_x' produced by the axial load P, plus the stress S_x'' produced by the internal pressure. Then if $d =$ the internal diameter and $t =$ the thickness of the tube wall,

$$S_x = S_x' + S_x'' = \frac{P}{A} + \frac{(p\pi d^2/4)}{t\pi d}$$

or
$$S_x = \frac{P}{t\pi d} + \frac{pd}{4t} \tag{3-1a}$$

The stress S_y in the lateral or circumferential direction of the tube is obtained from the equation for equilibrium of stresses on a semi-

[1] Two subscripts are used to denote the shear stress S_{xy}, the first indicating the direction of the normal to the plane in which the shear stress is acting (subscript x) and the second indicating the direction of the shear stress (subscript y).

[2] Subscripts x and y for the normal stresses S_x and S_y denote the directions of these stresses or the normal to the plane on which the stresses act.

circular section of the tube for a length L.   That is,

$$(S_y)(2tL) = pLd$$

or $$S_y = \frac{pd}{2t} \tag{3-1b}$$

For a thin-walled tube the shear stress is essentially uniform and the total shear stress is $(S_{xy})(t\pi d)$.   For equilibrium, the moment of this stress about the axis of the tube must be equal to the applied torque T.   That is,

$$(S_{xy}t\pi d)\left(\frac{d}{2}\right) = T$$

or $$S_{xy} = \frac{2T}{t\pi d^2} \tag{3-1c}$$

The stress components in the foregoing example represent the general case of stresses acting in one plane and in two directions.   These stresses are called biaxial or two-dimensional stresses.   Inside the element represented by Fig. 3-2(a), normal stresses greater than S_x or S_y, and shear stresses greater than S_{xy}, may occur.   For this reason it is necessary to consider the stresses on some plane FE in the element $ABCD$ of Fig. 3-2(a) and to determine the variation in the normal and shear stresses acting on this plane with change in direction θ.   To determine the stresses on plane FE, consider the free-body diagram of FEC as shown in Fig. 3-2(b).   The element FEC has dimensions as shown, with a constant thickness b perpendicular to the xy plane.   The stresses on the plane FE can be considered as made up of a normal stress component S_n and a shear stress component S_{xy}'.   To determine the normal stress S_n, the summation of the forces in the normal direction x_1 is written.   This gives

$$S_n b \, dm = S_x b \, dy \sin\theta + S_y b \, dx \cos\theta + S_{xy} b \, dx \sin\theta + S_{xy} b \, dy \cos\theta$$

Dividing by $b \, dm$ and noting that $\sin\theta = dy/dm$ and $\cos\theta = dx/dm$,

$$S_n = S_x \sin^2\theta + S_y \cos^2\theta + 2S_{xy}\sin\theta\cos\theta \tag{a}$$

Noting   that $2\sin\theta\cos\theta = \sin 2\theta$, $\sin^2\theta = (1 - \cos 2\theta)/2$,   and $\cos^2\theta = (1 - \cos 2\theta)/2$, eq. (a) becomes

$$S_n = \frac{S_x + S_y}{2} + \frac{S_y - S_x}{2}\cos 2\theta + S_{xy}\sin 2\theta \tag{b}$$

Equation (b) gives the value of the normal stress S_n on the plane FE

for any angle θ in terms of the known stress components S_x, S_y, and S_{xy}.

It is of interest to consider the variation in the normal stress S_n as the angle θ varies and to determine the maximum value of S_n. For this purpose the calculus condition $dS_n/d\theta = 0$ for defining

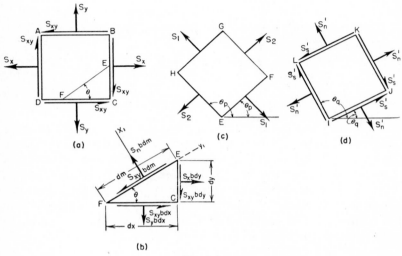

Fig. 3-2.

the maximum or minimum value of S_n can be used. Applying this condition to eq. (b), the direction of the maximum or minimum normal stress is defined by the angle $2\theta_p$, whose tangent is

$$\tan 2\theta_p = \frac{2S_{xy}}{S_y - S_x} \tag{c}$$

Before this value of θ_p can be substituted in eq. (b) it is necessary to determine the sine and cosine of $2\theta_p$. The values of $\sin 2\theta_p$ and $\cos 2\theta_p$ can best be evaluated graphically, as shown in Fig. 3-3. Referring to Fig. 3-3(a), the possible values of sine and cosine of the angle $2\theta_p$ are

$$\left.\begin{aligned}
\sin 2\theta_p &= \frac{\pm S_{xy}}{\sqrt{(S_y - S_x)^2/4 + S_{xy}^2}} \\
\cos 2\theta_p &= \frac{\pm(S_y - S_x)/2}{\sqrt{(S_y - S_x)^2/4 + S_{xy}^2}}
\end{aligned}\right\} \tag{d}$$

The maximum and minimum values of S_n can now be found by placing in eq. (b) the values of $\sin 2\theta_p$ and $\cos 2\theta_p$ from eqs. (d). Then the values of the maximum and minimum normal stresses are, respectively,

$$\left.\begin{array}{l} (S_n)_{\max} = \dfrac{S_x + S_y}{2} + \sqrt{\left(\dfrac{S_x - S_y}{2}\right)^2 + S_{xy}^2} \\[4mm] (S_n)_{\min} = \dfrac{S_x + S_y}{2} - \sqrt{\left(\dfrac{S_x - S_y}{2}\right)^2 + S_{xy}^2} \end{array}\right\} \quad \text{(e)}$$

The stresses $(S_n)_{\max}$ and $(S_n)_{\min}$ will be designated as S_1 and S_2. These stresses are called the *principal stresses* and represent the

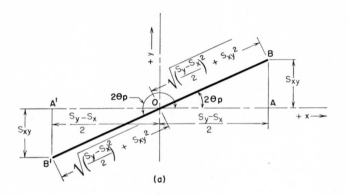

(a)

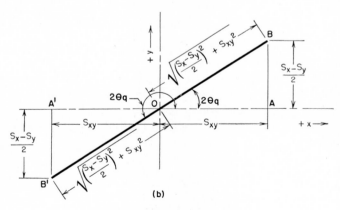

(b)

Fig. 3-3.

maximum and minimum values of the normal stresses considering all possible planes *FE* in the element of Fig. 3-2(a). Equations (e) can be written more conveniently as

$$\left.\begin{matrix} S_1 \\ S_2 \end{matrix}\right\} = \frac{S_x + S_y}{2} \pm \sqrt{\left(\frac{S_x - S_y}{2}\right)^2 + S_{xy}{}^2} \tag{3-2}$$

The values of the principal stresses S_1 and S_2 are given in eq. (3-2) in terms of the applied stress components S_x, S_y, and S_{xy}. In using eqs. (3-2), tensile normal stresses S_x and S_y will be considered positive, and compressive stresses negative. The orientation of these stresses with relation to the applied stresses is represented by Fig. 3-2(c), which shows the planes for the principal stresses as 90° apart. This can be verified by eqs. (d) which show that the angles $2\theta_p$ differ by 180°. Principal stress planes shown in Fig. 3-2(c) are free from shear stresses. This can be verified by summing the stresses in the y_1 direction for the angle $\theta = \theta_p$. It will then be found that the shear stress in the plane *FE* is zero.

Maximum Shear Stress. To determine the value of the maximum shear stress on the plane *FE* in Fig. 3-2(b) as θ varies, the shear stress for any angle θ will first be found by writing the equation of equilibrium for the stresses in the y_1 direction. Then

$$S_{xy}'b \, dm = S_x b \, dy \cos \theta - S_y b \, dx \sin \theta + S_{xy} b \, dx \cos \theta - S_{xy} b \, dy \sin \theta$$

Dividing by $b \, dm$ and noting that $\sin \theta = dy/dm$ and $\cos \theta = dx/dm$, then

$$S_{xy}' = S_x \sin \theta \cos \theta - S_y \sin \theta \cos \theta + S_{xy} \cos^2\theta - S_{xy} \sin^2\theta$$

or

$$S_{xy}' = \frac{S_x - S_y}{2} \sin 2\theta + S_{xy} \cos 2\theta \tag{f}$$

The maximum value of S_{xy}' is for an angle defined by $dS_{xy}'/d\theta = 0$ or by eq. (f), for an angle defined by

$$\tan 2\theta_q = -\frac{(S_y - S_x)}{2S_{xy}} \tag{g}$$

To determine the values of the sine and cosine of $2\theta_q$, the angle defined by eq. (g) is represented graphically as shown in Fig. 3-3(b). Then the sine and cosine of angle $2\theta_q$ is, by Fig. 3-3(b),

$$\left.\begin{aligned} \sin 2\theta_q &= \frac{\pm (S_x - S_y)/2}{\sqrt{(S_x - S_y)^2/4 + S_{xy}{}^2}} \\[2mm] \cos 2\theta_q &= \frac{\pm S_{xy}}{\sqrt{(S_x - S_y)^2/4 + S_{xy}{}^2}} \end{aligned}\right\} \tag{h}$$

Substituting the values of the trigonometric functions from eqs. (h) in eq. (f), the *maximum and minimum shear stress* values are

$$S_s' = \pm \sqrt{\left(\frac{S_x - S_y}{2}\right)^2 + S_{xy}^2} \qquad (3\text{-}3)$$

The plus value of S_s' in eq. (3-3) denotes the maximum shear stress, and the minus value denotes the minimum shear stress. The orientation of the planes on which these shear stresses act is shown in Fig. 3-2(d). There are two sets of planes on which the shear stresses S_s' act, since eqs. (h) define two angles having values of θ_q that differ by 90°. On the planes of maximum and minimum shear stresses, the normal stresses shown can be determined by substituting the values of the sine and cosine from eqs. (h) in eq. (b).

In determining the values of the principal stresses and maximum shear stress from eqs. (3-2) and (3-3), the tensile stresses S_x and S_y will be considered positive and the maximum principal stress will be considered as the algebraic maximum value. Shear stresses with directions as shown in Fig. 3-2(a) will be considered positive.

NUMERICAL EXAMPLE. For the element in Fig. 3-2(a), if $S_x = -2000$ psi, $S_y = 10,000$ psi, and $S_{xy} = 4500$ psi, determine: (a) the stress components for a plane at an angle $\theta = 30°$, (b) the principal stresses and their directions, and (c) the maximum shear stresses and the direction of the planes in which the shear stress acts.

SOLUTION. The normal stress component for the plane at an angle $\theta = 30°$ is given by eq. (b), or

$$S_n = \frac{S_x + S_y}{2} + \frac{S_y - S_x}{2} \cos 2\theta + S_{xy} \sin 2\theta$$

$$= \frac{-2000 + 10,000}{2} + \frac{10,000 + 2000}{2} \cos 60° + 4500 \sin 60°$$

$$= 4000 + 3000 + 3900 = 10,900 \text{ psi}$$

The shear stress component for the plane at an angle $\theta = 30°$ is given by eq. (f), or

$$S_{xy}' = \frac{S_x - S_y}{2} \sin 2\theta + S_{xy} \cos 2\theta$$

$$= \frac{-2000 - 10,000}{2} \sin 60° + 4500 \cos 60°$$

$$= -5200 + 2250 = -2950 \text{ psi}$$

The principal stresses are determined from eqs. (3-2):

$$S_1 = \frac{S_x + S_y}{2} + \sqrt{\left(\frac{S_y - S_x}{2}\right)^2 + S_{xy}{}^2}$$

$$= \frac{-2000 + 10,000}{2} + \sqrt{(6000)^2 + (4500)^2}$$

$$= 4000 + 7500 = 11,500 \text{ psi}$$

and

$$S_2 = \frac{S_x + S_y}{2} - \sqrt{\left(\frac{S_y - S_x}{2}\right)^2 + S_{xy}{}^2} = -3500 \text{ psi}$$

The directions of the principal stresses are obtained from eq. (c), or

$$\tan 2\theta_p = \frac{2S_{xy}}{S_y - S_x} = \frac{2 \times 4500}{12,000} = 0.75$$

$$2\theta_p = 36° 53' \quad \text{or} \quad 216° 53'$$

That is,

$$\theta_p = 18° 26' \quad \text{or} \quad 108° 26'$$

As indicated in Fig. 3-2(c), $\theta_p = 18° 26'$ is in the first quadrant and therefore corresponds to the plane EF for the maximum principal stress. The angle $\theta_p = 108° 26'$, however, is in the second quadrant and defines the plane GF for the minimum principal stress.

The maximum shear stress, by eq. (3-3), is

$$S_s' = \pm\sqrt{\left(\frac{S_x - S_y}{2}\right)^2 + S_{xy}{}^2} = \pm\sqrt{(6000)^2 + (4500)^2}$$

$$= \pm 7500 \text{ psi}$$

The directions of the planes of maximum shear, as given by eq. (g), are defined by

$$\tan 2\theta_q = -\left(\frac{S_x - S_y}{2S_{xy}}\right) = -1.333$$

$$2\theta_q = 126° 52' \quad \text{or} \quad 306° 52'$$

That is,

$$\theta_q = 63° 26' \quad \text{or} \quad 153° 26'$$

The angles θ_q correspond to the two planes represented by IJ and KJ in Fig. 3-2(d).

For stresses in three directions, called *triaxial* or *three-dimensional stresses*, the state of stress can be completely defined by six stress components as shown in Fig. 3-4. It can also be shown,[3] in a manner

---

[3] See S. Timoshenko and J. N. Goodier, *Theory of Elasticity*, McGraw-Hill Book Co., Inc., New York, 1951.

similar to that used for two-dimensional stresses, that there are three principal stresses S_1, S_2, and S_3, whose values are the three roots of S in the cubic equation

$$S^3 - (S_x + S_y + S_z)S^2 + (S_x S_y + S_y S_z + S_x S_z - S_{yz}{}^2 - S_{zz}{}^2 - S_{xy}{}^2)S$$
$$- (S_x S_y S_z + 2S_{yz} S_{zz} S_{xy} - S_x S_{yz}{}^2 - S_y S_{zz}{}^2 - S_z S_{xy}{}^2) = 0 \qquad (3\text{-}4)$$

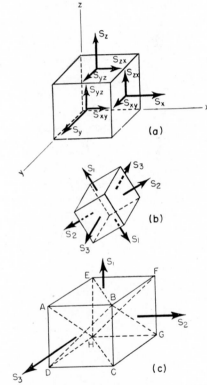

NOTE: PLANES OF MAXIMUM SHEAR STRESSES ARE
ABGH, EBCH AND BFHD

Fig. 3-4. Three dimensional stresses.

The stress components of Fig. 3-4(a) are replaced by the simpler principal stress system of Fig. 3-4(b). By considering all possible planes on the element of Fig. 3-4(a) it can be shown that the maximum shear stress is one of the following values:

$$S_s' = \pm\tfrac{1}{2}(S_1 - S_2)$$
$$S_s' = \pm\tfrac{1}{2}(S_2 - S_3)$$
$$S_s' = \pm\tfrac{1}{2}(S_3 - S_1)$$

$$(3\text{-}5)$$

The planes on which these shear stresses act are shown in Fig. 3-4(c). The greatest of the three shear stress values in eq. (3-5) depends upon the magnitude and sign of the principal stresses.

The principal stress equations have been stated for both two- and three-dimensional stresses, since it is found useful to express the theories of failure in terms of the principal stresses rather than the stress components. The maximum shear stress equations (3-3) and (3-5) have been given because they are used later to discuss the maximum shear theory.

Principal Strains. The deformations for states of combined stresses are usually expressed as the principal strains, or strains in the directions of the principal stresses. To determine the principal

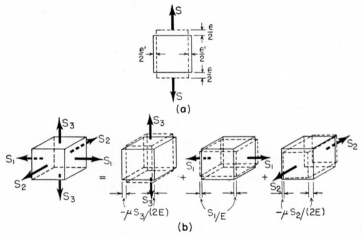

Fig. 3-5.

strains, consider first the element subjected to simple tension as shown in Fig. 3-5(a). The stress S produces a strain ϵ in the direction of the stress S and a lateral strain ϵ' at right angles to the stress direction S. The ratio of ϵ' to ϵ is called Poisson's ratio (μ), or

$$\mu = \frac{\epsilon'}{\epsilon} \qquad (3\text{-}6)$$

The principal strains, or strains in the directions of the principal stresses in Fig. 3-5(b), can now be expressed in terms of the principal stresses, the modulus of elasticity, and Poisson's ratio. The principal strain ϵ_1, in the direction of the principal stress S_1, can be obtained with the aid of Fig. 3-5(b). Referring to this figure, the strain in the direction of S_1 produced by S_1 is S_1/E. The strain in the S_1 direction produced by S_2 is $-\mu S_2/E$. The strain in the S_1 direction produced by S_3 is $-\mu S_3/E$. The resultant strain in the S_1 direction is $S_1/E - \mu S_2/E - \mu S_3/E$, or

$$\epsilon_1 = \frac{S_1}{E} - \frac{\mu}{E}(S_2 + S_3)$$

Similarly,
$$\epsilon_2 = \frac{S_2}{E} - \frac{\mu}{E}(S_3 + S_1)$$

$$\left.\right\} \quad (3\text{-}7)$$

and
$$\epsilon_3 = \frac{S_3}{E} - \frac{\mu}{E}(S_1 + S_2)$$

For two-dimensional stresses or stresses acting in one plane, $S_3 = 0$ and the principal strains become

$$\epsilon_1 = \frac{1}{E}(S_1 - \mu S_2)$$

$$\epsilon_2 = \frac{1}{E}(S_2 - \mu S_1)$$

$$\left.\right\} \quad (3\text{-}8)$$

$$\epsilon_3 = -\frac{\mu}{E}(S_1 + S_2)$$

Equations (3-7) and (3-8) express the strains for the element in Fig. 3-5(b) when all stresses are tensile. For compressive principal stresses, eqs. (3-7) and (3-8) can be employed, provided a minus value of the stress is used when a stress is compressive.

Strain Energy. In the development of the energy theories of failure for yielding it is necessary to determine the strain energy for an element subjected to principal stresses. The strain energy in the elastic range for the unit element in Fig. 3-5(b) subjected to combined stresses is equal to the work done by the three gradually applied stresses S_1, S_2, and S_3. That is, the stresses S_1, S_2, and S_3 produce strains ϵ_1, ϵ_2, and ϵ_3 in the direction of these stresses, and the work done, or strain energy, is

$$u = \frac{S_1\epsilon_1}{2} + \frac{S_2\epsilon_2}{2} + \frac{S_3\epsilon_3}{2} \qquad (3\text{-}9)$$

To express the strain energy u in terms of the stresses only, values of the principal stresses in terms of the principal strains from eqs. (3-7) can be substituted in eq. (3-9). Then the strain energy value reduces to

$$u = \frac{1}{2E} [S_1^2 + S_2^2 + S_3^2 - 2\mu(S_1S_2 + S_2S_3 + S_3S_1)] \quad (3\text{-}10)$$

Equation (3-10) gives the value of the elastic strain energy per unit volume in terms of the principal stresses, the modulus of elasticity, and Poisson's ratio. It should be noted that *the value given by eq. (3-10) can be used only in the elastic range and for materials where Hooke's law applies.*

For two-dimensional stresses $S_3 = 0$ and eq. (3-10) becomes

$$u = \frac{1}{2E} (S_1^2 - 2\mu S_1S_2 + S_2^2) \quad (3\text{-}11)$$

With the values of the principal stresses, principal strains, and strain energy determined in the foregoing, the theories of failure of materials subjected to combined stresses and yielding can now be considered.

3-2. THEORIES OF FAILURE FOR YIELD STRENGTH

A structural or machine member may fail to function for several reasons. Failure occurs by fracture of the member, and the ultimate strength or fracture strength is used as a measure of the resistance to this type of failure. However, failure may also be caused by excessive deformations of the part, produced by yielding In other words, the deformations become so large that clearances between parts are not maintained or change in shape makes the structure unserviceable.

For simple tension, failure by yielding is defined by a yield stress that is found experimentally by using a stress-strain diagram For an element subjected to combined stresses, as shown in Fig. 3-5(b), if S_1 is the greatest of the three stresses at all times during loading, it is of practical importance to know what the value of S_1 is to produce yielding of the element. It is not correct to suppose that yielding of the combined stress element will occur for a value of S_1 equal to the yield stress in simple tension. Experiments show that the value of S_1 at yield is influenced by the other values of the principal stresses.   Various theories of failure have been developed that define the value of the maximum principal stress at failure in terms of the other principal stresses and the yield stress in simple tension.[4] These theories are based on physical concepts as to how yielding might occur   By these theories, a member subjected to combined stresses yields when the maximum stress, deformation, strain energy, or some other function of stresses and strains has reached the value of maximum stress, deformation, or strain energy at yielding in simple tension.   In the following discussion, only those theories commonly recommended will be considered.

The *maximum stress theory*, sometimes called Rankine's theory, is based on the assumption that yielding of the element in Fig. 3-4(b) is dependent only upon the largest of the three principal stresses. Furthermore, by this theory, yielding occurs when the value of the numerically greatest principal stress equals the value S_{yp}' of the yield stress in simple tension if the greatest principal stress is tensile. If the numerically greatest principal stress is compressive, yielding of the element occurs when this stress equals the yield stress in simple compression, or S_{yp}''.   That is, if S_1 is the greatest principal stress, the yielding for combined stresses occurs when

$$S_1 = S_{yp}' \quad \text{or} \quad S_1 = -S_{yp}'' \qquad (3\text{-}12\text{a})$$

If S_2 is the greatest principal stress numerically, yielding occurs when

$$S_2 = S_{yp}' \quad \text{or} \quad S_2 = -S_{yp}'' \qquad (3\text{-}12\text{b})$$

If S_3 is the greatest principal stress numerically, yielding occurs when

$$S_3 = S_{yp}' \quad \text{or} \quad S_3 = -S_{yp}'' \qquad (3\text{-}12\text{c})$$

For two-dimensional stresses, $S_3 = 0$, and eqs. (3-12) reduce to

$$\left.\begin{array}{l} S_1 = S_{yp}' \quad \text{or} \quad S_1 = -S_{yp}'' \\ S_2 = S_{yp}' \quad \text{or} \quad S_2 = -S_{yp}'' \end{array}\right\} \qquad (3\text{-}13)$$

If the yield stresses in simple tension and simple compression are assumed to be equal and designated by the symbol S_{yp}, eqs. (3-13) can be written as

---

[4] For a complete discussion of these theories see A. Nadai, "Theories of Strength," *Trans. A.S.M.E.*, Vol. 55, 1933; A. Nadai, *Plasticity*, McGraw-Hill Book Co., Inc., 1930; S. Timoshenko, "Strength of Materials," D. Van Nostrand Co., Inc., 1942, Part II; J. Marin, *Mechanical Properties of Materials and Design*, McGraw-Hill Book Co., Inc., 1942.

$$S_1 = \pm S_{yp} \quad \text{and} \quad S_2 = \pm S_{yp}$$

or $\qquad S_1/S_{yp} = \pm 1 \quad \text{and} \quad S_2/S_{yp} = \pm 1 \qquad \left.\right\} \quad (3\text{-}14)$

where S_1/S_{yp} and S_2/S_{yp} are the stress ratios.

The maximum stress theory can be presented graphically by plotting eqs. (3-14) as shown in Fig. 3-6(a). That is, eqs. (3-14) are represented by the square formed by the vertical lines passing through the points $S_1/S_{yp} = +1$ and $S_1/S_{yp} = -1$, and the horizontal lines passing through the points $S_2/S_{yp} = +1$ and $S_2/S_{yp} = -1$. The lines defining the theory in Fig. 3-6(a) represent a boundary defining the beginning of yielding according to this theory. To explain, consider a point P in Fig. 3-6(a) having coordinates S_1/S_{yp} and S_2/S_{yp} corresponding to principal stresses S_1 and S_2. Let these stresses, for example, be the circumferential and longitudinal stresses in a thin-walled tube subjected to internal pressure and axial tension. Now consider the condition produced by increasing the internal pressure. An increase in pressure increases the value of the principal stresses and, therefore, the magnitudes of the coordinates S_1/S_{yp} and S_2/S_{yp} of the point P. When the pressure is increased so that point P moves to P', the material begins to yield according to the maximum stress theory. That is, in Fig. 3-6(a), the boundary defining a theory represents the beginning of yielding by this theory.

The maximum stress theory for yielding does not agree with test results. Differences between this theory and test results are quite large, particularly in the case of biaxial stresses of opposite sign. However, the theory is presented since it is a commonly used design procedure. That is, the maximum stress theory is automatically used when the influence of combined stresses is not considered, as can be seen by referring to eqs. (3-2). In using eqs. (3-2), if the value of S_1 is replaced by the tensile yield stress, the maximum stress theory results.

The *maximum shear theory*, also called Coulomb's theory, assumes that yielding is produced for a combined stress condition when the maximum shear stress reaches the value of the maximum shear stress at yield produced in an element subjected to simple tension. For the element in Fig. 3-4(b) the maximum shear stress is one of the values given in eqs. (3-5). For simple tension, the shear stress at yield can be determined from eqs. (3-3) by placing $S_x = S_{yp}'$, and $S_y = S_{xy} = 0$.   Then the shear stress at yield for simple tension is $S_{sy} = \pm S_{yp}'/2$.   By the maximum shear theory, yielding will occur for the combined stress element when the largest of the shear stresses in eqs. (3-5) equals the shear stress at yield in simple tension.   Since the maximum shear stresses given by eqs (3-5) may be negative or positive, the shear stress at yield for simple tension must equal that for simple compression.   That is, yielding is defined by

$$S_s' = \pm S_{sy} = \pm S_{yp}'/2 = \pm S_{yp}''/2 = \pm S_{yp}/2$$

Then, from eqs. (3-5),

$$\left.\begin{aligned}
S_1 - S_2 &= \pm S_{yp} \\
S_2 - S_3 &= \pm S_{yp} \\
S_3 - S_1 &= \pm S_{yp}
\end{aligned}\right\} \quad (3\text{-}15)$$

For two-dimensional stresses, $S_3 = 0$ and the equation that governs is dependent upon the sign of the principal stresses   That is, for principal stresses of opposite sign and with $S_3 = 0$, the maximum shear stress given by eqs. (3-5) is $S_s' = \pm\frac{1}{2}(S_1 - S_2)$.   Then by the maximum shear theory, yielding occurs when $S_{sy} = S_{yp}/2$, or $S_1 - S_2 = \pm S_{yp}$.   For principal stresses of the same sign, the maximum shear stress is defined by the second and third of eqs. (3-15), depending upon whether S_1 or S_2 is greatest.   That is, $S_1 = \pm S_{yp}$ or $S_2 = \pm S_{yp}$.   Based on the foregoing considerations of the relative signs of the principal stresses, the following equations define the maximum shear theory for biaxial stresses:

$$\left.\begin{aligned}
&\text{For } S_1 \text{ and } S_2 \text{ of opposite sign,}\\
&\qquad S_1 - S_2 = \pm S_{yp}\\
&\text{For } S_1 \text{ and } S_2 \text{ of the same sign,}\\
&\qquad S_1 = \pm S_{yp}, \qquad S_2 = \pm S_{yp}
\end{aligned}\right\} \quad (3\text{-}16)$$

Dividing both sides of eqs. (3-16) by S_{yp},

$$\left.\begin{aligned}
S_1/S_{yp} - S_2/S_{yp} &= \pm 1\\
S_1/S_{yp} = \pm 1, \qquad S_2/S_{yp} &= \pm 1
\end{aligned}\right\} \quad (3\text{-}17)$$

where S_1/S_{yp} and S_2/S_{yp} are the principal stress ratios.

Equations (3-17) are represented graphically in Fig. 3-6(b).   When both principal stresses are tensile or both compressive, a comparison of Figs. 3-6(a) and (b) shows that the maximum stress and the maximum shear theories coincide.   When the principal stresses are of opposite sign, however, there is considerable difference between these two theories.

Many designers use the maximum shear theory for ductile materials. Its wide use is indicated by its adoption in such codes as the A S.M.E. Code for the Design of Transmission Shafting, and the Code of the Army, Navy and Commerce Committee on Aircraft Requirements. Test results for ductile materials and for biaxial stresses show that, although the agreement between tests and theory is fair, the distortion energy or shear theory agrees best with the test results. One reason why the shear theory is widely used is that for both tension-tension and tension-compression biaxial stresses it is on the conservative side of the test data.

The *maximum strain theory*, also called St. Venant's theory, assumes that failure by yielding occurs when the maximum of the three principal strains becomes equal to the value of the strain at yielding in simple tension or simple compression that equals $\pm S_{yp}/E$. If you equate the strains given by eqs. (3-7) to the yield strain $\pm S_{yp}/E$, yielding occurs when

$$\left.\begin{aligned} S_1 - \mu(S_2 + S_3) &= \pm S_{yp} \\ S_2 - \mu(S_3 + S_1) &= \pm S_{yp} \\ S_3 - \mu(S_1 + S_2) &= \pm S_{yp} \end{aligned}\right\} \quad (3\text{-}18)$$

For two-dimensional stresses, $S_3 = 0$ and the governing equations defining failure by yielding are:

$$\begin{aligned} \text{For } S_1 \text{ greater than } S_2, \quad & S_1 - \mu S_2 = \pm S_{yp} \\ \text{For } S_2 \text{ greater than } S_1, \quad & S_2 - \mu S_1 = \pm S_{yp} \end{aligned} \right\} \quad (3\text{-}19)$$

Dividing eqs. (3-19) by S_{yp},

$$\left.\begin{aligned} S_1/S_{yp} - \mu S_2/S_{yp} &= \pm 1 \\ S_2/S_{yp} - \mu S_1/S_{yp} &= \pm 1 \end{aligned}\right\} \quad (3\text{-}20)$$

Equations (3-20) are presented graphically in Fig. 3-6(c) for a value of $\mu = 0.35$.

The *maximum strain energy theory* assumes that failure by yielding occurs when the total strain energy of deformation for an element of unit volume subjected to combined stresses is equal to the strain energy for a unit volume in simple tension or compression at yielding. From eq. (3-10) the total strain energy for a unit volume under simple tension or compression at yield is $u = S_{yp}{}^2/(2E)$. Equating this value of u to the value for an element un-

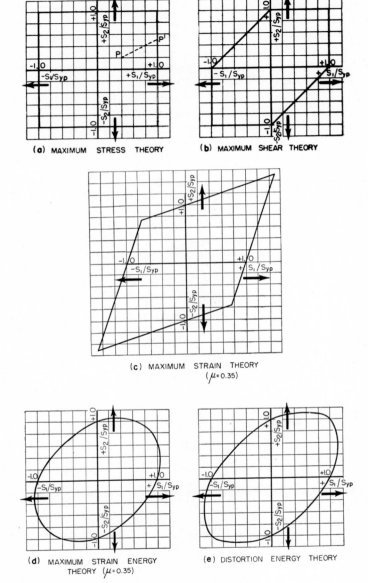

Fig. 3-6. Theories of failure.

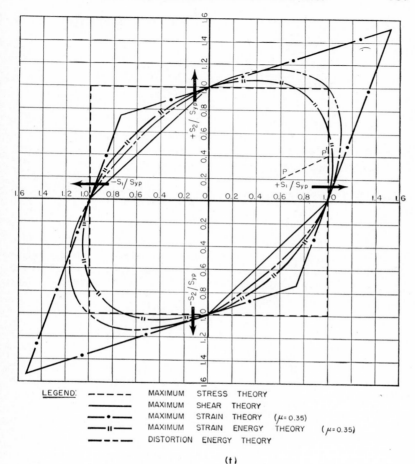

LEGEND:
- — — — — MAXIMUM STRESS THEORY
- ————— MAXIMUM SHEAR THEORY
- —•—•— MAXIMUM STRAIN THEORY ($\mu = 0.35$)
- —ıı—ıı— MAXIMUM STRAIN ENERGY THEORY ($\mu = 0.35$)
- — - — - DISTORTION ENERGY THEORY

(f)

Fig. 3-6 (Cont'd). Theories of failure.

der combined stresses, as defined by eq. (3-10), failure for combined stresses is expressed by the equation

$$S_1^2 + S_2^2 + S_3^2 - 2\mu(S_1 S_2 + S_2 S_3 + S_3 S_1) = S_{yp}^2 \tag{3-21}$$

For two-dimensional stresses, $S_3 = 0$ and eq. (3-21) becomes

$$S_1^2 - 2\mu S_1 S_2 + S_2^2 = S_{yp}^2 \tag{3-22}$$

Dividing eq. (3-22) by S_{yp}^2, the maximum strain-energy theory can be expressed by the equation

$$(S_1/S_{yp})^2 - \mu(S_1/S_{yp})(S_2/S_{yp}) + (S_2/S_{yp})^2 = 1 \tag{3-23}$$

Equation (3-23) is presented graphically in Fig. 3-6(d) for a value of $\mu = 0.35$.

The *distortion energy theory*, also called the Von Mises-Hencky theory, assumes that yielding of the element begins at stress values when the distortion energy produced by these stresses equals the distortion energy for simple tension at yield. To determine an expression for the distortion energy, note that the total strain energy of deformation u, as defined by eq. (3-10), is made up of two parts—the energy u_d required to produce distortion of the element, and the energy u_v required to change the volume of the element. That is,

$$u = u_v + u_d \quad \text{or} \quad u_d = u - u_v \tag{a}$$

The value of the distortion energy u_d could be determined from eq. (a) if the energy to change volume u_v were known, since the total strain energy u is defined by eq. (3-10). To obtain the strain energy u_v, the principal stresses shown in Fig. 3-7(a) will be considered to be made up of two parts, as indicated in Figs. 3-7(b) and (c), where

$$\left.\begin{aligned} S_1 &= S_1' + S_v \\ S_2 &= S_2' + S_v \\ S_3 &= S_3' + S_v \end{aligned}\right\} \tag{b}$$

Figure 3-7(c) shows an element subjected to equal tensile stresses S_v in the principal stress directions. The value of S_v will be selected so that the volume change of the original element in Fig. 3-7(a) is represented by the volume change in Fig. 3-7(c). Then the volume change in the element of Fig. 3-7(b) must be zero, or

$$\epsilon_1' + \epsilon_2' + \epsilon_3' = 0 \tag{c}$$

The value of the principal strains in eq. (c) are, by eqs. (3-7),

$$\left.\begin{aligned} \epsilon_1' &= \frac{S_1'}{E} - \frac{\mu}{E}(S_2' + S_3') \\ \epsilon_2' &= \frac{S_2'}{E} - \frac{\mu}{E}(S_3' + S_1') \\ \epsilon_3' &= \frac{S_3'}{E} - \frac{\mu}{E}(S_1' + S_2') \end{aligned}\right\} \tag{d}$$

Placing the values of the strains from eqs. (d) in eq. (c) and simplifying the resulting equation,

$$(1 - 2\mu)(S_1' + S_2' + S_3') = 0$$

or
$$S_1' + S_2' + S_3' = 0 \tag{e}$$

That is, for the volume change in Fig. 3-7(b) to be zero, the algebraic sum of the principal stresses must be zero. The value of the stress S_v can now be determined by adding eqs. (b) and noting by eq. (e) that $S_1' + S_2' + S_3' = 0$. Then the stress S_v has a value

$$S_v = \frac{S_1 + S_2 + S_3}{3} \tag{f}$$

With the value of S_v known in terms of the original stress values, the values of the stresses S_1', S_2', and S_3' can be found by substituting the value of S_v from eq. (f) in eqs. (b). This substitution gives

$$\left. \begin{array}{l} S_1' = \tfrac{2}{3}[S_1 - \tfrac{1}{2}(S_2 + S_3)] \\ S_2' = \tfrac{2}{3}[S_2 - \tfrac{1}{2}(S_3 + S_1)] \\ S_3' = \tfrac{2}{3}[S_3 - \tfrac{1}{2}(S_1 + S_2)] \end{array} \right\} \tag{g}$$

Equations (f) and (g) define the values of the stresses in the two new systems of stresses given in Figs. 3-7(b) and (c). Since the stresses in Fig. 3-7(c) are equal in all directions, there can be no distortion inside the element, and the distortion energy of the original element is completely represented by the distortion energy for the element in Fig. 3-7(b). Furthermore, all the

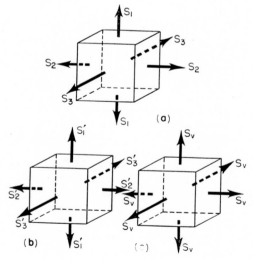

Fig. 3-7.

volume change and, hence, volume energy for the original element in Fig. 3-7(a) is made equal to the volume change or volume energy for the element in Fig. 3-7(c). The strain energy for the element in Fig. 3-7(c) is equal to

$$u_v = 3 \left(\frac{S_v \epsilon_v}{2} \right) \tag{h}$$

where ϵ_v = the strains in the directions of the stresses S_v.
Placing the value of S_v from eq. (f) in eq. (h),

$$u_v = \frac{3(S_1 + S_2 + S_3)}{3 \times 2} \epsilon_v$$

Noting that $\epsilon_v = (S_v - \mu S_v - \mu S_v)/E = (1 - 2\mu)S_v/E$, then

$$u_v = \frac{(S_1 + S_2 + S_3)}{2} \left(\frac{1 - 2\mu}{E} \right) S_v$$

or

$$u_v = \left(\frac{1 - 2\mu}{6E} \right) (S_1 + S_2 + S_3)^2 \tag{i}$$

With the value of u defined by eq. (3-10) and u_v defined by eq. (i), the distortion energy from eqs. (a) and (3-10) is

$$u_d = u - u_v = \frac{1}{2E} [S_1^2 + S_2^2 + S_3^2 - \mu(S_1 S_2 + S_2 S_3 + S_3 S_1)]$$

$$- \left(\frac{1 - 2\mu}{6E} \right) (S_1 + S_2 + S_3)^2$$

or

$$u_d = \left(\frac{1 + \mu}{3E} \right) (S_1^2 + S_2^2 + S_3^2 - S_1 S_2 - S_2 S_3 - S_3 S_1) \tag{j}$$

For simple tension at yield, $S_2 = S_3 = 0$, $S_1 = S_{yp}$, and the distortion energy by eq. (j) is

$$u_{dy} = \left(\frac{1 + \mu}{3E} \right) (S_{yp})^2 \tag{k}$$

Yielding of the three-dimensional or triaxial stressed element shown in Fig. 3-7(a) occurs by the distortion energy theory when the value of u_d, as given by eq. (j), equals the value at yielding for simple tension as defined by eq. (k), or

$$S_1^2 + S_2^2 + S_3^2 - S_1 S_2 - S_2 S_3 - S_3 S_1 = S_{yp}^2 \tag{3-24}$$

For two-dimensional stresses, $S_3 = 0$ and eq. (3-24) becomes

$$S_1^2 - S_1 S_2 + S_2^2 = S_{yp}^2 \tag{3-25}$$

Placing the values of the principal stresses from eqs. (3-2) in eq. (3-25) gives

$$S_x^2 - S_x S_y + S_y^2 + 3 S_{xy}^2 = S_{yp}^2 \tag{3-26}$$

Dividing eq. (3-25) by $(S_{yp})^2$,

$$\left(\frac{S_1}{S_{yp}}\right)^2 - \left(\frac{S_1}{S_{yp}}\right)\left(\frac{S_2}{S_{yp}}\right) + \left(\frac{S_2}{S_{yp}}\right)^2 = 1 \tag{3-27}$$

where S_1/S_{yp} and S_2/S_{yp} are stress ratios.

Equation (3-27) is the equation of an ellipse, as shown in Fig. 3-6(e). It should be noted that the maximum strain, maximum strain energy, and distortion energy theories, unlike the maximum stress and maximum shear theories, assume Hooke's law. For comparison, Fig. 3-6(f) shows all the foregoing theories plotted on one diagram.

For ductile materials and two-dimensional or biaxial stresses there is considerable test evidence to show that the distortion energy theory is in good agreement with test results for defining failure by yielding. It is, therefore, currently used by many research and design engineers. When the maximum shear and distortion energy theories are used, it is necessary to assume that the yield strengths in simple tension and simple compression are equal. Although this is a good assumption for many ductile materials, there are some ductile materials that show considerable difference between the tensile and compressive yield strengths. For the latter materials either the internal friction theory or Mohr's theory[4] gives a good approximation for biaxial stresses.

In general, the distortion energy theory is recommended for defining yielding of ductile materials, although the maximum shear theory is a reasonably good approximation.

NUMERICAL EXAMPLE. A circular shaft 10 in. in diameter is made of steel with a tensile yield stress of 90,000 psi. Determine the twisting moment required to produce yielding based on (1) the maximum stress theory, (2) the maximum shear theory, and (3) the distortion energy theory. Compare the values as given by the maximum stress and maximum shear theories with the value required by the distortion energy theory.

SOLUTION. The twisting moment T produces shear stresses $S_{xy} = Tr/J = Tr/(\pi r^4/2) = 2T/(\pi r^3)$ on the element of the shaft, as shown in Fig. 3-8(a). From eqs. (3-2) the principal stresses $S_1 = S_{xy}$ and $S_2 = -S_{xy}$ as indicated in Fig. 3-8(b). Then by each of the three theories of failure, the twisting moment T that will produce yielding can be obtained as follows:

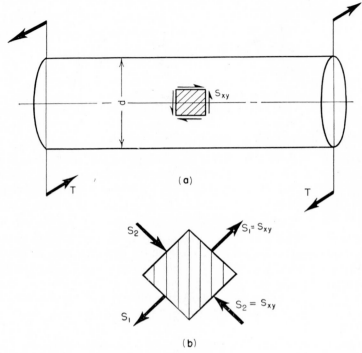

Fig. 3-8.

For the maximum stress theory, by eq. (3-14), $S_1 = S_{yp}$ and since $S_1 = S_{yp} = 2T/(\pi r^3)$, then $2T/(\pi r^3) = S_{yp}$, or

$$T = \frac{S_{yp}\pi r^3}{2} = 90,000 \times \pi \times \frac{5^3}{2} = 1.77 \times 10^7 \text{ in. lb.}$$

For the maximum shear theory, by eq. (3-16), $S_1 - S_2 = \pm S_{yp}$. And, since $S_1 = -S_2 = 2T/(\pi r^3)$, then $2S_1 = S_{yp} = (2 \times 2T)/(\pi r^3)$, or

$$T = \frac{\pi r^3 S_{yp}}{4} = \frac{\pi \times 5^3 \times 90,000}{4} = 0.88 \times 10^7 \text{ in. lb.}$$

For the distortion energy theory, by eq. (3-25), $S_1^2 - S_1 S_2 + S_2^2 = S_{yp}^2$. And, since $S_1 = -S_2$, $3S_1^2 = S_{yp}^2$. But $S_1 = S_{xy} = (2T)/(\pi r^3)$, so that $3S_1^2 = 3(2T)^2/(\pi r^3)^2 = S_{yp}^2$, or

$$T = \frac{\pi r^3 S_{yp}}{(\sqrt{3} \times 2)} = \frac{\pi \times 5^3 \times 90,000}{(\sqrt{3} \times 2)} = 1.02 \times 10^7 \text{ in. lb.}$$

A comparison of the yield torques, as predicted by the maximum stress and shear theories, with the value determined by the distortion energy theory is given by the torque ratios

$$R_1 = \frac{1.77 \times 10^7}{(1.02 \times 10^7)} = 1.73$$

and

$$R_2 = \frac{0.88 \times 10^7}{(1.02 \times 10^7)} = 0.87$$

NUMERICAL EXAMPLE. A cylindrical pressure vessel, closed at the ends, is 10 ft. in diameter and has a 3-in. wall thickness. The vessel is made of a steel with a yield strength in tension of 42,000 psi. Determine the internal pressure that will produce yielding according to (1) the maximum stress theory, (2) the maximum shear theory, and (3) the distortion energy theory.

SOLUTION. The stresses in a thin-walled cylinder subjected to internal pressure are represented by the longitudinal stress S_1 and circumferential stress S_2 as shown in Fig. 3-9. The values of these stresses are, by eqs. (3-1a) and (b),

$$S_1 = \frac{pd}{2t} \quad \text{and} \quad S_2 = \frac{pd}{4t}$$

where p = the internal pressure, d = the internal diameter, and t = the wall thickness.

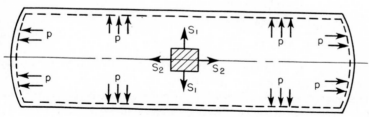

Fig. 3-9.   Pressure vessel.

The principal stresses S_1 and S_2 are both tensile, so that by eqs. (3-13) and (3-16) the results as given by the maximum shear and maximum stress theories are the same. Since S_1 is greater than S_2, then by eq. (3-16),

$$S_1 = S_{yp} = \frac{p_1 d}{2t} \quad \text{or} \quad p_1 = \frac{2t S_{yp}}{d} = \frac{2 \times 3 \times 42,000}{120} = 2100 \text{ psi}$$

Using the distortion energy theory, the yield pressure is defined by substituting the values of S_1 and S_2 in eq. (3-25), which gives

$$\left(\frac{p_3 d}{2t}\right)^2 - \left(\frac{p_3 d}{2t}\right)\left(\frac{p_3 d}{4t}\right) + \left(\frac{p_3 d}{4t}\right)^2 = S_{yp}{}^2$$

or $\qquad p_3 = \left(\frac{4}{\sqrt{3}}\right)\left(\frac{t S_{yp}}{d}\right) = \frac{4 \times 3 \times 42{,}000}{120\sqrt{3}} = 2420$ psi

3-3. THEORIES OF FAILURE FOR ULTIMATE STRENGTH

For brittle materials such as cast iron and concrete, failure for simple stresses cannot be defined by the yield strength, since a yield stress does not exist. For these materials, failure is defined by the ultimate stress. Plastic failure of ductile materials subjected to simple stresses is also defined by the ultimate stress. Several theories of failure for predicting the ultimate strength of materials subjected to combined stresses have been presented.[4] The maximum stress and maximum shear stress theories discussed in Article 3-2 have been applied to define ultimate strengths of materials subjected to combined stresses. Equations (3-12) to (3-18) for the yield strengths of materials, as defined by the maximum stress and shear theories, can be used for defining ultimate strengths provided the yield stress S_{yp} is replaced by the ultimate stress.

For two-dimensional stresses the *maximum stress theory* for defining the ultimate strength becomes

$$\begin{aligned} &\text{For } S_1 \text{ greater than } S_2, \quad S_1 = S_u', \quad \text{or} \quad S_1 = -S_u'' \\ &\text{For } S_2 \text{ greater than } S_1, \quad S_2 = S_u', \quad \text{or} \quad S_2 = -S_u'' \end{aligned} \quad (3\text{-}28)$$

where S_u' = the ultimate stress in tension and S_u'' = the ultimate stress in compression.

The *maximum shear theory* for ultimate strengths and two-dimensional stresses is expressed by one of the following equations:

$$\left.\begin{aligned} &\text{For principal stresses of the same sign,} \\ &\qquad S_1 = \pm S_u \quad \text{or} \quad S_2 = \pm S_u \\ &\text{For principal stresses of the opposite sign,} \\ &\qquad S_1 - S_2 = \pm S_u \quad \text{or} \quad S_2 - S_1 = \pm S_u \end{aligned}\right\} \quad (3\text{-}29)$$

In eqs. (3-29) S_u is the ultimate strength in tension or compression, whichever is the smallest. As in the case of the shear theory for

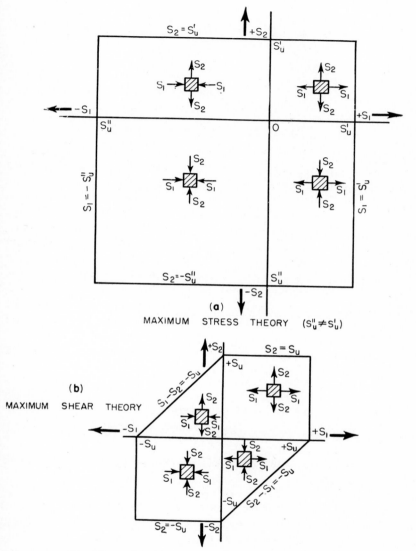

Fig. 3-10.   Theories of failure for ultimate strength.

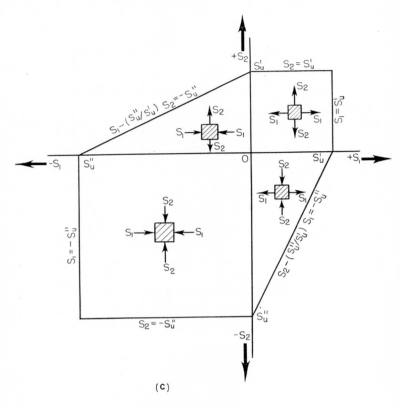

INTERNAL FRICTION THEORY

Fig. 3-10 (Cont'd).   Theories of failure for ultimate strength.

yield strength, it is necessary to assume equal strengths in tension and compression.

Figures 3-10(a) and (b) represent eqs. (3-28) and (3-29) or the maximum stress and shear theories for ultimate strength.

A special case of Mohr's theory of failure, the *internal friction theory*, assumes that failure is a function of the shear stress and internal friction, and that the limiting shear stress at failure depends upon the ratio of the principal stresses.   For biaxial stresses, the equations defining the ultimate strengths are, by this theory,[4]

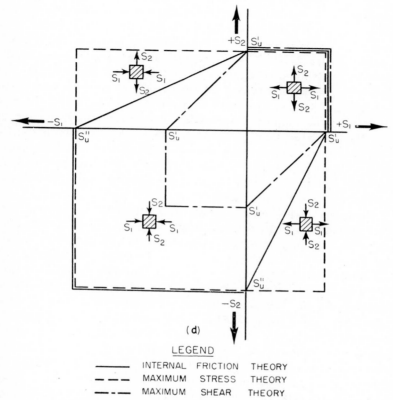

(d)

LEGEND

—————— INTERNAL FRICTION THEORY
— — — MAXIMUM STRESS THEORY
— · — MAXIMUM SHEAR THEORY

Fig. 3-10 (Cont'd).   Theories of failure for ultimate strength.

For principal stresses of the same sign,

$$S_1 = S_u{}', \; S_1 = -S_u{}'', \quad S_2 = S_u{}', \; S_2 = -S_u{}''$$

For principal stresses of opposite sign,

$$S_1 - \left(\frac{S_u{}''}{S_u{}'}\right)S_2 = -S_u{}'' \quad \text{and} \quad S_2 - \left(\frac{S_u{}''}{S_u{}'}\right)S_1 = -S_u{}''$$

$$(3\text{-}30)$$

The foregoing equations are shown graphically in Fig. 3-10(c) for the case where the ultimate strength in simple compression is greater than for simple tension.

Equations (3-30) show that the simple compressive strength of the material S_u'' is considered in this theory.   For biaxial stresses of the same sign, eqs. (3-30) agree with eqs. (3-29) for the maximum shear theory.   For biaxial stresses of opposite sign, however, the internal friction theory gives values intermediate between the maximum shear and maximum stress theories as indicated in Fig. 3-10(d).

For biaxial tensile stresses, all three theories coincide and there is a reasonably good agreement between the test data and theories for both ductile and brittle materials.   *For biaxial stresses of opposite sign,* the limited amount of test data show that for ductile materials with the same tensile and compressive strengths the maximum shear theory should be used.   For brittle materials and for ductile materials with values of S_u' and S_u'' that differ appreciably, the internal friction theory is recommended.

The above discussion of ultimate strengths refers to nominal ultimate strengths.   True ultimate strengths have also been compared with the maximum shear and stress theories using the true tensile and compressive strengths in place of their nominal strengths.

Attempts have been made to predict theoretically the fracture strengths of materials subjected to combined stresses.[5]   For ductile materials, the necking down that occurs in specimens after the ultimate loads have been reached introduces triaxial states of stress at the necked-down part of the specimen.   The magnitudes of these stresses are unknown, since the stress distribution over the specimen cross section varies with increase in load.   These rapid changes in states of stress, and the errors in the calculated stress values, make the stress-strain relation prior to fracture of questionable value.   For these reasons a comparison between theories and test results is not warranted.

NUMERICAL EXAMPLE.   Determine the force required to punch a 2-in. diameter hole in a 1-in. thick metal plate.   Assume that the shear stress is uniformly distributed.   The ultimate strengths in tension and compression are $S_u' = 50,000$ and $S_u'' = 90,000$ psi

---

[5] For a discussion of fracture of metals subjected to combined stress see M. Gensamer *et al.*, "Report on the Fracture of Metals," *Welding Research Supplement*, Aug., 1947, Vol. 12, pp. 443-484; *Seminar on "Fracturing of Metals,"* publ. by the A.S.M., 1948, pp. 1-312, in particular the paper by J. E. Dorn on "The Effect of Stress State on the Fracture Strengths of Metals," pp. 32-50. See also J. H. Holloman, *The Problem of Fracture*, pub. by the American Welding Society, 1946, pp. 1-92.

respectively. Solve by the maximum shear and internal friction theories.

SOLUTION. Figure 3-11(a) shows a punch with diameter d, subjected to a load P, and a plate of thickness t. The shear stresses

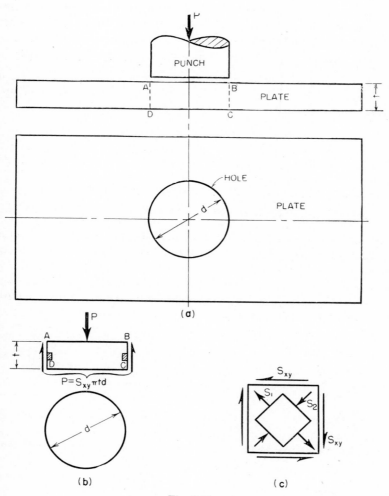

(a)

(b)

(c)

$P = S_{xy} \pi t d$

Fig. 3-11.

produced on the core of the plate $ABCD$ are shown in Fig. 3-11(b). For equilibrium, and if the shear stresses are assumed to be uniform, $P = (S_{xy})(t\pi d)$. The shear stresses S_{xy} produce principal stresses $S_1 = -S_2$, as shown in Fig. 3-11(c).

By the *maximum shear theory* the value of the ultimate shear strength S_{xy} is determined from the second of eqs. (3-29) or from $S_1 - S_2 = \pm S_u$, or $2S_{xy} = S_u$, or $S_{xy} = S_u/2$. Then by the maximum shear theory the ultimate load is

$$P = (S_{xy})(t\pi d) = (S_u/2)(t\pi d) = (50,000/2)(1 \times \pi \times 2) = 157,000\,\text{lb}.$$

By the *internal friction theory* the ultimate shear strength S_{xy} is determined from the last of eqs. (3-30) for principal stresses of opposite sign. Then for $S_1 = -S_2 = S_{xy}$,

$$-S_{xy} - (S_u''/S_u')S_{xy} = -S_u''$$

or
$$S_{xy} = \frac{S_u''}{(1 + S_u''/S_u')} = \frac{90,000}{(1 + 9/5)} = 32,000 \text{ psi}$$

Then, by the internal friction theory, the load required is

$$P = (S_{xy})(t\pi d) = (32,200)(1 \times \pi \times 2) = 202,000 \text{ lb}.$$

NUMERICAL EXAMPLE.   A thin-walled tube with internal diameter $d = 2$ in. and wall thickness $t = 0.1$ in. is subjected to a twisting moment T.   Determine the maximum twisting moment that can be applied if the ultimate strengths in tension and compression are $S_u' = 40,000$ psi and $S_u'' = 80,000$ psi respectively.   Solve by both the maximum shear and internal friction theories.

SOLUTION.   For a thin-walled tube in torsion the total shear stress in the tube wall times the radius equals the applied torque.   That is,

$$T = (S_{xy}t\pi d)\frac{d}{2} = \frac{t\pi d^2 S_{xy}}{2}$$

For torsion of a thin-walled tube, the principal stresses are $S_1 = -S_2 = S_{xy}$, as shown in Fig. 3-8.

By the *maximum shear theory*, for $S_1 = -S_2 = S_{xy}$, the ultimate shear strength is, by the second of eqs. (3-29),

$$S_1 - S_2 = \pm S_u, \quad \text{or} \quad 2S_1 = 2S_{xy} = S_u, \quad \text{or} \quad S_{xy} = S_u/2.$$

The ultimate torque by the maximum shear theory is then

$$T = \frac{t\pi d^2 S_{xy}}{2} = \frac{t\pi d^2 S_u}{2 \times 2}$$

$$= \frac{0.1 \times \pi \times 2^2 \times 40,000}{4} = 12,600 \text{ in. lb.}$$

By the *internal friction theory* the ultimate shear strength is defined by eq. (3-30). That is, for $S_1 = -S_2 = S_{xy}$, by the last of eqs. (3-30),

$$-S_{xy}(1 + S_u''/S_u') = \pm S_u''$$

or

$$-S_{xy}\left(1 + \frac{80,000}{40,000}\right) = -80,000$$

and

$$S_{xy} = 26,700 \text{ psi}$$

Then the ultimate torque by the internal friction theory is

$$T = \frac{t\pi d^2 S_{xy}}{2} = \frac{0.1 \times \pi \times 2^2 \times 26,700}{2} = 16,800 \text{ in. lb.}$$

3-4. THEORIES FOR PLASTIC STRESS-STRAIN RELATIONS AND DUCTILITY

In the design of some machine and structural members it is necessary to know the stress-strain relations in the plastic range for various states of combined stresses. These plastic stress-strain relations also are of importance in the improvement of forming operations where sheets of metal are plastically deformed and subjected to combined stresses in such processes. Information on ductility under combined stresses is particularly important, as it makes it possible to determine such things as the limiting angles through which metal sheets can be bent without fracture. It is also essential to know the ductility of metals under combined stresses because, in some designs, the ductility may be the controlling factor.

The widely used *deformation theory for plastic flow* will be presented in this article. This theory is employed to define the stress-strain relations and ductility for combined stresses. In presenting and recommending the deformation theory for plastic flow it should be noted that there is only a limited amount of test data available. However, the test results that have been presented are in approximately good agreement with the theory for conditions where the ratios of the principal stresses remain constant.

The *deformation theory for plastic flow* is based on the following assumptions:

1. The directions of the true principal plastic strains δ_1, δ_2, and δ_3 coincide with the directions of the true principal stresses S_1, S_2, and S_3. The symbol δ for true plastic strains will be used to distinguish this type of strain from the nominal elastic strain ϵ.

2. The volume remains constant in the plastic range, or if δ_1, δ_2, and δ_3 are the true principal strains,

$$\delta_1 + \delta_2 + \delta_3 = 0 \tag{a}$$

3. The ratios of the three principal shear strains to the principal shear stresses are equal. That is, it can be shown that the principal shear strains are $(\delta_1 - \delta_2)$, $(\delta_2 - \delta_3)$, and $(\delta_3 - \delta_1)$,[6] and the principal stresses are $(S_1 - S_2)/2$, $(S_2 - S_3)/2$, and $(S_3 - S_1)/2$. Then

$$\frac{\delta_1 - \delta_2}{(S_1 - S_2)/2} = \frac{\delta_2 - \delta_3}{(S_2 - S_3)/2} = \frac{\delta_3 - \delta_1}{(S_3 - S_1)/2} = k$$

or
$$\frac{\delta_1 - \delta_2}{S_1 - S_2} = \frac{\delta_2 - \delta_3}{S_2 - S_3} = \frac{\delta_3 - \delta_1}{S_3 - S_1} = k_1 \tag{b}$$

The value of k_1 in eq. (b) is usually determined from the true plastic stress-strain relation in simple tension.

With the above assumptions, as defined by eqs. (a) and (b), equations for principal strains in terms of principal stresses can be determined by solving these equations simultaneously. That is,

$$\left.
\begin{aligned}
\delta_1 &= \frac{2k_1}{3}\left[S_1 - \frac{1}{2}(S_2 + S_3) \right] \\
\delta_2 &= \frac{2k_1}{3}\left[S_2 - \frac{1}{2}(S_3 + S_1) \right] \\
\delta_3 &= \frac{2k_1}{3}\left[S_3 - \frac{1}{2}(S_1 + S_2) \right]
\end{aligned}
\right\} \tag{c}$$

Equations (c) define the true principal strains in terms of the true principal stresses and a quantity k_1. The quantity $3/(2k_1)$ is sometimes called the *plasticity modulus*. To determine k_1, eqs. (c) will be applied to simple tension. For simple tension, $S_2 = S_3 = 0$, $S_1 = S'$, the true stress in simple tension, and $\delta_1 = \delta$, the true strain in simple tension. Then by the first of eqs. (c),

$$\delta = \frac{2}{3}k_1 S' \quad \text{or} \quad k_1 = \frac{3}{2}\frac{\delta}{S'} \tag{d}$$

Placing the value of k_1 from eq. (d) in eqs. (c),

$$\left.
\begin{aligned}
\frac{\delta_1}{S_1 - \frac{1}{2}(S_2 + S_3)} &= \frac{\delta}{S'} \\
\frac{\delta_2}{S_2 - \frac{1}{2}(S_3 + S_1)} &= \frac{\delta}{S'} \\
\frac{\delta_3}{S_3 - \frac{1}{2}(S_1 + S_2)} &= \frac{\delta}{S'}
\end{aligned}
\right\} \tag{e}$$

[6] See M. M. Frocht, *Photoelasticity*, John Wiley & Sons, Inc., 1941, Vol. 1, p. 31.

Squaring both sides of eqs. (e) and adding the numerators and denominators,

$$\frac{\delta}{S'} = \frac{\sqrt{\frac{2}{3}(\delta_1{}^2 + \delta_2{}^2 + \delta_3{}^2)}}{\sqrt{\frac{1}{2}[(S_1 - S_2)^2 + (S_2 - S_3)^2 + (S_3 - S_1)^2]}} \tag{3-31}$$

Equation (3-31) gives the relation between the principal stresses and principal strains in the plastic range in terms of the true stress S' and true strain δ in simple tension. Equation (3-31) can also be written as

$$\frac{\bar{S}}{\bar{\delta}} = \frac{S'}{\delta} \tag{3-32}$$

where $\bar{S} = \sqrt{\frac{1}{2}[(S_1 - S_2)^2 + (S_2 - S_3)^2 + (S_3 - S_1)^2]}$

and $\bar{\delta} = \sqrt{\frac{2}{3}(\delta_1{}^2 + \delta_2{}^2 + \delta_3{}^2)}$ $\Bigg\}$ (3-33)

The stress $\bar{S}$ and strain $\bar{\delta}$, as defined by eqs. (3-33), are usually called the *effective stress* and *effective strain*.[7] Combined stress test data in terms of plastic stresses and strains can be represented by plotting the effective stress $\bar{S}$ versus the effective strain $\bar{\delta}$. Then, by the deformation theory, as defined in eqs. (3-31) or (3-32), the $\bar{S}$–$\bar{\delta}$ relation should coincide with the stress-strain or S'–δ relation for simple tension. Test data show that, for biaxial tension, the agreement between the $\bar{S}$–$\bar{\delta}$ and S'–δ relations is a reasonably good approximation for engineering design purposes.

The effective stress and strain have also been called the *significant stress and strain*.[8] These stresses and strains are also equivalent to the *octahedral stress and strain*.[9]

The theoretical relationship between the principal stresses and principal strains, as determined by eqs. (3-31) or (3-32), was evaluated on the basis of three assumed laws of yielding. It should be noted that the above theory assumes that the loads are applied slowly, the strains are small, the elastic strains can be neglected compared to the plastic strains, and the principal axes of stress and strain do not rotate. It is also assumed that the principal stresses are gradually increased in value, with the ratio of the principal stresses remaining constant.

To determine equations for the principal strains in terms of the principal stresses it is necessary to express the relation between the true stress and true strain in simple tension. An approximate relation for the true stress-true strain relation in simple tension is given by eq. (1-20) in Chapter 1,

---

[7] See, for example, H. E. Davis, and E. R. Parker, "Behavior of Steel under Biaxial Stress as Determined by Tests on Tubes," *Trans. A.S.M.E.*, 1948, Vol. 70, paper No. 48—A.P.M. 20.

[8] See for example W. T. Lankford and Edward Saibel, "Some Problems in Unstable Plastic Flow under Biaxial Tension," Am. Inst. of Min. and Met. Engrs., 1947, *Tech. Pub. No. 2238.*

[9] See for example A. Nadai, *Theory of Flow and Fracture of Solids*, McGraw-Hill Book Co., Inc., 1950, Vol. 1.

or $S' = k\delta^n$. Since the effective stress-strain relation in the foregoing theory coincides with the tensile stress-strain relation, $\bar{S} = k\bar{\delta}^n$ and eq. (3-32) can be written as

$$\frac{\delta}{S'} = \frac{\bar{\delta}}{\bar{S}} = \left(\frac{\bar{S}}{k}\right)^{1/n} \left(\frac{1}{\bar{S}}\right) = \frac{(\bar{S})^{\frac{1-n}{n}}}{k^{1/n}}$$

Placing the value of $\bar{S}$ from eq. (3-33) in the foregoing equation,

$$\frac{\delta}{S'} = \left(\frac{1}{k^{1/n}}\right)(S_1^2 + S_2^2 + S_3^2 - S_1S_2 - S_2S_3 - S_3S_1)^{\frac{1-n}{2n}} \qquad (3\text{-}34)$$

The principal strains in terms of the principal stresses and the simple tension constants k and n of the material can be determined by placing the value of δ/S' from eq. (3-34) in eqs. (e). Then the values of the true plastic principal strains become

$$\delta_1 = \left(\frac{1}{k^{1/n}}\right)(S_1^2 + S_2^2 + S_3^2 - S_1S_2 - S_2S_3 - S_3S_1)^{\frac{1-n}{2n}}$$
$$\left(S_1 - \frac{S_2}{2} - \frac{S_3}{2}\right)$$

$$\delta_2 = \left(\frac{1}{k^{1/n}}\right)(S_1^2 + S_2^2 + S_3^2 - S_1S_2 - S_2S_3 - S_3S_1)^{\frac{1-n}{2n}}$$
$$\left(S_2 - \frac{S_3}{2} - \frac{S_1}{2}\right) \qquad (3\text{-}35)$$

$$\delta_3 = \left(\frac{1}{k^{1/n}}\right)(S_1^2 + S_2^2 + S_3^2 - S_1S_2 - S_2S_3 - S_3S_1)^{\frac{1-n}{2n}}$$
$$\left(S_3 - \frac{S_1}{2} - \frac{S_2}{2}\right)$$

Equations (3-35) can be used to determine the strains at rupture provided the values of the stresses S_1, S_2, and S_3 at rupture are known. To determine the values of the stresses S_1, S_2, and S_3 at rupture, a rupture theory for combined stresses must be introduced. A conservative theory for this purpose, and for use with ductile materials, is the maximum shear theory. By this theory, if S_1 is the maximum principal stress and S_3 is the minimum principal stress, the maximum shear theory for rupture can be expressed by eqs. (3-15) if S_{yp} is replaced by S_r, the rupture strength for simple tension. Then the greatest shear stress is $(S_1 - S_3)/2$ and the third of eqs. (3-15) governs. That is, rupture is defined by

$$S_1 - S_3 = S_r$$

or
$$S_1 = \frac{S_r}{1 - \beta} \qquad (3\text{-}36)$$

where $\beta = S_3/S_1$.

Placing the value of S_1 from eq. (3-36) for the value of S_1 in eqs. (3-35), the principal strains at rupture are

$$
\begin{aligned}
\delta_{1r} &= \left[\frac{S_r}{k(1-\beta)}\right]^{1/n}[\alpha^2+\beta^2-\alpha\beta-\alpha-\beta+1]^{\frac{1-n}{2n}} \\
&\qquad\qquad\qquad\qquad\qquad\left(1-\frac{\alpha}{2}-\frac{\beta}{2}\right) \\
\delta_{2r} &= \left[\frac{S_r}{k(1-\beta)}\right]^{1/n}[\alpha^2+\beta^2-\alpha\beta-\alpha-\beta+1]^{\frac{1-n}{2n}} \\
&\qquad\qquad\qquad\qquad\qquad\left(\alpha-\frac{\beta}{2}-\frac{1}{2}\right) \\
\delta_{3r} &= \left[\frac{S_r}{k(1-\beta)}\right]^{1/n}[\alpha^2+\beta^2-\alpha\beta-\alpha-\beta+1]^{\frac{1-n}{2n}} \\
&\qquad\qquad\qquad\qquad\qquad\left(\beta-\frac{\alpha}{2}-\frac{1}{2}\right)
\end{aligned}
\tag{3-37}
$$

where $\qquad\qquad \alpha = S_2/S_1 \quad \text{and} \quad \beta = S_3/S_1 \qquad\qquad$ (3-38)

The ductility of materials subjected to combined stresses is usually measured by the greatest of the three principal fracture strains in eqs. (3-37). The influence of combined stresses on the ductility can be obtained, for example, in the case of biaxial tensile stresses of equal values by placing $S_3 = 0$ or $\beta = 0$, and $\alpha = S_2/S_1 = 1$ in eqs. (3-37). Then from eqs. (3-37),

$$
\delta_{1r} = \left(\frac{S_r}{k}\right)^{1/n}(1-1+1)^{\frac{1-n}{2n}}\left(1-\frac{1}{2}\right) = \frac{1}{2}\left(\frac{S_r}{k}\right)^{1/n}
$$

$$
\delta_{2r} = \left(\frac{S_r}{k}\right)^{1/n}(1-1+1)^{\frac{1-n}{2n}}\left(1-\frac{1}{2}\right) = \frac{1}{2}\left(\frac{S_r}{k}\right)^{1/n}
$$

$$
\delta_{3r} = \left(\frac{S_r}{k}\right)^{1/n}(1-1+1)^{\frac{1-n}{2n}}\left(-\frac{1}{2}-\frac{1}{2}\right) = -\left(\frac{S_r}{k}\right)^{1/n}
$$

That is, $\delta_{1r} = \delta_{2r} = \delta_{r/2}$ and $\delta_{3r} = -\delta_r$ where δ_r = the strain at rupture for simple tension. In other words, in the direction of the principal stresses the strain at rupture is one-half the value in simple tension. Test results indicate that for this combination of stresses the reduction in ductility predicted is approximately correct. It should be noted again, however, that the uncertainties in both the stress and strain values near and at fracture can give at best only rough approximations.

NUMERICAL EXAMPLE. A structural steel was tested in tension and from the true stress-strain curve values of $k = 108{,}000$ psi and $n = 0.33$ were determined. The true fracture stress was 120,000 psi. A thin-walled cylindrical boiler made of this steel is subjected to internal pressure. The boiler has an internal diameter of 18 in. and a wall thickness of 0.25 in. Using the above theory, determine (1) the true maximum strain or ductility and compare with the true strain at fracture or true ductility in simple tension, and (2) the pressure at fracture.

SOLUTION. For a thin-walled cylindrical boiler subjected to internal pressure the state of stress can be assumed to be two-dimensional so that $S_3 = 0$ and, in eqs. (3-37), $\beta = S_3/S_1 = 0$. Furthermo e, since $S_2 = (pd)/(4t)$ and $S_1 = (pd)/(2t)$, $\alpha = S_2/S_1 = \frac{1}{2}$. With $\alpha = \frac{1}{2}$ and $\beta = 0$, eqs. (3-37) reduce to

$$\delta_{1r} = \left(\frac{S_r}{k}\right)^{1/n}\left(\frac{3}{4}\right)^{\frac{1-n}{2n}}\left(\frac{3}{4}\right) = \left(\frac{S_r}{k}\right)^{1/n}\left(\frac{3}{4}\right)^{\frac{1+n}{2n}}$$

$$\delta_{2r} = \left(\frac{S_r}{k}\right)^{1/n}\left(\frac{3}{4}\right)^{\frac{1-n}{2n}}(0) = 0$$

$$\delta_{3r} = \left(\frac{S_r}{k}\right)^{1/n}\left(\frac{3}{4}\right)^{\frac{1-n}{2n}}\left(-\frac{3}{4}\right) = -\delta_{1r}$$

That is, the circumferential strain δ_{1r} equals in magnitude the radial strain δ_{3r}, while the longitudinal strain $\delta_{2r} = 0$. Placing values of S_r, k and n in the above equation for δ_{1r},

$$\delta_{1r} = \left(\frac{120,000}{108,000}\right)^{1/0.33}\left(\frac{3}{4}\right)^{1.33/0.66} = 0.77 \text{ in. per in.}$$

The value $\delta_{1r} = 0.77$ in. per in. measures the true ductility for the boiler. The true ductility or strain at fracture in simple tension is the value of δ in the equation $S' = k\delta^n$ when S' is equal to the fracture stress of 120,000 psi. That is,

$$\delta_r = \left(\frac{S'}{k}\right)^{1/n} = \left(\frac{120,000}{108,000}\right)^{1/0.33} = 1.37 \text{ in. per in.}$$

The true ductility for the boiler is less than the true ductility in simple tension. That is, $\delta_{1r}/\delta_r = 0.77/1.37 = 0.56$.

For the shear theory, the pressure at fracture can be obtained if the value of $\delta_{1r} = (p_r d)/(2t)$ is substituted in eq. (3-36). That is,

$$S_{1r} = \frac{S_r}{1 - \beta} \quad \text{or} \quad \frac{p_r d}{2t} = S_r$$

or

$$p_r = \frac{2tS_r}{d} = \frac{2 \times 0.25 \times 120,000}{18} = 3333 \text{ psi}$$

3-5. COMPARISON OF THEORIES AND TEST RESULTS

The necessity of using special testing equipment has resulted in relatively few investigations on the behavior of materials subjected to combined stresses. Furthermore, for certain stress combinations, test specimens have not been devised.

Some of the earlier investigations were made on solid round specimens subjected to torsion combined with axial tension [Fig. 3-12(b)],
or torsion combined with bending [Fig. 3-12(a)]. Although these
loadings produce combined stresses in the specimens, the magnitude
of these stresses varies from the center of the specimen to the outside. This non-uniform stress distribution introduces a strengthening effect. That is, the yielding of the outer fibers in these specimens

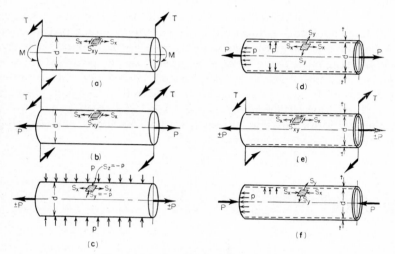

Fig. 3-12.   Combined stress specimens.

is restrained by the lower-stressed inner fibers that are below the
yield stress value. This strengthening effect is also present in some
of the earlier tests on thick-walled cylindrical specimens subjected
to internal pressure and axial tension. In recent years, notched
tension specimens have been used for triaxial stress tests. The
stress variation in these notched specimens makes them unsatis-
factory when they are used to determine quantitatively the influence
of the state of stress on the mechanical properties.

Lately attempts have been made to select and test specimens in
such a manner that a uniform state of stress is produced. Most
combined stress tests have been made on thin-walled tubes subjected
to internal pressure and axial tension [Fig. 3-12(d)], or torsion and
axial tension [Fig. 3-12(e)]. A few biaxial stress tests have been

made on thin-walled tubes subjected to torsion and axial compression [Fig. 3-12(f)], and thin-walled tubes subjected to torsion and internal pressure.   Biaxial compression stresses have been obtained by subjecting solid round specimens to radial compression.   Some triaxial tests have been made by subjecting round specimens to radial compression and axial tension [Fig. 3-12(c)].   Some of the testing machines used for combined stress tests are described in Chapter 11.

For the most commonly used combined stress specimen, that is, the thin-walled tube subjected to internal pressure and axial tension [Fig. 3-12(d)], the stress components are a circumferential stress S_y and an axial stress S_x.   These stresses are also the principal stresses S_1 and S_2, since there is no shear stress component.   The values of S_x and S_y in terms of the diameter d, the wall thickness t, pressure p, and axial load P are given by eqs. (3-1a) and (3-1b).

For a thin-walled tube subjected to axial tension P and twisting moment T, the stress components are

$$S_x = \frac{P}{A} = \frac{P}{t\pi d}$$

and, by eq. (3-1c), $$S_{xy} = \frac{2T}{t\pi d^2}$$

The principal stresses for the thin-walled tube subjected to axial tension and torsion are obtained from eq. (3-2) by placing $S_y = 0$ and using the above values of S_x and S_{xy}.

In most biaxial stress tests the ratio of the principal stresses S_2/S_1 is maintained essentially constant throughout the test.   For example, in the test of thin-walled circular tubes subjected to internal pressure and axial tension, the axial tension is usually applied by a Universal testing machine and the internal pressure is supplied by a pump unit.   The loads are applied in predetermined amounts such that the ratio of the principal stresses remains constant.   At each load increment, strains are measured in the axial and circumferential directions at one or more locations on the outside of the specimen. The strains are measured by mechanical, optical, or electrical strain gages and the stresses are determined in the elastic range by eqs. (3-1a) and (3-1b).   For the plastic range the true stresses are determined by these equations with the true values of the wall thickness t and the diameter d in place of the original values.   Nominal stress-strain diagrams for the elastic range and true stress-strain diagrams for the plastic range are plotted for each principal stress, as shown in Fig. 3-13. From the nominal elastic stress-strain plots, the values of the principal stresses at yield can be determined and compared with the values predicted by the theories of failure. Figures 3-14(a) to (e) show a comparison of test results and theories for tension-tension and tension-compression biaxial stresses. From the true stress-strain values of the principal stresses, the ultimate and fracture strengths can be compared with the theories of failure. The

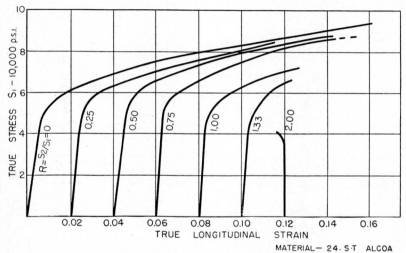

Fig. 3-13. True stress-strain relations for longitudinal stress and various stress ratios.

true plastic stress-strain relations are compared with the deformation theory for the plastic range by plotting values of the effective stresses versus the effective strains, as calculated by eqs. (3-33). By the deformation theory, the effective stress-strain relation should coincide with the true stress-strain relation for simple tension. For example, Fig. 3-15(a) shows plots of effective stresses and strains for various ratios of the principal stresses. The true ductility values or maximum principal strains at fracture can also be determined from the final strain readings, or readings at fracture, and compared to the theoretical ductility values as obtained by eqs. (3-37). How-

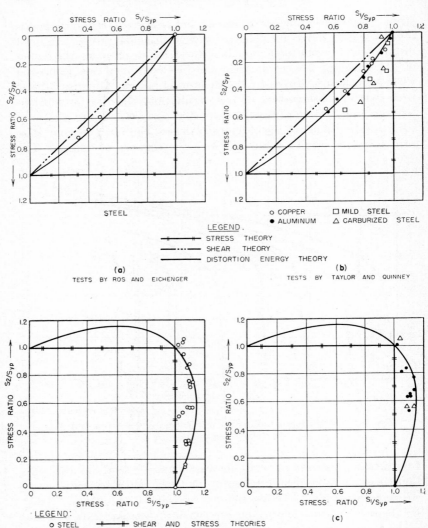

Fig. 3-14.   Comparison of biaxial strengths with theories of failures.

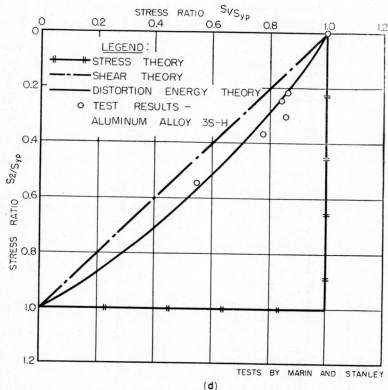

Fig. 3-14 (Cont'd).   Comparison of biaxial strengths with theories of failures.

ever, the non-uniform stress distribution that accompanies the neck-ing down of the specimen before fracture makes it impossible to obtain values of true ductility or fracture strength that have much significance.   Figure 3-15(b) shows the type of fractures produced for various principal stress ratios.

Figures 3-14(a) to (e) show that, for ductile materials and for biaxial tension-tension and biaxial tension-compression stresses, the *distortion energy theory* is a good approximation.   Figure 3-14(e) shows that, for brittle materials such as cast iron, the *maximum stress theory* is a good approximation for biaxial tension-tension and biaxial tension-compression stresses.   The fracture strength for duc-tile materials can be approximately defined by the *maximum shear*

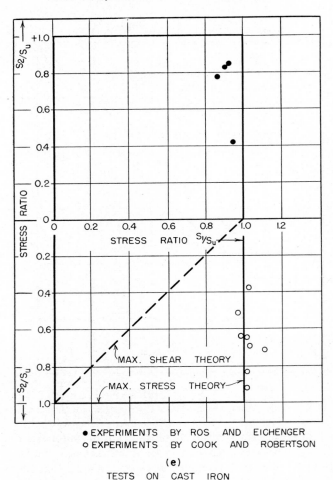

● EXPERIMENTS BY ROS AND EICHENGER
○ EXPERIMENTS BY COOK AND ROBERTSON

(e)

TESTS ON CAST IRON

Fig. 3-14 (Cont'd). Comparison of biaxial strengths with theories of failures.

theory. The plastic stress-strain relations for ductile materials have been shown to be approximately defined for biaxial tension-tension stresses using the effective stress-strain relations given in eqs. (3-33).[10]

[10] See, for example, D. M. Cunningham, E. G. Thomsen, and J. E. Dorn, "Plastic Flow of a Magnesium Alloy under Biaxial Stresses," *Proc. A.S.T.M.*, 1947, Vol. 47, p. 546; and W. R. Osgood, "Combined Stress Tests on 24S-T Aluminum Alloy Tubes," *Trans. A.S.M.E.*, 1947, Vol. 69, p. A-147.

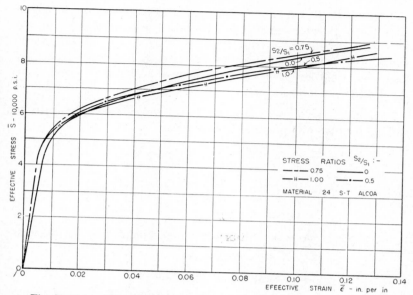

Fig 3-15(a). Effective stress-strain relations for various principal stress ratios.

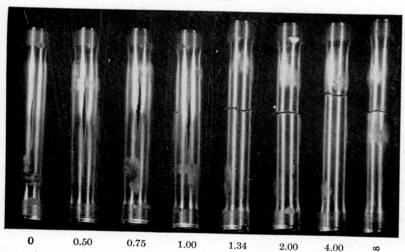

rig. 3-15(b). Type of fracture for various principal stress ratios. *Note:* Numbers below fractured specimens indicate ratios of longitudinal to lateral stress. Material tested: Alcoa 24 S-T.

NUMERICAL EXAMPLE. A thin-walled circular tube of aluminum alloy has an inside diameter of 2 in. and a wall thickness of 0.1 in. It is subjected to an internal pressure of 2000 psi. Determine the value of the axial tensile load that must be applied to produce yielding if the yield stress in simple tension is 36,000 psi. Solve using the distortion energy theory.

SOLUTION. By eqs. (3-1b) and (3-1c) the stress components S_x and S_y, equal to the principal stresses, are

$$S_1 = \frac{pd}{2t} = \frac{2000 \times 2}{2 \times 0.1} = 20,000 \text{ psi}$$

and
$$S_2 = \frac{pd}{4t} + \frac{P}{t\pi d} = \frac{2000 \times 2}{4 \times 0.1} + \frac{P}{0.1 \times \pi \times 2}$$

$$= 10,000 + 1.59P$$

In the distortion energy theory, yielding is defined by eq. (3-25), or

$$S_1{}^2 - S_1 S_2 + S_2{}^2 = S_{yp}{}^2$$

Placing the values of S_1 and S_2 in this equation,

$$20,000^2 - (20,000)(10,000 + 1.59P) + (10,000 + 1.59P)^2 = 36,000^2$$

or $4 - (2 + 3.18P \times 10^{-4}) + (1 + 1.59P \times 10^{-4})^2 = 3.6^2$

and $3 + 2.53 \times 10^{-8}P^2 = 3.6^2$

hence $P = 19,850 \text{ lb.}$

NUMERICAL EXAMPLE. A thin-walled tubular specimen of inner diameter $d = 2.00$ in. and wall thickness $t = 0.05$ in. is subjected to an axial tensile load of 4000 lb. Determine the value of the twisting moment required to produce yielding if the yield stress of the material in tension is 40,000 psi. Solve by both the shear and distortion energy theories. Assume that the area of the wall $= t\pi d$.

SOLUTION. The stress components S_x and S_{xy} are, by eqs. (3-37),

$$S_x = \frac{P}{t\pi d} = \frac{4000}{0.05 \times \pi \times 2} = 12,740 \text{ psi}$$

and
$$S_{xy} = \frac{2T}{t\pi d^2} = \frac{2T}{0.05 \times \pi \times 4} = 3.19T$$

From eqs. (3-2) the principal stresses are

$$S_1 = \frac{12,740}{2} + \sqrt{\left(\frac{12,740}{2}\right)^2 + (3.19T)^2}$$

and
$$S_2 = \frac{12,740}{2} - \sqrt{\left(\frac{12,740}{2}\right)^2 + (3.19T)^2}$$

By the *maximum shear theory* and for stresses of opposite sign, the first of eqs. (3-16) defines yielding, or
$$S_1 - S_2 = S_{yp}$$
Placing the values of S_1 and S_2 in this equation,
$$2\sqrt{6370^2 + 10.1T^2} = S_{yp} = 40,000$$
or
$$T^2 = \left(\frac{1}{10.1}\right)(4 \times 10^8 - 6370^2)$$
and
$$T = 5970 \text{ in. lb.}$$

Since $S_x = P/(t\pi d) = 12,740$ psi, $S_y = 0$, and
$$S_{xy} = \frac{T}{0.05 \times \pi \times 2} = 3.19T,$$
then by the distortion energy theory or eq. (3-26),
$$S_x^2 - S_x S_y + S_y^2 + 3S_{xy}^2 = S_{yp}^2$$
or
$$12,740^2 + (3 \times 10.1)(T)^2 = 40,000^2$$
thus
$$T^2 = \frac{1}{30.3}(40,000^2 - 12,740^2)$$
and
$$T = 6880 \text{ in. lb.}$$

NUMERICAL EXAMPLE. A solid rod 4 in. in diameter is subjected to a lateral pressure of 20,000 psi. What is the value of the axial tensile load required to produce yielding? Solve using the distortion energy theory. The yield stress of the material in simple tension is 54,000 psi.

SOLUTION. Figure 3-16 shows the rod subjected to axial tension and lateral pressure. The principal stresses are $S_1 = S_2 = -20,000$ psi,

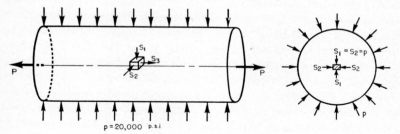

Fig. 3-16.

and $S_3 = P/(\pi r^2) = P/(4\pi)$. By the distortion energy theory, yielding is defined by eq. (3-24), so

$$S_1^2 + S_2^2 + S_3^2 - (S_1 S_2 + S_2 S_3 + S_3 S_1) = S_{yp}^2$$

or

$$(2 \times 10^4)^2 + (2 \times 10^4)^2 + \frac{P^2}{16\pi^2} - (2 \times 10^4)^2$$

$$+ 2 \times (2 \times 10^4) \left(\frac{P}{4\pi}\right) = (5.4 \times 10^4)^2$$

and $P = 430{,}000$ lb.

3-6. DESIGN STRESSES FOR STATIC COMBINED STRESSES

In machine and structural design, many considerations influence the determination of the dimensions selected. These factors include operational and service effects, magnitude and character of the loads applied, and the properties, cost, and availability of the material selected. Modern developments in design have led to a more rational estimate of the design stresses. Improvements in design have been made necessary by the increased speeds of operation of machinery, greater use of light-weight constructions, and scarcity of materials. Although there are many factors other than the mechanical properties that govern the dimensions selected for a part, the mechanical properties are often the controlling factors in machine and structural design.

The design stress is governed not only by the factor of safety, but also by the strength of the material. The discussion in Articles 3-4 and 3-5 has shown that the strength may be appreciably changed by the state of stress. In order to define design stresses, materials will be classified into two groups—*ductile materials*, or materials with an elongation in simple tension of more than 5 per cent for a 2-in. gage length, and *brittle materials*, or materials having an elongation of less than 5 per cent. The strength of ductile materials in simple tension will be defined by the yield strength, as indicated by the lower yield point when one exists, or by the A.S.T.M. offset yield stress when a yield point does not exist. For ductile materials the yield strengths in tension and compression will be assumed to be equal. For brittle materials the strength usually must be defined by the ultimate stress in tension or compression. The design stresses for combined states of stress and for brittle and ductile materials will now be defined.

Biaxial Stresses—Ductile Materials. The distortion energy theory agrees better with the test results than any other theory for ductile materials and biaxial stresses. Replacing the yield strength S_y in eq. (3-25) by the design stress in simple tension S_w, the relation between the allowable values of S_1 and S_2 is

$$S_1^2 - S_1 S_2 + S_2^2 = S_w^2 \qquad (3\text{-}38)$$

That is, for given values of S_2 and S_w, the value of S_1 as given by eq. (3-38) is the allowable value of S_1. For example, in a thin-walled cylindrical pressure vessel, if the circumferential stress $S_2 = 10,000$ psi and the simple tension working stress of the material $S_w = 20,000$ psi, the allowable value of S_1 in tension is, by eq. (3-38), 23,000 psi.

In terms of the stress components S_x, S_y, and S_{xy}, the allowable relation between the stress components is obtained by replacing S_{yp} in eq. (3-26) by S_w, or

$$S_x^2 - S_x S_y + S_y^2 + 3S_{xy}^2 = S_w^2 \qquad (3\text{-}39)$$

To show the influence of the biaxial stress ratios on the design stress, eq. (3-38) can be divided by S_w and the resulting equation solved for (S_1/S_w). Then

$$\frac{S_1}{S_w} = \frac{1}{\sqrt{1 - R + R^2}} \qquad (3\text{-}40)$$

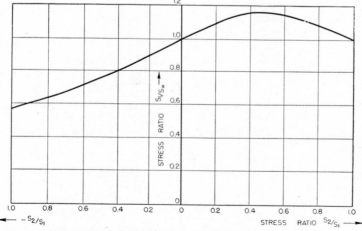

Fig. 3-17. Influence of biaxial stress ratio on working stress using distortion energy theory.

where $R = S_2/S_1$ = the ratio of the principal stresses, a quantity less than one, since S_1 is selected as the numerically greater stress. The variation in the ratio S_1/S_w with R, as given by eq. (3-40), shows the influence of the state of stress on the design stress ratio S_1/S_2 and is plotted in Fig. 3-17.

By studying the variation in the stress ratio S_1/S_w with change in the principal stress ratio S_2/S_1, the influence of biaxiality of stresses on the allowable value of S_1 can be found. Figure 3-17 shows, for example, that when the principal stress ratio $S_2/S_1 = +0.5$, there is an increase in the allowable value of S_1 above the uniaxial tensile value, since $S_1/S_w = 1.15$ or $S_1 = 1.15S_w$. For a value of $S_2/S_1 = -1.0$, on the other hand, since $S_1/S_w = 0.57$, the allowable value of $S_1 = 0.57S_w$, which represents a 43 per cent decrease in the allowable stress S_1 as compared to the allowable simple tension stress.

Biaxial Stresses—Brittle Materials. There is little test data available for brittle materials subjected to biaxial stresses. The internal friction theory as defined by eqs. (3-30), however, is recommended in place of the maximum stress theory since it is more conservative. Replacing S_u' by S_w, eqs. (3-30) become

For S_1 and S_2 of the same sign,

$$\left. \begin{array}{l} S_1 = S_w \quad \text{or} \quad S_1 = -r_c S_w \\ S_2 = S_w \quad \text{or} \quad S_2 = -r_c S_w \end{array} \right\} \quad (3\text{-}41)$$

For S_1 and S_2 of opposite sign,

$$\left. \begin{array}{l} S_1 - r_c S_2 = -r_c S_w \\ S_2 - r_c S_1 = -r_c S_w \end{array} \right\} \quad (3\text{-}42)$$

where $r_c = S_u''/S_u'$ = the ratio of the compressive to the tensile ultimate strength.

To show the influence of the combined stress ratio $R = S_2/S_1$ on the allowable or design stress S_1, eqs. (3-41) and (3-42) can be written

For S_1 and S_2 of the same sign and S_1 greater than S_2,

$$\frac{S_1}{S_w} = 1 \quad \text{or} \quad \frac{S_1}{S_w} = -r_c \quad (3\text{-}43)$$

For S_1 and S_2 of opposite sign and S_1 greater than S_2,

$$\frac{S_1}{S_w} = -\frac{r_c}{1 - r_c R} \tag{3-44}$$

where $r_c = S_u''/S_u'$ and $R = S_2/S_1$.

The variation in the allowable or design stress S_1 with stress ratio $R = S_2/S_1$ is given in Fig. 3-18 by showing the variation between the stress ratios S_1/S_w and $R = S_2/S_1$.

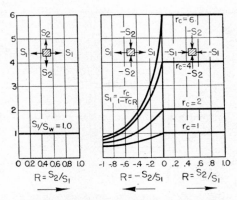

Fig. 3-18.   Variation in design stress with principal stress ratio R, using internal friction theory.

There is very little test data available for triaxial stresses and ductile materials. For this reason the conservative strain energy theory is recommended. For triaxial stresses and brittle materials there is also a lack of test data and the conservative internal friction theory is recommended.

3-7. UTILIZATION OF THEORIES IN DESIGN

The theories of failure are used to determine either the required dimensions or the allowable loads in members subjected to combined stresses. A few examples of these applications are given in the following.

NUMERICAL EXAMPLE. A circular steel shaft is subjected to a bending moment of 2000 in. lb. and a twisting moment of 10,000 in. lb., as shown in Fig. 3-19. Determine the required diameter of the

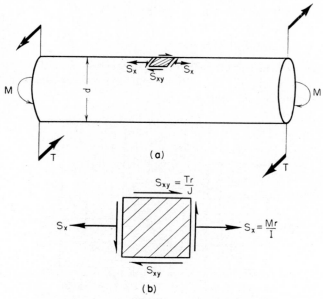

Fig. 3-19.   Shaft subjected to torsion and bending.

shaft by the distortion energy theory if the design stress in simple tension S_w for the steel is 40,000 psi.   Compare the value obtained with that required by the maximum shear theory.

SOLUTION.   The stress components S_x and S_{xy} produced by the bending moment M and twisting moment T, as shown in Figs. 3-19(a) and (b) are, respectively,

$$S_x = \frac{Mr}{I} = \frac{Mr}{\pi r^4/4} = \frac{2000 \times 4}{\pi r^3}$$

and
$$S_{xy} = \frac{Tr}{J} = \frac{Tr}{\pi r^4/2} = \frac{10,000 \times 2}{\pi r^3}$$

By the *distortion energy theory*,

$$S_x{}^2 - S_x S_y + S_y{}^2 + 3 S_{xy}{}^2 = S_w{}^2$$

Using the foregoing values of S_x and S_{xy}, and noting that $S_y = 0$ and $S_w = 40,000$ psi,

$$\left(\frac{4 \times 2000}{\pi r^3}\right)^2 + 3\left(\frac{2 \times 10,000}{\pi r^3}\right)^2 = 40,000^2$$

or $r = 0.655$ and $d = 1.31$ in.

By the *maximum shear theory*, $S_1 - S_2 = S_w$, or since

$$S_1 = \frac{S_x}{2} + \sqrt{\frac{S_x^2}{4} + S_{xy}^2}$$

and

$$S_2 = \frac{S_x}{2} - \sqrt{\frac{S_x^2}{4} + S_{xy}^2}$$

then

$$2\sqrt{\frac{S_x^2}{4} + S_{xy}^2} = S_w$$

Substituting the values of S_x and S_{xy} in this equation,

$$\frac{1}{4}\left(\frac{4 \times 2000}{\pi r^3}\right)^2 + \left(\frac{2 \times 10,000}{\pi r^3}\right)^2 = \frac{1}{4}(40,000)^2$$

or $r = 0.69$ in.   and $d = 1.38$ in.

NUMERICAL EXAMPLE.   *Allowable Pressure in a Thin-walled Pipe Subjected to Twisting.*   A thin-walled circular pipe with an inside diameter of 2 in. and a wall thickness of 0.10 in. is subjected to a twisting moment of 2000 in. lb., as shown in Fig. 3-20(a).   What is the allowable internal pressure if the design stress in simple tension is 20,000 psi and the cylinder is assumed to have closed ends?   Solve using the distortion energy and shear theories.

SOLUTION.   For a thin-walled tube subjected to an internal pressure p and a twisting moment T, the stress components as represented in Figs. 3-20(a) and (b) were shown, by eqs. (3-1a), (3-1b) and (3-1c), to be

$$S_x = \frac{pd}{4t}, \quad S_y = \frac{pd}{2t}, \quad \text{and} \quad S_{xy} = \frac{2T}{t\pi d^2}$$

Placing these values in eq. (3-39), the allowable pressure by the *distortion energy theory* is determined by the equation

$$\left(\frac{pd}{4t}\right)^2 - \left(\frac{pd}{4t}\right)\left(\frac{pd}{2t}\right) + \left(\frac{pd}{2t}\right)^2 + 3\left(\frac{2T}{t\pi d^2}\right)^2 = S_w^2$$

Solving this equation for the pressure p,

$$p = \left(\frac{4t}{d}\right) \sqrt{\frac{S_w{}^2}{3} - \left(\frac{2T}{t\pi d^2}\right)^2}$$

$$= \left(\frac{4 \times 0.10}{2}\right) \sqrt{\frac{(2 \times 10^4)^2}{3} - \left(\frac{2 \times 2000}{0.1 \times \pi \times 2^2}\right)^2}$$

$$= 0.2 \sqrt{\frac{4}{3} \times 10^8 - \left(\frac{10,000}{\pi}\right)^2} = 2000\sqrt{1.33 - 0.101} = 2220 \text{ psi}$$

By the *shear theory*, since it is not known whether S_1 and S_2 are of the same or opposite signs, both eqs. (3-16) must be considered. Placing values of S_1 and S_2 from eqs. (3-2) in eqs. (3-15) and replacing S_{yp} by the allowable stress S_w,

$$2 \sqrt{\frac{(S_x - S_y)^2}{4} + S_{xy}{}^2} = S_w$$

and $S_y = S_w$.

Placing the values of the stress components in these equations,

$$4 \left[\left(\frac{pd}{8t}\right)^2 + \left(\frac{2T}{t\pi d^2}\right)^2 \right] = S_w{}^2$$

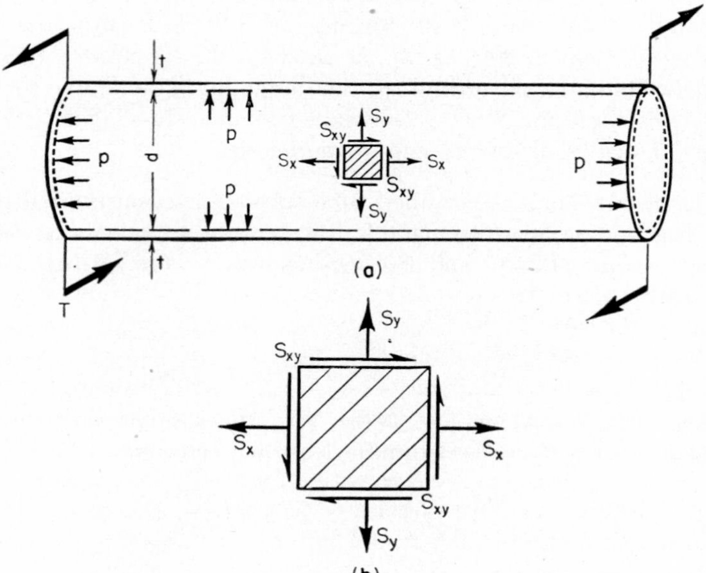

(a)

(b)

Fig. 3-20.

or
$$p = \frac{8t}{d} \sqrt{\frac{S_w^2}{4} - \left(\frac{2T}{t\pi d^2}\right)^2}$$

$$= \frac{8 \times 0.10}{2} \sqrt{\frac{(2 \times 10^4)^2}{4} - \left(\frac{2 \times 2000}{0.1 \times \pi \times 2^2}\right)^2}$$

$$= 0.4\sqrt{10^8 - (0.101)10^8} = 3790 \text{ psi}$$

and $\dfrac{pd}{2t} = S_w$ or $p = \dfrac{2tS_w}{d} = \dfrac{2 \times 0.1}{2} \times 20{,}000 = 2000 \text{ psi}$

That is, by the shear theory the allowable pressure is the smaller of the two values 3790 and 2000, or 2000 psi.

3-8. STRESS CONCENTRATION

Most machines and structural parts fail at points of stress concentration such as are produced by scratches, notches, screw threads, grooves, holes, or abrupt changes of cross section. At points of stress concentration the stresses cannot be determined by the ordinary methods of stress analysis. For example, in Fig. 3-21(a) the stress distribution is shown across a section AB for a bar with a circular hole subjected to axial tension. The actual stress at the edge of the hole in the direction of the load is found to be about three times the average value obtained by using the formula $S = P/A$, where A is the net area of the cross section. In the same way the axial stresses in the edge of the notch in Fig. 3-21(b) are much greater than the average stress.

In addition to increasing the axial stress, the hole and notch shown in Figs. 3-21(a) and (b) change the state of stress near these discontinuities from uniaxial tensile stress to biaxial and triaxial states of stress. In the plate of Fig. 3-21(a), in addition to axial stress, there is a lateral stress for sections near the hole. For sections near the notch in the rod of Fig. 3-21(b), radial and tangential stresses are produced in addition to the axial stress. The presence of these combined stresses naturally influences the yield and ultimate strengths of the material compared to what that strength would be if the material were free from stress concentration. Some test results have been reported that give the strengths of bars with notches and other discontinuities. The non-uniform state of stress existing in members with discontinuities makes it difficult to evaluate the strength of these members.

It should be noted that there are two distinct aspects in the con-

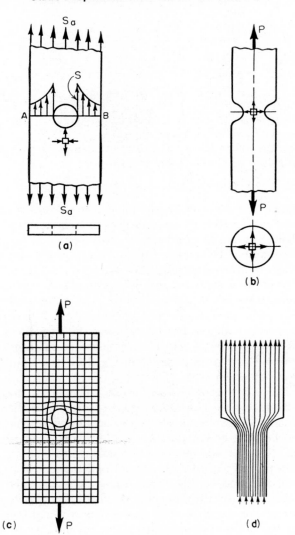

Fig. 3-21.

sideration of members with discontinuities; namely, the increase in the stresses produced, and the influence of the combined stresses on the strength of the material. It has usually been the practice to neglect the influence of the combined stresses and to consider only the increase in the maximum stress as produced by the discontinuity.

In the case of static stresses, the stress values at points of stress concentration can be obtained, in some cases, by theoretical procedures. The photoelastic, strain gage, or stress coat experimental procedures are sometimes used to obtain stress values at points of stress concentration. By either theoretical or experimental methods a *stress concentration factor* k_s is obtained which is defined as

$$k_s = \frac{S}{S_a} \tag{3-45}$$

where S is the maximum stress in the member, as determined by experimental or theoretical methods, and S_a is called the nominal average stress and is the stress obtained by the usual formulas derived in Strength of Materials. For example, in a plate with a small central circular hole subjected to axial loading, Fig. 3-21(a), the theoretical stress S at the edge of the hole, as obtained by the theory of elasticity or by experiment, is approximately three times the usually calculated stress value S_a, which is equal to the load divided by the net area. That is, the stress concentration factor in this case is $k_s = S/S_a = 3S_a/S_a = 3.0$.

A picture of the physical action producing stress concentration can be obtained by considering the deformation of the rubber model shown in Fig. 3-21(c). Before the tensile loading was applied the lines shown formed squares. After loading, large strains are produced as indicated by the distorted lines in Fig. 3-21(c). These strains, and hence stresses, are large near the edge of the hole. In other words, a stress concentration is produced.

The maximum stress produced at the point of highest stress concentration is somewhat proportional to the velocity of streamline flow through a channel whose shape is similar to that of the bar. Using this analogy it can be seen that in the region where the size is changing the velocity of flow will be higher and the streamlines become closer together, as indicated in Fig. 3-21(d). These regions of higher velocity of flow and closer spaced streamlines correspond to points of greater stress, or stress concentration. This analogy does not give correct quantitative results but is helpful in forming a physical picture of the state of stress.

The damaging influence of stress concentration is much more pronounced in brittle materials than for ductile materials. In ductile materials the stress distribution at the section of discontinuity changes after the stress exceeds the proportional limit. For example, in Fig. 3-21(a), if the load is increased, yielding will start at the point of highest stress or at the edge of the hole. Further increase in the load produces increase in the strain at the edge of the hole without increase in the stress. This means that the stresses are redistributed and the material away from the hole must develop an

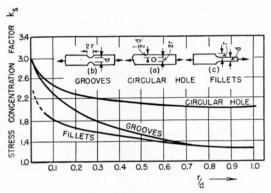

Fig. 3-22. Stress concentration factors for flat plates in tension.

increase in stress. If the material is sufficiently ductile, further increase in load increases the strain at the edge of the hole and eventually a uniform stress distribution on section AB is produced. That is, the stress concentration initially present no longer exists. For a brittle material, however, the foregoing plastic redistribution of stress cannot occur and the stress concentration is not reduced with increase in load. Stress concentration is therefore of particular importance in the case of brittle materials.

Values of stress concentration factors for some of the common types of discontinuities are given in Fig. 3-22, based on the net area of the cross section.

Stress concentrations are produced not only by design discontinuities such as threads, notches, and fillets, but also by accidental stress raisers. Examples of such stress raisers are cracks, slag inclusions, scratches, tool marks, blow holes, and flaws of various types arising from the manufacturing processes. These accidental stress raisers are particularly to be avoided in parts subjected to fluctuating loads, since such flaws serve as starting points for progressive fracture. This will be discussed further in Chapter IV on fatigue properties of materials.

PROBLEMS

3-1. A thin-walled cylinder of internal diameter $d = 3$ in. and wall thickness $t = \frac{1}{8}$ in. is subjected to an axial tensile load of 15,000 lb. and a twisting moment of 8000 in. lb. Determine the principal stresses and maximum shear stresses.

Ans. $S_1 = 14,170$ psi, $S_2 = -1430$ psi, $S_s' = \pm 7800$ psi.

3-2. For a hub-and-axle assembly the stresses on the outer fiber are $S_1 = S_2 = -10,000$ psi, and the bending stress is $S_3 = +12,000$ psi. If the transverse shear stress components are neglected, so that S_1, S_2, and S_3 are the principal stresses, determine (a) the maximum shear stress, (b) the principal strains, (c) the strain energy, and (d) the change in volume per unit volume. Use values of $E = 30 \times 10^6$ psi and Poisson's ratio $= 0.3$.

Ans. $S_s' = \pm 11,000$ psi, $\epsilon_1 = \epsilon_2 = -3.53 \times 10^{-4}$ in. per in., $\epsilon_3 = 6.0 \times 10^{-4}$ in. per in., $u = 7.13$ in. lb. per cu. in., and $\Delta V/V = 1.06 \times 10^{-4}$ cu. in. per cu. in.

3-3. What is the ratio of the distortion energy to the total strain energy for the following states of stress:

(a) $S_1 = S_2 = S_3$,
(b) $S_1 = S_2 = -S_3$,
(c) $S_1 = -S_2 = -S_3$,
(d) $S_1 = S_2, S_3 = 0$,
(e) $S_1 = -S_2, S_3 = 0$.

Use a value of Poisson's ratio $= 0.3$.

3-4. A solid circular shaft is subjected to a bending moment of 120,000 in. lb. and a twisting moment. If the diameter of the shaft is 4 in., what is the value of the twisting moment that will produce yielding? The yield stress in tension is 40,000 psi. Solve using (a) the maximum shear theory, and (b) the distortion energy theory.

Ans. (a) 220,500 in. lb., (b) 256,000 in. lb.

3-5. A boiler is 15 in. in diameter and has a wall thickness of $\frac{1}{4}$ in. Determine the internal pressure required to produce yielding at the outer surface if the yield stress of the material in tension is 40,000 psi. Solve using (a) the maximum shear theory, and (b) the distortion energy theory.

Ans. (a) 1330 psi, (b) 1540 psi.

3-6. Solve Prob. 3-5 for yielding at the inner surface.

3-7. A solid steel rod 2 in. in diameter is subjected to a lateral compressive pressure of 25,000 psi. What is the axial compressive load that will produce yielding? Solve using (a) the maximum stress theory, (b) the maximum shear theory, and (c) the distortion energy theory. The yield strength of the material in simple tension or compression is 40,000 psi.

Ans. (a) 126,000 lb., (b) 204,000 lb., (c) 204,000 lb.

3-8. A rod 2 in. in diameter is subjected to an axial tension of 10,000 lb. and a lateral compressive pressure of 25,000 psi. The simple tensile yield stress is 50,000 psi. What is the factor of safety based on the distortion energy theory?

3-9. A boiler is 15 in. in diameter and has a wall thickness of $\frac{1}{4}$ in. What is the maximum pressure that can be applied if $S_u = 78,000$ psi? Solve using the maximum shear theory.

3-10. What is the axial compressive load that can be applied to a 3-in.-diameter rod subjected to a radial compressive pressure of 40,000 psi? The yield tensile and compressive strengths of the materials are 80,000 psi. Solve by (a) the maximum shear theory, and (b) the distortion energy theory.

Ans. (a) 850,000 lb., (b) 846,000 lb.

3-11. A thin-walled tube with an internal diameter of 14 in. and a wall thickness of $\frac{1}{4}$ in. is subjected to an internal pressure of 1000 psi, an axial tensile load of 20,000 lb., and a twisting moment. If the ultimate strength in simple tension is 80,000 psi and the simple compressive strength is 96,000 psi, determine the maximum twisting moment that can be applied. Solve by (a) the maximum stress theory, (b) the maximum shear theory, (c) the distortion energy theory, and (d) the internal friction theory. Consider that the tube is closed at the ends.

3-12. Determine by means of eq. (3-37) the true principal strains at fracture at the outer surface for a cylindrical tube 20 in. inside diameter with a wall thickness of 0.25 in. The tube is closed at the ends and is subjected to an axial tensile load of 40,000 lb. and an internal pressure $p = 1000$ psi. The material constants are $k = 108,000$ psi and $n = 0.33$. The true fracture stress in simple tension for the material is 120,000 psi.

Ans. 0.742, 0.066, −0.806 in. per in.

3-13. Determine expressions for the true strains at fracture in a thin-walled spherical shell subjected to internal pressure. The material constants $k = 110,000$ psi, $n = 0.33$, and the true tensile fracture strength is 120,000 psi. Use the maximum shear theory and eq. (3-37).

3-14. For a 24S-T aluminum alloy with $k = 10^5$ psi and $n = 0.16$ plot the S_1–δ curves for each of the following stress ratios:

(a) $S_2/S_1 = 0.5$, $S_3 = 0$,
(b) $S_2/S_1 = 1.0$, $S_3 = 0$,
(c) $S_2/S_1 = -0.5$, $S_3 = 0$,
(d) $S_2/S_1 = S_3/S_1 = 0.5$,
(e) $S_2/S_1 = S_3/S_1 = -0.2$.

3-15. A circular shaft is subjected to an axial compression load of 12,000 lb. and a twisting moment of 5000 ft. lb. If the yield stress in simple tension is 40,000 psi and a factor of safety $N = 2$ is used, determine the shaft diameter by (a) the maximum shear theory, and (b) the distortion energy theory.

3-16. (a) A thin-walled cylinder of diameter $d = 4$ in. is subjected to an axial load of 12,000 lb. and a twisting moment of 10,000 in. lb. Determine the required wall thickness by the maximum shear theory. The design stress $S_w = 20,000$ psi.

(b) Solve Prob. 3-16(a) by the distortion energy theory.

(c) Solve Prob. 3-16(a) by the internal friction theory if $r_c = 1.8$.

3-17. (a) What is the wall thickness required for a pipe with an inside diameter $d = 4$ in. subjected to an internal pressure of 500 psi and a twisting moment of 12,000 in. lb.? Solve by the distortion energy theory and for a design stress $S_w = 35,000$ psi. The pipe is closed at the ends.

(b) Solve Prob. 3-17(a) by the maximum shear theory.

Ans. (a) 0.0342 in., (b) 0.0368 in.

3-18. (a) A bolt is subjected to a twisting moment of 160 in. lb. and an axial tensile load of 15,000 lb. If the design stress $S_w = 24,000$ psi, determine the bolt diameter by the maximum shear theory.

(b) Solve Prob. 3-18(a) by the distortion energy theory.

Ans. (a) 0.893 in., (b) 0.893 in.

3-19. (a) Determine an equation for the diameter d of a circular shaft subjected to a twisting moment T, a bending moment M, and axial tension P. Solve by the distortion energy theory.

(b) Solve Prob. 3-19(a) if the shaft is hollow with an internal diameter d_i and external diameter d_o.

3-20. Find the maximum allowable load that may be applied to the bar in Fig. 3-23 using an allowable stress of 20,000 psi. Use stress concentration factors as given in Fig. 3-22.   *Ans.* 7150 lb.

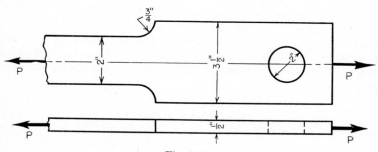

Fig. 3-23.

3-21. Determine the maximum axial stress produced in the member of Fig. 3-23 if $P = 20{,}000$ lb. Use stress concentration factors given in Fig. 3-22.   *Ans.* 56,000 psi.

3-22. For the member in Fig. 3-24 what is the factor of safety based on yielding if the tensile yield stress is 80,000 psi and $P = 20{,}000$ lb.

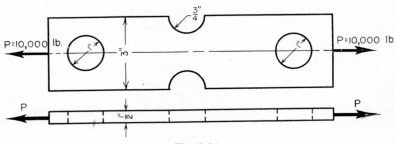

Fig. 3-24.

3-23. Find the allowable load P for the bar in Fig. 3-25 if the allowable stress for the material is 30,000 psi and the stress concentration factor in bending is 2.0.   *Ans.* 16,600 lb.

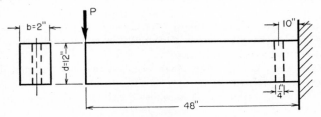

Fig 3-25.

3-24. What is the maximum stress in Fig. 3-25 if the load is 5000 lb.? Use a stress concentration factor $k_s = 2.0$.

3-25. Find the allowable bending load P for the bar in Fig. 3-25 if the allowable stress is 30,000 psi and there is an axial compressive load of 5000 lb. acting in addition to an end vertical load of 5000 lb. Use a stress concentration factor of 2.0.

BIBLIOGRAPHY

Freudenthal, A. M., *The Inelastic Behavior of Engineering Materials and Structures*, John Wiley and Sons, Inc., New York, 1950.

Hill, R., *The Mathematical Theory of Plasticity*, Oxford University Press, New York, 1950.

Iterson, V., *Plasticity in Engineering*, Blackie & Son, Ltd., London, 1947.

Nadai, A., *Theory of Flow and Fracture of Solids*, McGraw-Hill Book Co., Inc., New York, 1950, Vol. 1.

Reiner, M., *Deformation and Flow*, K. K. Lewis Co., London, 1949.

Timoshenko, S., *Strength of Materials*, D. Van Nostrand Co., Inc., New York, 1942, Part II, Chapter IX.

Chapter 4

Fatigue Properties

4-1. NATURE OF FATIGUE

In previous chapters the loads and stresses were considered to be gradually increased to fixed static values. Machine and structural members, however, are often subjected to loads and stresses that vary in magnitude with time. For example, locomotive driving rods are subjected to axial stresses that do not remain constant, but vary with the rotation of the locomotive wheels. A stress that varies in this manner is referred to as a *fluctuating, repeated, alternating,* or *fatigue stress.* Sometimes loads are applied by moving bodies that impart a suddenly applied, or *impact load,* to a machine or structural part.

Two types of fatigue stress members should be distinguished. In one type, stress variations occur continuously over relatively long periods of time as, for example, in railway axles, crank shafts, connecting rods of engines, turbine shafts, and many other machine members. There are several engineering structures, however, such as railway bridges, in which the stress fluctuations occur in only a fraction of the life of the structure and the damaging effect is less pronounced. Therefore, the type of application considered is a significant factor in determining the importance of the fatigue properties.

The repeated loading conditions described above often produce a so-called fatigue failure. Such failures are produced by progressive fracture beginning at points of high stress. Failure is produced by the gradual spreading of a small crack until complete rupture of the part is produced. This progressive fracture may be produced by irregularities of outline as, for example, an abrupt change of cross section, or by internal cracks and pieces of slag.   It is apparent that this type of failure is serious, since a small crack, one that may be overlooked in a magnaflux or X-ray inspection of the material, could be sufficient to be a source of fatigue failure.

The type of fracture produced in ductile metals under fatigue loading differs greatly from that produced with static loading (Fig. 4-1). Under static loading, plastic flow of the material precedes fracture and the surfaces of the ruptured section show a fibrous structure produced by stretching of the crystals.   A fatigue crack, however, looks entirely different; such a crack starts at a local defect and spreads progressively until the stressed section becomes so small that the remaining portion fractures suddenly under the load.   In a fatigue fracture, two zones of failure can be distinguished, one produced by the gradual development of the crack, and the other produced by sudden fracture.   The zone produced by sudden fracture resembles the fractured surface of a static tensile specimen of a brittle material such as cast iron (Fig. 4-1).   Hence, the fractured surface is said to be of the *brittle* type.

Although no adequate theory has been formulated to explain fatigue failure of materials, the mechanism of fatigue failure is at least partially known.   As previously noted, fatigue failure starts with a crack forming at a point of weakness in the material.   Microscopic examination of metals shows that there are many small cracks and points of weakness oriented in various directions.   This random orientation accounts for the fact that widely different values of strength may be obtained using different specimens cut from the same piece of material.   This element of possible variation indicates that the fatigue strength value should be stated as the most probable value.   This statistical nature of fatigue has led in recent years to the interpretation of fatigue strengths by mathematical statistical procedures.   By these procedures, test data are interpreted in such a way that a probable strength is specified rather than an exact value.   For example, it is stated by this statistical interpretation that the fatigue strength of a material will be at least 50,000 psi for 80 per cent of the time and lower than 50,000 psi for the remaining 20 per cent of the time.[1]

The concept that fatigue failure is dependent upon a crack or

---

[1] See W. Weibull, "A Statistical Representation of Fatigue Failures in Solids," *Trans. Royal Inst. of Tech.*, Stockholm, 1949, No. 22.

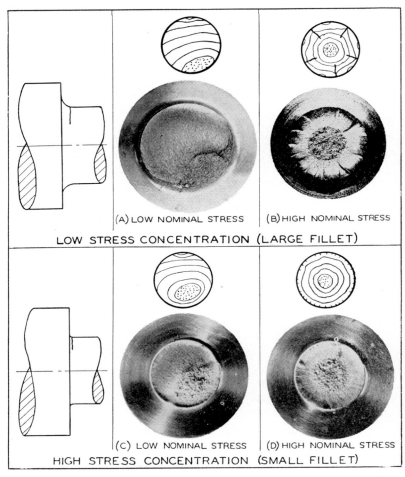

(A) LOW NOMINAL STRESS   (B) HIGH NOMINAL STRESS

LOW STRESS CONCENTRATION (LARGE FILLET)

(C) LOW NOMINAL STRESS   (D) HIGH NOMINAL STRESS

HIGH STRESS CONCENTRATION (SMALL FILLET)

Fig. 4-1(a).   Laboratory fatigue fractures-stress concentration case of shaft with fillet (Rotating shaft subjected to bending in a fixed plane.) (Courtesy R. E. Peterson from *Handbook on Experimental Stress Analysis*, John Wiley and Sons.)

"weakest link" is consistent with the fact that volume of the material tested is an important factor.   That is, a large-sized specimen with a correspondingly large number of flaws or points of weakness has a greater chance of fatigue failure than a smaller specimen with

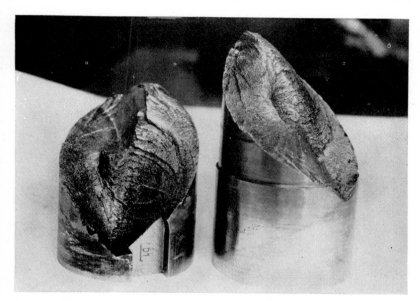

Fig. 4-1(b).   Service failure produced by alternating torsion.

fewer points of weakness.   This conclusion is confirmed by tests, since large specimens have lower fatigue strengths than smaller specimens.

The behavior of materials subjected to repeated stresses has been studied in three ways.   A limited amount of work has been done on the fatigue strength of single crystals.[2]   A second type of fatigue testing uses small specimens which, in the case of metals, are made up of many crystals.   A third type of fatigue testing studies the performance of large-scale models of actual machine and structural parts when subjected to repeated stresses.[3]   The following discussion deals only with the second type of testing.

For ferrous metals and alloys the strength of the material under repeated stresses is sometimes defined as the *endurance* or *fatigue limit*.   *This limit is the maximum stress that can be applied repeatedly*

[2] See, for example, H. J. Gough and W. A. Wood, "The Crystalline Structure of Steel at Fracture," *Proc. Royal Soc.*, London, 1938, A, No. 992, Vol. 165, p. 358.

[3] For example, machines for fatigue testing of built-up beams, columns, and other structural parts are described by R. L. Templin, "Fatigue Machines for Testing Structural Units," *Proc. A.S.T.M.*, 1939, Vol. 39.

an infinite number of times without fracturing the material.   Non-ferrous metals do not have an endurance or fatigue limit.   For this reason, and the fact that the required service life of parts varies considerably, the strength of materials under repeated stresses is more commonly defined by the endurance or fatigue strength rather than the endurance or fatigue limit.   *The endurance or fatigue strength is the maximum stress that can be applied repeatedly for a specified number of stress cycles without producing rupture of the material.*

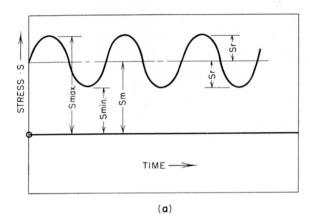

(a)

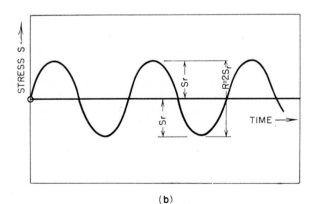

(b)

Fig. 4-2.   Stress-time variation.

To explain the determination of the fatigue strength it is desirable first to define certain stress values. For this purpose consider the stress variation in a bar subjected to fluctuating axial stress as, for example, a connecting rod. The variation of stress with time may be represented as shown in Fig. 4-2(a). The shape of the stress-time curve will depend upon the mechanism producing the stress fluctuations. The sinusoidal type of variation shown is commonly found in many fatigue testing machines, and represents simple harmonic motion. There are many applications in which the stress variation is of this type. Regardless of the shape of the stress-time curve, the stress varies from a maximum value S_{max} to a minimum value S_{min} [Fig. 4-2(a)]. For sinusoidal variation of stress, the stress S at any time t is expressed by the equation

$$S = S_m + S_r \sin \frac{2\pi t}{T} \tag{4-1}$$

where T is the time for one complete cycle, and the mean stress S_m and variable stress S_r are expressed in terms of the maximum and minimum stresses by the following equations:

$$S_m = \frac{S_{max} + S_{min}}{2} \tag{4-2}$$

$$S_r = \frac{S_{max} - S_{min}}{2} \tag{4-3}$$

The stress variation $R = 2S_r$ is called the *range of stress*. The stress variation can be considered as a static mean stress S_m upon which a completely reversed stress S_r is superimposed. The case of *completely reversed stress* is shown in Fig. 4-2(b) where the mean stress $S_m = 0$.[4]

The fatigue strengths of materials have been obtained for various kinds of simple stresses including alternating tension and compression, alternating torsion, and alternating bending. A few investigations have also been made to determine fatigue strengths for combined stresses. Most fatigue tests have been made on specimens subjected to bending, since the simplest type of fatigue test is obtained with bending stresses.

---

[4] Other symbols and nomenclature used in describing fatigue are given in "Manual on Fatigue Testing," Special Publication No. 91, *A.S.T.M.*, 1949.

4-2. FATIGUE STRENGTH FOR REPEATED AXIAL STRESSES— DETERMINATION OF FATIGUE STRENGTH

The shape and dimensions of fatigue specimens have not been standardized as for static test specimens, as indicated in Fig. 4-3. Figure 4-3(c) shows one type of specimen used for axial fatigue tests. The axial fluctuating force or variable stress S_r is applied by an eccen-

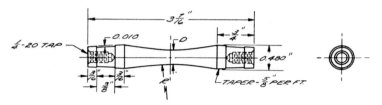

(a) Simple rotating-beam fatigue specimen (R. R. Moore Type). D— 0.200 to 0.400 in. selected on basis of ultimate strength of material. R—3.5 to 10 in.

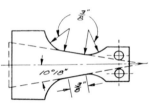

(b) Sheet contilever fatigue specimen (Bureau of Standards Type).

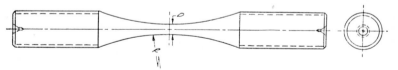

(c) Fatigue specimen for axial loading (Wright Field Type). D—Selected on basis of ultimate strength of material. R—3 to 10 in.

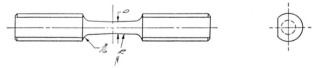

(d) Torsion fatigue specimen (H. F. Moore Type). D—Selected on basis of ultimate strength of material. R—5 in.

Fig. 4-3. Fatigue test specimens.

tric, a rotating weight, or by magnetic means. A prestressed helical spring is usually used to apply the static mean stress. Several specimens are required to determine the fatigue or endurance strengths for various numbers of cycles. To determine the fatigue strengths for complete reversal, for example, a specimen is first subjected to a maximum repeated stress of magnitude somewhat less than the ultimate static tensile strength. For this large completely reversed

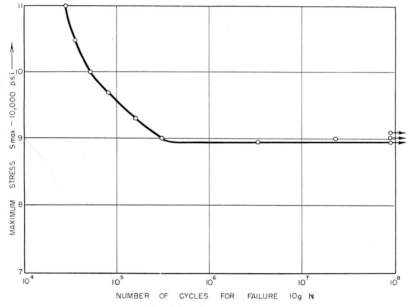

Fig. 4-4.   *S-N* diagrams.

stress, only a small number of cycles are required to produce fracture. A second specimen is tested in the same way but under a stress slightly less than the first specimen. For the second specimen a larger number of cycles of stress are required to produce rupture. This procedure is continued for a series of specimens and the data obtained are plotted as shown in Fig. 4-4. That is, the variation between the stress producing fracture, or fatigue strength, and the number of cycles to produce fracture is shown. The ordinate to the *S-N* curve in Fig. 4-4 gives the fatigue or endurance strength for the corresponding value of the number of cycles N. For large values of

N, the S-N curve becomes approximately a horizontal straight line. That is, the S-N curve approaches an asymptote. The stress value corresponding to the horizontal asymptote is called the *fatigue* or *endurance limit.* An endurance limit is found for ferrous metals and alloys, but for non-ferrous metals and alloys, such as aluminum alloys, the fracture stress continues to decrease with increase in the number of cycles. In these cases the curve does not approach an asymptote. In place of a semi-log plot, as shown in Fig. 4-4, the test data are sometimes plotted on Cartesian coordinates or log-log coordinates. Plotting on Cartesian coordinates may lead the investigator to assume that the fatigue limit has been reached at comparatively low values of N when this is not actually the case.

Interpretation of Fatigue Strength Test Results. Most fatigue tests have been made for the condition in which the stresses are completely reversed. This is partly due to the fact that this is the most severe condition and partly because, for some stresses such as bending, it is more convenient to make tests with completely

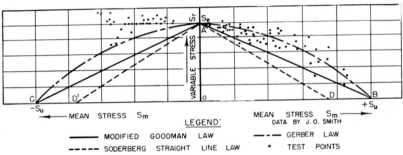

Fig. 4-5.   Influence of range of repeated axial stress (for ductile metals).

reversed stresses. Sometimes, however, it is important to obtain more complete information by obtaining the fatigue strengths for various ratios of the variable to the mean stress. For this purpose it is necessary to obtain S-N diagrams for various stress ratios of S_r/S_m. From these S-N diagrams the fatigue strengths for various S_r/S_m ratios, corresponding to a given number of stress cycles, can be selected. These values can be represented graphically in various ways.[5] One method of presentation is shown in Fig. 4-5, where the

[5] See J. O. Smith, "The Effect of Range of Stress on the Fatigue Strength of Metals," Bulletin No. 334, Univ. of Ill., 1939; and G. C. Noll and C. Lipson,

mean stress S_m is plotted against the variable stress S_r.   In Fig. 4-5,
point B denotes failure in static tension, since it represents a value
of $S_m = S_u$ and $S_r = 0$.   On the other hand, point C represents
values of $S_m = -S_u$ and $S_r = 0$, and corresponds to failure under
static compression for equal static strength in tension and compression.   Point A represents complete stress reversal since, for point A,
$S_m = 0$ and $S_r = S_e$.   That is, for point A, the mean stress S_m is
zero and, therefore, indicates complete stress reversal.   Typical test
points in Fig. 4-5 between A and B and between A and C denote
stress combinations with various ratios of S_r/S_m for which failure
occurs after N cycles.   A number of attempts have been made to
interpret the test data shown in Fig. 4-5.   Three of the most common
empirical relations used to define the test points are referred to as
the *Modified Goodman law*, the *Gerber law*, and the *Soderberg law*.
The Modified Goodman law is indicated by the straight line AB
which joins the point A, representing complete stress reversal, with
point B, representing the ultimate static tensile strength.   The
Gerber law is obtained by passing a parabola through points A, B,
and C as shown.   The Soderberg law is indicated by the straight line
AD which joins the point A, representing complete reversal, with
point D, representing the tensile yield strength.   The Soderberg law
has been recommended in recent years by several investigators.[6]
It is recommended for use in design because it is the only relation
that is on the safe side of the test results and is, therefore, the most
conservative of the relations proposed.   Furthermore, a straight-
line relation is a simple one to use.   The equation for a straight line
AD can be written as

$$y = mx + b \qquad (4\text{-}4)$$

Referring to Fig. 4-5, for $x = 0$, $y = b = S_e$; and when $y = 0$,
$x = S_{yp}$, or $m = -b/x = -S_e/S_{yp}$.   Placing values of $y = S_r$,
$x = S_m$, $m = -S_e/S_{yp}$, and $b = S_e$ in eq. (4-4),

$$S_r = S_e - \left(\frac{S_e}{S_{yp}}\right) S_m \qquad (4\text{-}5)$$

"Allowable Working Stresses," *Proc. S.E.S.A.*, Vol. III, No. II, pp. 89-101; also
Product Engineering, Vol. 17, No. 3, 1946, pp. 205-209.

[6] See, for example, C. R. Soderberg, "Working Stresses," *Trans. A.S.M.E.*,
1935, p. A-106; and J. B. Kommers, "Design Diagrams for Alternating plus
Steady Loads," *Product Engineering*, 1938, Vol. 7, No. 10, p. 395.

Equation (4-5) gives the value of the variable stress S_r that produces failure by fatigue for a specified number of cycles and for a given value of the mean stress S_m. Equation (4-5) applies to line AD for which the mean stress S_m is tensile or positive. If the mean stress S_m is compressive and negative, eq. (4-5) can be used provided the absolute values of S_m and S_r are used.

It is sometimes preferable to express eq. (4-5) in terms of the strength $S_{\max}$. This can be done by replacing S_r in eq. (4-5) by its value ($S_{\max} - S_m$). Making this substitution, eq. (4-5) becomes

$$S_{\max} = (1 - p)S_m + S_e \qquad (4\text{-}5a)$$

where $p = S_e/S_{yp}$ = the ratio of the fatigue strength for complete reversal to the static tensile yield strength. The approximate value of the strength $S_{\max}$ can be obtained from eq. (4-5a) for a given mean stress S_m.

In terms of the variable and mean stresses, the modified Goodman law becomes

$$S_r = S_e - mS_m \qquad (4\text{-}6)$$

where $m = S_e/S_u$ = the ratio of the fatigue strength for complete reversal to the static ultimate tensile stress.

The Gerber law may be a better approximation than the straight-line law for aluminum alloys. In terms of the maximum and mean stresses the Gerber law becomes

$$S_r = S_e - \frac{mS_m^2}{S_u} \qquad (4\text{-}7)$$

Of the three relations for the fatigue strength $S_{\max}$, as defined by eqs. (4-5), (4-6), and (4-7), the first one, eq. (4-5), representing the Soderberg law is recommended unless available test data for the material indicates that eq. (4-6) or (4-7) is suitable.

NUMERICAL EXAMPLE. A steel alloy is tested under fluctuating axial stresses. For $N = 10^5$, the fatigue strength for complete reversal is 80,000 psi. The yield tensile stress is 140,000 psi, and the ultimate tensile strength is 160,000 psi. Determine the fatigue strength S_r for the material when the ratio $S_m/S_{yp} = 0.5$ and $N = 10^5$. Solve by the three foregoing laws and compare the strengths with the Soderberg law.

SOLUTION. By the Soderberg law, as given by eq. (4-5),

$$S_r = S_e - \left(\frac{S_e}{S_{yp}}\right)S_m$$

or $\qquad S_r = 80{,}000 - \dfrac{80{,}000}{140{,}000}\,(0.5 \times 140{,}000) = 40{,}000 \text{ psi}$

Using eq. (4-6), or the modified Goodman law,

$$S_r = S_e - \left(\frac{S_e}{S_u}\right) S_m$$

or $\qquad S_r = 80,000 - \dfrac{80,000}{160,000} (0.5 \times 140,000) = 45,000$ psi

By eq. (4-7), or the Gerber law,

$$S_r = S_e - \left(\frac{mS_m^2}{S_u}\right) = S_e - S_e \left(\frac{S_m}{S_u}\right)^2$$

or $\qquad S_r = 80,000 - 80,000 \left(\dfrac{0.5 \times 140,000}{160,000}\right)^2 = 64,700$ psi

The ratio of the fatigue strengths as determined by the modified Goodman law, to the value predicted by the Soderberg law is $45,000/40,000 = 1.13$. The corresponding ratio for the Gerber law is $64,700/40,000 = 1.62$.

Design Stresses for Fluctuating Axial Stress. The Soderberg law, as expressed by eq. (4-5), will be used as the basis for defining the design stresses, since this law gives safe values and is expressed by a simple equation. For a given material, the right-hand side of eq. (4-5) gives the approximate value of the variable stress S_r that will produce failure in a specified number of cycles and for a mean stress S_m. To determine the allowable or design value for S_r, consider the case of complete stress reversal. The allowable stress value corresponding to complete reversal, or the stress S_e, is S_e/N_e, where N_e is the factor of safety for complete stress reversal. For an entirely static stress, failure is represented by the stress S_{yp}, the yield stress of the material. The design stress corresponding to a static stress only is represented by S_{yp}/N_y, where N_y is the factor of safety for static stress. For a combination of static and variable stresses between the conditions of completely reversed stress and static stress, the allowable value of the variable stress is, by eq. (4-4),

$$S_r = \left(\frac{S_e}{N_e}\right) - \frac{(S_e/N_e)}{(S_{yp}/N_y)} S_m$$

or $\qquad S_r = \left(\frac{S_e}{N_e}\right) - \frac{(S_e N_y)}{(S_{yp} N_e)} S_m \qquad\qquad (4\text{-}8)$

Equation (4-8) defines the value of the design stress S_r for a given mean stress S_m in terms of the factors of safety N_e and N_y and the material constants p and S_e. In some cases it may be satisfactory to assume the factors of safety N_e and N_y to be equal. Then eq. (4-8) becomes

$$S_r = \frac{S_e}{N} - \left(\frac{S_e}{S_{yp}}\right) S_m$$

or

$$S_r = \left(\frac{S_e}{S_{yp}}\right) (S_w - S_m) \qquad (4\text{-}9)$$

where $S_w = S_y/N$ = the static working stress.

Equations (4-8) and (4-9) will now be applied to the design of members subjected to fluctuating axial stresses.

Design of Members Subjected to Axial Fluctuating Stresses. Connecting rods and bolts are examples of members subjected to fluctuating axial stresses.

NUMERICAL EXAMPLE. *Bolt Subjected to Fluctuating Stresses.* A bolt is subjected to an axial tensile load that varies from a value of 100,000 lb. to 40,000 lb. The material to be used has a tensile yield strength $S_{yp} = 60,000$ psi and a fatigue strength for complete reversal $S_e = 40,000$ psi. Determine the required cross-sectional area, using Soderberg's law and factors of safety of $N_e = 4.0$ and $N_y = 2.0$. What is the required cross-sectional area if the 100,000-lb. load is statically applied?

SOLUTION. Let $P_{\max}$, P_m, and $P_{\min}$ be the maximum, mean, and minimum loads respectively. Then the variable and mean axial stresses in terms of the loads are

$$S_r = \frac{P_{\max} - P_{\min}}{2A} \quad \text{and} \quad S_m = \frac{P_m}{A} = \frac{P_{\max} + P_{\min}}{2A}$$

or

$$S_r = \frac{100,000 - 40,000}{2A} = \frac{30,000}{A}$$

and

$$S_m = \frac{100,000 + 40,000}{2A} = \frac{70,000}{A}$$

where A is the cross-sectional area.

By eq. (4-5) the failure stress S_r is $S_r = S_e - (S_e/S_{yp})S_m$. Then for design, the stress S_r is

$$S_r = \left(\frac{S_e}{N_e}\right) - \frac{(S_e/N_e)}{(S_{yp}/N_y)} S_m$$

$$= \frac{40,000}{4} - \frac{(40,000/4)}{(60,000/2)} S_m = 10,000 - \left(\frac{S_m}{3}\right)$$

Since $S_r = 30,000/A$ and $S_m = 70,000/A$,

$$\frac{30,000}{A} = 10,000 - \left(\frac{1}{3}\right)\frac{70,000}{A}$$

or $A = 5.33$ sq. in.

If the load is considered to be statically applied,

$$A = \frac{P_{\max}}{S_w} = \frac{P_{\max}N_y}{S_y}$$

$$= \frac{100,000 \times 2}{60,000} = 3.33 \text{ sq. in.}$$

NUMERICAL EXAMPLE. *Connecting Rod Subjected to Repeated Axial Stresses.* A connecting rod of circular cross section is subjected to an axial load that varies from a tensile value of 80,000 lb. to a compressive value of 100,000 lb. The yield compressive strength $S_{yp} = 60,000$ psi and the fatigue strength $S_e = 40,000$ psi. Determine the diameter required if $N_y = N_e = 4.0$. Use Soderberg's law.

SOLUTION. Since the compressive load is greater than the tensile load, the straight line AD' in Fig. 4-5 will be used to define failure in place of AD. For this purpose eq. (4-5) can be used provided the absolute value of S_m is used. That is, the mean stress S_m is

$$S_m = \frac{P_m}{A} = \frac{P_{\max} + P_{\min}}{2A}$$

$$= \frac{80,000 - 100.000}{2A} = -\frac{10,000}{A}$$

and the absolute value of $S_m = \dfrac{10,000}{A}$.

The variable stress S_r is

$$S_r = \frac{P_r}{A} = \frac{P_{\max} - P_{\min}}{2A} = \frac{(80,000 + 100,000)}{2A} = \frac{90,000}{A}$$

From eq. (4-5) the allowable relation between S_r and S_m is

$$S_r = \frac{S_e}{N_e} - \frac{S_e/N_e}{S_{yp}/N_y} S_m$$

Placing the values of the stresses and factors of safety in this equation,

$$\frac{90,000}{A} = \frac{40,000}{4} - \left(\frac{40,000/4}{60,000/4}\right)\left(\frac{10,000}{A}\right)$$

or $A = 9.67$ sq. in.

The diameter of the connecting rod is then

$$d = \sqrt{\frac{4A}{\pi}} = \sqrt{\frac{4 \times 9.67}{\pi}} = 3.51 \text{ in.}$$

In the examples considered it is assumed that the member is of constant cross section throughout its length or that the change in cross section is gradual. For many machine and structural parts this is not the case and the cross section changes suddenly. The stresses produced are then different from those calculated by the ordinary strength of materials formulas. These stresses must be considered in design since their values are higher than those obtained by the usual methods of calculation. As noted in Chapter 3, these regions of high stresses are called *regions of stress concentration.* Stress concentrations are produced in members with holes, circular shafts with fillets, U-shaped notches, shafts with keyways, screw threads, welded joints, and any other part of a member in which there is a non-uniform change in cross section. In the case of fatigue, the stress concentration is a function of the fatigue strength of the material as well as the discontinuity. The ratio of the fatigue strength of a member or specimen with no stress concentration to the fatigue strength with stress concentration is called the *fatigue strength reduction factor.*[4] This factor has no meaning unless the geometry, size, and material of the member or specimen, and stress range are stated. Strength reduction factors may be as high as 2.0 and differ in value from the static stress concentration factors.[7]

Internal and external flaws in the material are also an important source of strength reduction. The danger of these weak spots is that fatigue or fluctuating loads produce a progressive extension of even a minute crack. Inspection methods have been developed to detect internal flaws. It is very important, however, to avoid stress concentrations by exercising care in the fabrication of the part and by avoiding abrupt changes in cross section in the design.

---

[7] For a summary of stress concentration factors see R. J. Roark, "Formulas for Stress and Strain," McGraw-Hill Book Co., Inc., 1938. The factors affecting stress concentration are discussed by R. E. Peterson, "Stress Concentration Phenomena in Fatigue of Metals," *Trans. A.S.M.E.*, 1933, Vol. 55, p. 157. See also *Stress and Strength of Manufactured Parts*, by C. Lipson, G. C. Noll, and L. S. Clock, McGraw-Hill Book Co., Inc., 1950.

NUMERICAL EXAMPLE. *Repeated Loading of a Threaded Bolt.* A threaded bolt is subjected to a completely reversed axial load of 50,000 lb. The fatigue strength reduction factor is 1.5. (a) What is the required root diameter of the bolt if the fatigue strength S_e of the material is 50,000 psi? Use a factor of safety of 3. (b) What is the root diameter if the load is statically applied? The yield stress is 60,000 psi, the static stress concentration factor[3] is 2.0, and the factor of safety is 2.

SOLUTION. The required root area for the fatigue condition is

$$A = \frac{P}{(S_e/N_e)} = \frac{50,000}{50,000/(3 \times 1.5)} = 4.5 \text{ sq. in.}$$

or

$$d = \sqrt{\frac{4A}{\pi}} = \sqrt{\frac{4 \times 4.5}{\pi}} = 2.40 \text{ in.}$$

Considering the static condition, the required root area is

$$A = \frac{P}{S_{yp}/N_y} = \frac{50,000}{60,000/(2 \times 2)} = 3.33 \text{ sq. in.}$$

or

$$d = \sqrt{\frac{4A}{\pi}} = \sqrt{\frac{4 \times 3.33}{\pi}} = 2.06 \text{ in.}$$

4-3. FATIGUE STRENGTH FOR REPEATED TORSIONAL STRESSES

Some torsion fatigue tests have been made on metals and alloys for the case of complete stress reversal. The average of the test results for ductile materials indicates that the torsional fatigue strength for complete reversal is about 0.60 the fatigue strength for axial stresses and complete reversal. For purpose of design and for ductile materials, the design stress for torsion and for complete stress reversal will be selected, therefore, as

$$(S_s)_w = 0.6 S_{ew} \tag{4-10}$$

where $(S_s)_w$ is the design torsional stress for complete reversal and S_{ew} is the design axial fatigue stress for complete reversal. For brittle materials such as cast iron, the ratio is higher and, in some cases, equal to about 1.0.

---

[3] Based on some test results, it has been recommended that a static stress concentration factor be applied only for brittle materials. See, for example, *Handbook on Experimental Stress Analysis*, Chapter X on "Working Stresses," by C. R. Soderberg, John Wiley & Sons, Inc., 1950, p. 438; and *Design of Machine Elements*, by M. F. Spotts, Prentice-Hall, Inc., 1948.

Some test data have been obtained for various ratios of the mean to the maximum shear stress on the fatigue strength in shear.[9] These tests show that the value of the mean stress has no affect on the shear fatigue strength. This result can be expressed by the equation

$$(S_s)_{\max} = S_{se} \tag{4-11}$$

NUMERICAL EXAMPLE. *Circular Shaft Subjected to Fluctuating Torsion.* A circular shaft is subjected to a completely reversed twisting moment of 4000 ft. lb. The fatigue strength S_e for completely reversed axial stress is 42,000 psi. The shaft has a keyway with a fatigue strength reduction factor of 1.8. Determine the shaft diameter using a factor of safety of 2.5.

SOLUTION. The design shear stress is, by eq. (4-10),

$$S_{sw} = 0.6 S_{ew} = 0.6 \frac{S_e}{k_f N_f} = \frac{0.6 \times 42,000}{1.8 \times 2.5} = 5600 \text{ psi}$$

The required diameter can now be determined from the equation

$$S_{sw} = \frac{Tr}{J} = \frac{16T}{\pi d^3}$$

or

$$d = \sqrt[3]{\frac{16T}{\pi S_{sw}}} = \sqrt[3]{\frac{16 \times 48,000}{\pi \times 5600}} = 3.52 \text{ in.}$$

4-4. FATIGUE STRENGTH FOR REPEATED BENDING STRESSES

Most fatigue tests have been made on specimens subjected to completely reversed bending stresses, since the fatigue machine for this type of test is a simple one. In the rotating-beam type of fatigue testing machine a specimen of circular cross section (Fig. 4-3) is supported in bearings and subjected to a bending moment of constant value. A description of this machine is given in Chapter 11. A motor is used to rotate the specimen. Then for a point A on the cross section [Fig. 4-6(a)] the stress is

$$S = \frac{My}{I} = \frac{Mr}{I} \sin \theta$$

---

[9] J. O. Smith, "The Effect of Range of Stress on the Torsional Fatigue Strength of Steel," *Bulletin 316*, Eng. Exp. Sta., Univ. of Ill., 1939; and "The Effect of Range of Stress on the Fatigue Strength of Metals," *Bulletin 334*, Eng. Exp. Sta., Univ. of Ill., 1942.

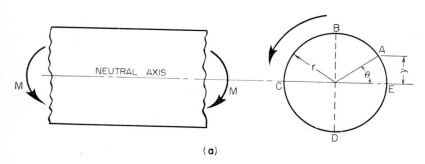

(a)

ROUND   SPECIMEN   SUBJECTED
TO A   REVERSED   BENDING   STRESS

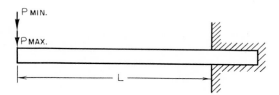

(b)

NON-ROTATING   TYPE   SPECIMEN
FOR   FLUCTUATING   BENDING   TESTS

Fig. 4-6.

With rotation of the specimen the stress varies as the angle θ changes.   When A moves to B, the value of $\theta = 90°$ and $S = Mr/I$. When A moves to C, $\theta = 180°$ and $S = 0$.   When the element at A is at the lower point D, $\theta = 270°$ and $S = -Mr/I$.   For the element A at E, $\theta = 0$ and $S = 0$.   That is, the stress varies sinusoidally as shown in Fig. 4-2(b).

The fatigue strength and S-N diagram in reversed bending are obtained in a manner similar to that described for fluctuating axial stresses.

Sometimes the fatigue strength in bending is obtained by applying an end fluctuating load on a specimen that does not rotate [Fig.

4-6(b)]. In this case, values of the fatigue strength are found to be different from values found using the rotating-type specimen. The non-rotating-type specimen is commonly used for fatigue tests of plastics and is also used for determining the bending fatigue strength of flat metal stock.

Design of Members Subjected to Bending Fatigue Loads.
The fatigue strengths in reversed bending are found to be approximately equal to those for reversed axial stress. In the design of members subjected to bending, in which the stresses are not completely reversed, it is recommended that the design stress equations used for fluctuating axial stress be applied. To explain the application of eq. (4-8) to prismatic members subjected to fluctuating bending moments, consider a straight bar that is subjected to plane bending so that the moment varies from a value M_{max} to M_{min}. In order to determine the section modulus required, the variable and mean stresses for the critical outer fiber will be determined first. The values of these stresses are

$$S_r = \frac{M_r c}{I} = \frac{(M_{max} - M_{min})c}{2I}$$

and
$$S_m = \frac{M_m c}{I} = \frac{(M_{max} + M_{min})c}{2I}$$

Placing these values of S_r and S_m in eq. (4-8) and solving for the section modulus (I/c),

$$\frac{I}{c} = \left(\frac{M_{max} - M_{min}}{2S_e}\right) N_e + \left(\frac{M_{max} + M_{min}}{2S_{yp}}\right) N_y \qquad (4\text{-}12)$$

The first term on the right-hand side of eq. (4-12) is the correction factor for fatigue loading, since, for static loading only, $M_{max} - M_{min} = 0$ and eq. (4-12) reduces to $I/c = N_y M_{max}/S_{yp}$, the value determined for static loading only.

NUMERICAL EXAMPLE. *Cantilever Beam Subjected to a Fluctuating End Load.* A steel cantilever beam 30 in. long and 4 in. wide is subjected to an end downward fluctuating load that varies from a value of 12,000 lb. to 2000 lb. Determine the required depth of the beam if the material constants are $S_e = 30,000$ psi and $S_{yp} = 25,000$ psi. Use values of $N_e = 3.0$ and $N_y = 2.0$.

SOLUTION. The maximum and minimum moments at the critical section are $P_{max}L$ and $P_{min}L$, where L is the length of the beam.

Placing these moment values in eq. (4-12),

$$\frac{I}{c} = \frac{(P_{max} - P_{min})LN_e}{2S_e} + \frac{(P_{max} + P_{min})LN_y}{2S_{yp}}$$

$$= \frac{10{,}000 \times 30 \times 3}{2 \times 30{,}000} + \frac{14{,}000 \times 30 \times 2}{2 \times 25{,}000}$$

$$= 15 + 16.8 = 31.8 \text{ in.}^3$$

For a cross section of width b and depth d the value of I/c is $bd^2/6$. That is,

$$\frac{bd^2}{6} = 31.8 \quad \text{or} \quad d = \sqrt{\frac{6 \times 31.8}{4}} = 6.9 \text{ in.}$$

4-5. MEMBERS SUBJECTED TO REPEATED BENDING AND AXIAL LOADS

In many machine and structural members the fluctuating bending stress is accompanied by an axial stress. The following example shows how fluctuating axial and bending stresses can be considered.

NUMERICAL EXAMPLE. *Member Subjected to Bending and Axial Fatigue Stresses.* A member of circular cross section with a diameter of 2 in. is subjected to a static axial load P of 20,000 lb. What completely reversed bending moment can be applied so that failure will be produced at the end of $N = 10^6$ cycles? The yield strength is 40,000 psi and the fatigue strength S_e for $N = 10^6$ cycles is 30,000 psi.

SOLUTION. The variable and mean stresses for the critical outer fiber are

$$S_r = \frac{M_r r}{I} = \frac{M_r r}{\pi r^4/4}$$

and

$$S_m = \frac{P}{A} = \frac{P}{\pi r^2}$$

where r = the radius of the cross section.

Placing the foregoing values of the stresses in eq. (4-5),

$$S_r = S_e - \left(\frac{S_e}{S_{yp}}\right) S_m$$

or

$$\frac{4M_r}{\pi r^3} = S_e - \left(\frac{S_e}{S_{yp}}\right)\left(\frac{P}{\pi r^2}\right)$$

and
$$\frac{4M_r}{\pi \times 1^3} = 30{,}000 - \left(\frac{30{,}000}{40{,}000}\right)\left(\frac{20{,}000}{\pi \times 1^2}\right)$$

hence
$$M_r = 19{,}850 \text{ in. lb.}$$

4-6. FATIGUE STRENGTH FOR COMBINED STRESSES

Fluctuating loads on structures and machines may produce stresses that act in more than one direction and that vary in magnitude with time. These combined fatigue stresses are present in many operating machine parts. Fluctuating combined stresses are produced in rotating or reciprocating parts such as axles, connecting rods, rotating shafts, crank shafts, cam shafts, and ship and aircraft propeller shafts. In these parts the stresses are not acting in one direction only, as in the case of the simple stresses considered above. The fatigue strengths of materials for stresses acting in more than one direction differ from the strength for uniaxial stresses. There have been only a few experimental studies made to determine the fatigue strengths of materials when subjected to fluctuating combined stresses. This lack of test data is due to the fact that this is a comparatively new field of study and that there are difficulties in the design and operation of combined fatigue stress testing machines. There have been some theories of failure proposed for defining strength of materials under combined fatigue stresses.

Theories of Failure for Combined Fatigue Stresses. The theories given herein are restricted to cases in which the directions of the principal

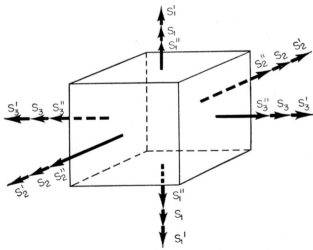

Fig. 4-7. Element subjected to fluctuating triaxial stress.

stresses do not vary during the stress variation. It is assumed, furthermore, that the maximum and minimum values of the principal stresses occur at the same instant of time. There are many applications in design where these limitations apply.

The theories of failure for combined fatigue stresses are based on physical concepts of failure similar to those used for static combined stresses. In other words, failure under combined fatigue stresses is assumed when a limiting normal stress, shear stress, or energy is reached that corresponds to the values at failure under uniaxial fluctuating stress.

Maximum Stress Theory. Figure 4-7 represents an element subjected to fluctuating triaxial stresses. The principal stresses S_1, S_2, and S_3 vary so that their maximum stress values are S_1', S_2', and S_3', and their mean values are S_1'', S_2'', and S_3'' respectively. By the maximum stress theory, failure is assumed when the maximum value of the greatest principal stress becomes equal to the value of S_{max} at failure under uniaxial fluctuating stress for the same number of stress cycles, as defined by the Soderberg law or eq. (4-5a). The foregoing hypothesis requires that the mean stresses for the uniaxial and combined stress conditions be the same. That is, considering all three principal stresses, failure is defined by one of the following equations:

$$\left. \begin{array}{l} S_1' = (1 - p)S_1'' + S_e \\ S_2' = (1 - p)S_2'' + S_e \\ S_3' = (1 - p)S_3'' + S_e \end{array} \right\} \quad (4\text{-}13)$$

If S_1' is the greatest principal stress, then for a given mean stress S_1'' the right-hand side of the first of eqs. (4-13) gives the value of S_1' for failure by fatigue.

For two-dimensional stresses, $S_3' = S_3'' = 0$, and the first two of eqs. (4-13) apply. For the two-dimensional element shown in Fig. 4-8 subjected to normal and shearing stress components, it can be shown that the relation between the stress components at failure is[10]

$$\tfrac{1}{2}[(S_x' + S_y') - (1 - p)(S_x'' + S_y'')]$$
$$\pm \tfrac{1}{2}\sqrt{[(S_y' - S_x') - (1 - p)(S_y'' - S_x'')]^2 + 4[S_{xy}' - (1 - p)S_{xy}'']^2}$$
$$= \pm S_e \quad (4\text{-}14)$$

Equation (4-14) may be interpreted as defining the maximum stress S_x' for given values of the remaining stresses.

Maximum Shear Theory. A shear theory of failure for fatigue stresses was proposed by Soderberg.[11] This theory is based on the failure relation

---

[10] J. Marin, *Mechanical Properties of Materials and Design*, McGraw-Hill Book Company, Inc., 1942.

[11] C. R. Soderberg, "Working Stresses," *Trans. A.S.M.E.*, 1935, Vol. 57, p. A-106.

for uniaxial stress as defined by eq. (4-5a) and assumes that the maximum shear stress is the criterion for failure. For the three-dimensional element of Fig. 4-7, the maximum and mean values of the principal shear stresses are

$$S_{xy}' = \pm\frac{S_1' - S_2'}{2}, \quad S_{xy}' = \pm\frac{S_2' - S_3'}{2}, \quad S_{xy}' = \pm\frac{S_3' - S_1'}{2}$$
$$S_{xy}'' = \pm\frac{S_1'' - S_2''}{2}, \quad S_{xy}'' = \pm\frac{S_2'' - S_3''}{2}, \quad S_{xy}'' = \pm\frac{S_3'' - S_1''}{2} \tag{a}$$

For uniaxial tensile stress the shear stress S_{xy} equals one-half the tensile stress S. Then the maximum and mean shear stresses are $S_{xy}' = \pm S_{max}/2$ and $S_{xy}'' = \pm S_m/2$. Placing these values of S_{max} and S_m in eq. (4-5a), failure by uniaxial fatigue can then be written as

$$S_{xy}' = (1 - p)S_{xy}'' \pm \frac{S_e}{2} \tag{b}$$

Placing the values of the principal shear stresses from eqs. (a) in eq. (b), fatigue failure under combined stresses is defined by one of the following equations·

$$\left.\begin{aligned}
S_1' &= S_2' + (1 - p)(S_1'' - S_2'') + S_e \\
S_2' &= S_3' + (1 - p)(S_2'' - S_3'') + S_e \\
S_3' &= S_1' + (1 - p)(S_3'' - S_1'') + S_e
\end{aligned}\right\} \tag{4-15}$$

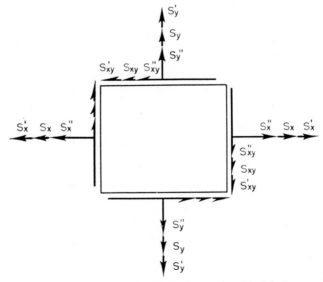

Fig. 4-8. Element subjected to fluctuating biaxial stress.

For two-dimensional stresses eqs. (4-15) can be used by placing $S_3' = S_3'' = 0$. Then, as represented in Fig. 4-8, the equations[10] defining failure by the maximum shear theory can be shown to be

$$
\left.
\begin{aligned}
S_x' &= (1 - p)S_x'' \pm S_e \\
S_y' &= (1 - p)S_y'' \pm S_e
\end{aligned}
\right\}
$$

or

$$
\sqrt{[(1 - p)(S_x'' - S_y'') - (S_x' - S_y')]^2 + 4[(1 - p)(S_{xy}'' - S_{xy}')]^2} = \pm S_e
$$

$$(4\text{-}15a)$$

The relative values of the stress components will determine which one of eqs. (4-15a) should be used. For principal stresses of the same sign, the first two of eqs. (4-15a) are used, while for principal stresses of opposite sign, the last of eqs. (4-15a) is used

Distortion Energy Theory. A theory based on distortion energy as the criterion of failure has also been proposed.[12] This theory is based on the assumption that failure occurs in the case of combined stresses when the distortion energy corresponding to the maximum values of the stress components equals the distortion energy at failure for the maximum uniaxial stress value at failure. To apply this criterion it is necessary first to express eq. (4-5a) in terms of distortion energy. To do so, eq. (k), Chapter 3, is used first to determine the distortion energies for uniaxial stress corresponding to the maximum and mean stresses. The distortion energies will be designated by u_d' and u_d'' respectively. Their values are

$$
u_d' = \left(\frac{1 + \mu}{3E}\right)(S_{\max})^2 \quad \text{and} \quad u_d'' = \left(\frac{1 + \mu}{3E}\right)(S_m)^2 \tag{c}
$$

Placing the values of the distortion energies from eqs. (c) in eq. (4-5a), the failure relation for fluctuating axial stresses becomes

$$
\sqrt{u_d'} = (1 - p)\sqrt{u_d''} + \sqrt{\frac{1 + \mu}{3E}}\, S_e \tag{d}
$$

The distortion energy values u_d' and u_d'', corresponding to the maximum stress values S_1', S_2', and S_3' and to the mean stress values S_1'', S_2'', and S_3'' respectively, can be obtained from eq. (j), Chapter III. These values, when substituted for u_d' and u_d'' in eq. (d), give the failure relation for combined fatigue stresses, or

$$
\sqrt{(S_1')^2 + (S_2')^2 + (S_3')^2 - (S_1'S_2' + S_2'S_3' + S_3'S_1')}
$$
$$
- (1 - p)\sqrt{(S_1'')^2 + (S_2'')^2 + (S_3'')^2 - (S_1''S_2'' + S_2''S_3'' + S_3''S_1'')} = S_e \tag{4-16}
$$

[12] J. Marin, "Working Stresses for Members Subjected to Fluctuating Loads," *Trans. A.S.M.E.*, Vol. 59, p. 55, 1937.

Equation (4-16) can be used for defining fatigue failures under combined biaxial stresses by placing $S_3' = S_3'' = 0$. For the two-dimensional element in Fig. 4-8, the distortion energy theory can be shown to be expressed by the following equation:

$$\sqrt{(S_x')^2 - S_x'S_y' + (S_y')^2 + 3(S_{xy}')^2} -$$
$$[(1 - p) \sqrt{(S_x'')^2 - S_x''S_y'' + (S_y'')^2 + 3(S_{xy}'')^2}] = S_e \quad (4\text{-}16a)$$

That is, if all the stresses in eq. (4-16a) except S_x' are known, then the value of S_x' as determined by eq. (4-16a) is the value of the stress that will produce failure by this theory.

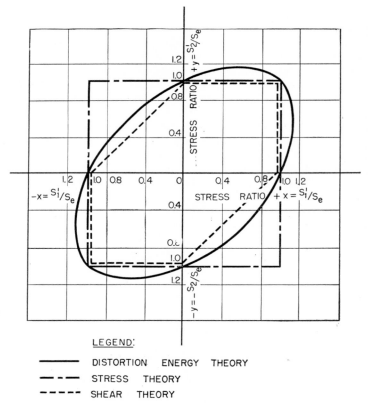

LEGEND:

——————— DISTORTION ENERGY THEORY

— · — · — STRESS THEORY

— — — — SHEAR THEORY

Fig. 4-9. Comparison of theories of failure in fatigue for completely reversed stresses.

The three foregoing theories are shown in Fig. 4-9 for biaxial stresses that are completely reversed. That is, for $S_1'' = S_2'' = 0$.

Test Results for Combined Fatigue Stresses. Combined fatigue tests have been made primarily to determine fatigue strengths in two directions at right angles; that is, for biaxial tension-tension and biaxial tension-compression. Biaxial tension-tension tests have been made with thin-walled

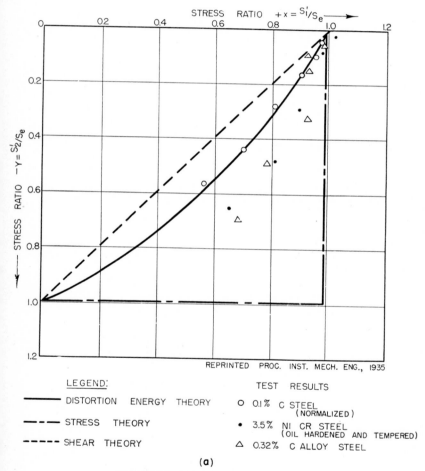

REPRINTED   PROC.   INST.   MECH.   ENG.,   1935

LEGEND: TEST   RESULTS

———— DISTORTION   ENERGY   THEORY   O   0.1%   C STEEL
                                                         (NORMALIZED)
— — — STRESS   THEORY   •   3.5%   NI CR STEEL
                                                         (OIL HARDENED AND TEMPERED)
– – – – – SHEAR   THEORY   △   0.32%   C ALLOY STEEL

(a)

STRENGTHS   FOR   DUCTILE   METALS

Fig. 4-10.   Biaxial fatigue strengths for metals.

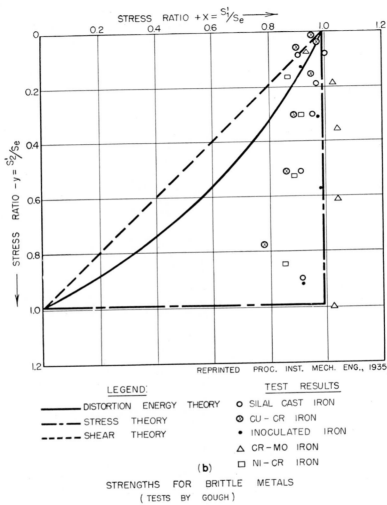

STRESS RATIO $+X = S'_1/S_e$ ⟶

STRESS RATIO $-y = S'_2/S_e$

REPRINTED PROC. INST. MECH. ENG., 1935

LEGEND:

———— DISTORTION ENERGY THEORY

—·—·— STRESS THEORY

— — — — SHEAR THEORY

TEST RESULTS

○ SILAL CAST IRON

⊗ CU – CR IRON

• INOCULATED IRON

△ CR – MO IRON

□ NI – CR IRON

(b)

STRENGTHS FOR BRITTLE METALS

(TESTS BY GOUGH)

Fig. 4-10 (Cont'd). Biaxial fatigue strengths for metals.

tubes subjected to fluctuating int rnal pressure and fluctuating axial tensile loading.   For biaxial tension-compression stresses, round rods subjected to combined torsion and bending have been the most commonly used specimens. Combined torsion and bending o a round rod gives a combination of shear and normal tensile stresses.   These stresses then produce principal stresses of opposite sign.   Tubular specimens subjected to internal pressure and axial

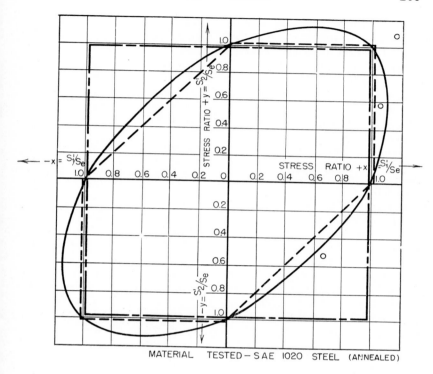

MATERIAL   TESTED — S AE 1020 STEEL (ANNEALED)

(C)

STRENGTHS   FOR   STEEL

(TESTS BY MAJORS AND   MAC GREGOR)

Fig. 4-10 (Cont'd).   Biaxial fatigue strengths for metals.

compression have also been used for compression-tension fatigue tests. Gough[13] has conducted a comprehensive investigation on the fatigue strengths of steels and cast irons subjected to tension-compression biaxial stresses. Round rod specimens subjected to combined bending and torsion were used in these tests.   The effect on the strength of various ratios of the principal stress was investigated for completely reversed stresses.   Figure 4-10 shows a comparison between the test results and the theories of failure, and shows that for the steel alloys the distortion energy theory is a good approximation, while for cast iron the maximum stress theory agrees best with the test results.

[13] H. J. Gough and H. V. Pollard, "Strength of Metals under Combined Alternating Stresses," *Proc. Inst. Mech. Eng.*, London, 1935, Vol. 131, p. 3.   See also *Proc. Inst. Mech. Eng.*, 1935, Vol. 132, p. 549, and *Proc. Inst. Automobile Engs.*, London, 1937, Vol. 31, p. 821.

In Fig. 4-10, stresses S_1' and S_2' represent the maximum values of the principal stresses S_1 and S_2 corresponding to fatigue failure. The stress S_e is the uniaxial strength value for failure in fatigue.

Sawert[14] made fatigue tests on disks in which the principal stress ratio could be varied. For biaxial stresses of opposite sign and for three steels, the distortion energy theory was found to be in best agreement with the test results. For notched-bar specimens subjected to tension-tension and completely reversed stresses the distortion energy theory again agreed best with the test results.

Tests by Majors et al.[15] on steel tubes subjected to internal pressure and axial tension or compression show best agreement with the distortion energy theory [Fig. 4-10(c)]. In these tests the stresses were not completely reversed.

Marin[16] and Griffis[17] made tests on steel tubes subjected to fluctuating internal pressure and axial loads. Various ratios of the mean to the maximum stresses from $+0.5$ to $+1.0$ were investigated for ratios of the principal stresses from 0 to $+1.0$. The shear theory agreed best with these test results.

Summarizing the foregoing, it can be seen from the limited test data on ductile metals that the distortion energy theory is in best agreement with the test results. For conservative design it is recommended that the maximum shear theory be used. For brittle metals such as cast iron, the maximum stress theory agrees approximately with the few available test results.

NUMERICAL EXAMPLE. A thin-walled tube with a 4-in. diameter and $\frac{1}{4}$-in. wall thickness is subjected to an internal pressure that varies from a value of $-p'/4$ to p'. If the yield stress of the material S_{yp} is 42,000 psi and the fatigue strength S_e is 35,000 psi at $N = 10^8$ cycles, determine the pressure p' required to produce fracture in 10^8 cycles. Solve by both the shear and distortion theories.

SOLUTION. The principal stresses are

$$S_1' = \frac{p'd}{2t} = 8p', \quad S_1'' = \frac{p''d}{2t} = \frac{\frac{1}{2}(p' - p'/4)d}{2t} = 3p'$$

$$S_2' = \frac{p'd}{4t} = 4p', \quad S_2'' = \frac{p''d}{4t} = 1.5p'$$

[14] W. Sawert, "The Behavior of Steel under Reversed Multi-Axial Stresses," Zeitschrift des Vereines Deutscher Ingenieure, Vol. 87, 1943, p. 609.

[15] H. Majors, B. D. Mills, and C. W. MacGregor, "Fatigue under Combined Pulsating Stresses," Trans. A.S.M.E., 1949, Vol. 71.

[16] J. Marin, "Strength of Steel Subjected to Biaxial Fatigue Stresses," The Welding Journal, Research Supplement, Nov. 1942.

[17] G. K. Morikawa, and LeVan Griffis, "The Biaxial Fatigue Strength of Low Carbon Steels," The Welding Journal, Research Supplement, March 1945, p. 1678.

For the *shear theory* the third of eqs. (4-15) with $S_3' = S_3'' = 0$ will be used, since S_1' is greater than S_2'.   Then

$$S_1' = (1 - p)S_1'' + S_e$$

or

$$8p' = (1 - p)(3p') + S_e$$

Since

$$p = \frac{S_e}{S_y} = \frac{35,000}{42,000} = \frac{5}{6}$$

then

$$8p' = (1 - p)(3p') + S_e = \frac{1}{6}(3p') + 35,000$$

or

$$p' = 4667 \text{ psi}$$

For the *distortion energy theory*, eq. (4-16) will be used with $S_3' = S_3'' = 0$, or

$$\sqrt{(S_1')^2 - S_1'S_2' + (S_2')^2} - (1 - p)\sqrt{(S_1'')^2 - S_1''S_2'' + (S_2'')^2} = S_e$$

Placing the values of S_1', S_1'', S_2', and S_2'' in this equation,

$$\sqrt{64(p')^2 - 32(p')^2 + 16(p')^2} - (1 - p)\sqrt{9(p')^2 - 4.5(p')^2 + 2.25(p')^2} = S_e$$

or

$$6.93p' - \left(1 - \frac{5}{6}\right)2.6p' = 35,000$$

and

$$p' = 5380 \text{ psi}$$

NUMERICAL EXAMPLE.   A circular shaft 2 in. in diameter is subjected to a static bending moment of 8000 in. lb.   What is the value of the maximum twisting moment that varies from a value of 0 to T' required to produce fracture in 10^7 cycles?   The tensile yield strength S_{yp} of the material is 90,000 psi and the fatigue strength S_e for 10^7 cycles is 60,000 psi.   Solve by both the maximum shear and the distortion energy theories.

SOLUTION.   The stress components for a circular shaft subjected to fluctuating torsion and static bending are

$$S_x = S_x' = S_x'' = \frac{Mc}{I} = \frac{Mr}{\pi r^4/4} = \left(\frac{4}{\pi}\right)8000 = 1.02 \times 10^4 \text{ in. lb.}$$

$$S_{xy}' = \frac{T'r}{J} = \frac{T'r}{\pi r^4/2} = 0.638T'$$

$$S_{xy}'' = \frac{T''r}{J} = \frac{T''r}{\pi r^4/2} = 0.319T'$$

By the maximum shear theory the third of eqs. (4-15a) governs since the principal stresses are of opposite sign. That is, for $S_y' = S_y'' = 0$ and $p = \frac{2}{3}$,

$$\sqrt{[(1 - p)S_x'' - S_x']^2 + 4[(1 - p)S_{xy}'' - S_{xy}']^2} = S_e$$

or $\sqrt{[(1 - \frac{2}{3})(1.02 \times 10^4) - 1.02 \times 10^4]^2}$

$$\overline{+ 4[(1 - \frac{2}{3})(0.319T') - 0.638T']^2} = 60,000$$

and $\qquad T' = \sqrt{\dfrac{35.54 \times 10^8}{1.132}} = 55,900$ in. lb.

By the *distortion energy theory*, eq. (4-16a) applies when $S_y' = S_y'' = 0$, or

$$\sqrt{(S_x')^2 + 3(S_{xy}')^2} - (1 - p)\sqrt{(S_x'')^2 + 3(S_{xy}'')^2} = S_e$$

or $\qquad \sqrt{1.04 \times 10^8 + 1.22(T')^2} - \frac{1}{3}\sqrt{1.04 \times 10^8 + 0.305(T')^2} = 60,000$

and $\qquad T' = 6.52 \times 10^4 \quad$ or $\quad 4.53 \times 10^4$ in. lb.

The larger value $T' = 65,200$ in. lb. governs, since by substituting this value of T' in eq. (4-16a) and solving for S_e, the correct value of $S_e = 60,000$ psi is obtained. The smaller value of T' gives a value of S_e which is meaningless.

Design Stresses for Combined Fatigue Stresses. The limited amount of test data available indicate that the distortion energy theory gives a good approximation for the case of biaxial stresses. The design stress relation using the distortion energy theory can be obtained from eq. (4-16) if $S_3' = S_3'' = 0$ and S_e is replaced by the allowable or design value $(S_e/S_y)(S_y/N) = pS_w$, where S_w is the static design stress. That is, the relation for the allowable principal biaxial fatigue stresses by the distortion energy theory becomes

$$\sqrt{(S_1')^2 - S_1'S_2' + (S_2')^2} - (1 - p)\sqrt{(S_1'')^2 - S_1''S_2'' + (S_2'')^2} = pS_w$$
$$(4\text{-}17)$$

Thus, for known values of S_1'', S_2', S_2'', p, and S_w, the value of S_1', as calculated by eq. (4-17), is the allowable value for this stress.

Equation (4-16a) can be used to define allowable stress values in terms of the stress components S_x, S_y, and S_{xy}, provided S_e is replaced by $(S_e/S_y)(S_y/N) = pS_w$. That is,

$$\sqrt{(S_x')^2 - S_x'S_y' + (S_y')^2 + 3(S_{xy}')^2} -$$
$$(1 - p)\sqrt{(S_x'')^2 - S_x''S_y'' + (S_y'')^2 + 3(S_{xy}'')^2} = pS_w \quad (4\text{-}18)$$

Equation (4-18) assumes that the factors of safety $N_y = N_e = N$, since it is based on S_e being replaced by $pS_w = (S_e/S_y)(S_y/N)$. The application of the foregoing design relations will be illustrated in the following examples.

NUMERICAL EXAMPLE. *Tube Subjected to Internal Pressure and Fluctuating Axial Loading.* A thin-walled tube has an internal diameter of 4 in. It is subjected to a static internal pressure of 1000 psi and a fluctuating axial tensile load that varies from 10,000 to 60,000 lb. Determine the required wall thickness if $S_y = 50{,}000$ psi, $S_e = 25{,}000$ psi, and $S_w = 20{,}000$ psi. Solve by the distortion energy theory.

SOLUTION. The axial stress S_1 in the tube is the sum of the stress produced by the internal pressure plus that produced by the axial load, or

$$S_1 = \frac{p\pi d^2/4}{t\pi d} + \frac{P}{t\pi d}$$

or

$$S_1 = \frac{pd}{4t} + \frac{P}{t\pi d}$$

The lateral stress S_2 is $S_2 = \frac{pd}{2t}$. Then the maximum and mean principal stresses are

$$S_1' = \frac{pd}{4t} + \frac{P'}{t\pi d}, \qquad S_2' = \frac{pd}{2t}$$

$$S_1'' = \frac{pd}{4t} + \frac{P''}{t\pi d}, \qquad S_2'' = \frac{pd}{2t}$$

Placing these values in eq. (4-17),

$$\sqrt{\left(\frac{pd}{4t} + \frac{P'}{t\pi d}\right)^2 - \left(\frac{pd}{4t} + \frac{P'}{t\pi d}\right)\left(\frac{pd}{2t}\right) + \left(\frac{pd}{2t}\right)^2}$$

$$- (1-p)\sqrt{\left(\frac{pd}{4t} + \frac{P''}{t\pi d}\right)^2 - \left(\frac{pd}{4t} + \frac{P''}{t\pi d}\right)\left(\frac{pd}{2t}\right) + \left(\frac{pd}{2t}\right)^2} = pS_w$$

or

$$\frac{1}{t}[\sqrt{(5760)^2 - (5760)(2000) + (2000)^2}$$

$$- \frac{1}{2}\sqrt{(3780)^2 - (3780) \times (2000) + (2000)^2}] = 10{,}000$$

and

$$t = \frac{1000(\sqrt{25.68} - \frac{1}{2}\sqrt{10.74})}{10{,}000} = 0.34 \text{ in.}$$

NUMERICAL EXAMPLE. *Circular Shaft Subjected to Twisting and Axial Loading.* A circular shaft 4 in. in diameter is subjected to a fluctuating twisting moment that varies from 4000 to 20,000 in. lb. Determine the allowable value of the axial static tensile load that can be applied to the shaft. The tensile yield strength S_{yp} of the material is 90,000 psi and the fatigue strength S_e is 60,000 psi. Solve by the distortion energy theory and use a working stress $S_w = 40{,}000$ psi.

SOLUTION. The maximum and mean stress components are

$$S_x' = S_x'' = \frac{P}{\pi r^2} = \frac{P}{\pi \times 2^2} = 0.0795P$$

$$S_{xy}' = \frac{T'r}{J} = \frac{T'r}{\pi r^4/2} = \frac{20{,}000 \times 2}{\pi \times 2^4/2} = 1590 \text{ psi}$$

$$S_{xy}'' = \frac{T''r}{J} = \frac{T''r}{\pi r^4/2} = \frac{12{,}000 \times 2}{\pi \times 2^4/2} = 955 \text{ psi}$$

Substituting these stress values in eq. (4-18) for the distortion energy theory and noting that $p = S_e/S_y = 2/3$ and $S_w = 40{,}000$ psi,

$$\sqrt{(0.0795P)^2 + 3 \times 1590^2} - \tfrac{1}{3}\sqrt{(0.0795P)^2 + 3 \times 955^2} = 40{,}000 \times \tfrac{2}{3}$$

and
$$P = 5.00 \times 10^5 \quad \text{or} \quad 2.48 \times 10^5 \text{ lb.}$$

The larger value of $P = 5.00 \times 10^5$ lb. governs, since this value when substituted in eq. (4-18) gives the correct magnitude of S_w.

4-7. FACTORS AFFECTING THE FATIGUE STRENGTH

There are many factors other than the states of stress discussed in the foregoing paragraphs that influence the value of the fatigue strength. Some of these factors are:

Chemical Composition. Test results do not show that there is any chemical ingredient or alloying element that gives great fatigue strength directly to a metal. A marked indirect beneficial effect is provided, however, by certain alloying elements. For example, the fatigue properties of steel are indirectly improved by the addition of nickel, chromium, vanadium, molybdenum, manganese, and silicon. This indirect effect is accomplished by lessening the rate at which crystalline changes take place in steel. In this way the time and temperature tolerances for heat treatment are widened.

Surface Treatment. Various methods are used to improve the surface properties of a part, including carburizing, nitriding, cold working, shot-peening, and localized heat treatment by flame or by induction heating. For example, surface cold-rolling of railway axles at the press-fit was found in one investigation to double the fatigue strength. A strength increase of 30 per cent by surface cold-rolling of plain specimens has been reported. By strengthening the surface of a structural or machine part its strength in direct tension-compression is usually increased slightly, while the strength in bending or torsion is appreciably increased. For bending or torsion, the largest percentage of the higher stresses are carried by the surface and, hence, with surface treatment, improvement is made where it is most needed.

Localized Stresses. Localized stresses may have an appreciable effect on the fatigue strength. These stresses are produced in various ways, including rough surface finish, internal nonhomogeneity such as flaws in the material, and irregularities of outline. The influence of surface conditions on the fatigue strength is indicated in Fig. 4-11.[18] For example, when a material with a tensile strength of 160,000 psi

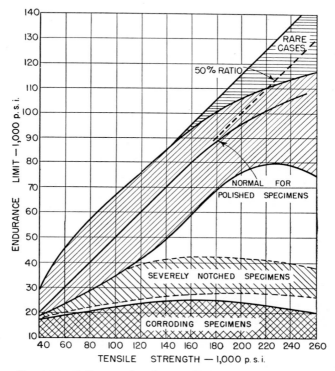

Fig. 4-11.   Influence of surface condition on fatigue strength. (Reproduced by permission from "Prevention of the Failure of Metals Under Repeated Stress" by Battelle Memorial Institute Staff; published by John Wiley and Sons.)

[18] Staff of the Battelle Memorial Institute, *Prevention of the Failure of Metals under Repeated Stress*, John Wiley & Sons, Inc., New York, 1946.

is used, the average endurance limit is about 80,000 psi for polished specimens and about 35,000 psi for notched specimens.

Methods of Fabrication. The method of fabrication influences the fatigue strength in producing both internal and external changes in the material. The fatigue strengths of materials with ground, machined, hot-rolled, or forged surfaces are quite different. The influence of surface finish is indicated in Fig. 4-12. For a steel with a tensile strength of 200,000 psi, Fig. 4-12 shows that the endurance strength for a ground surface is about 85,000 psi, while for a hot-rolled surface it is only about 25,000 psi.

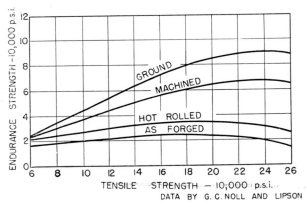

Fig. 4-12. Influence of surface finish on fatigue strength of steel. Unnotched specimens in reversed bending. (Courtesy Addison-Wesley Press.)

Stress Concentration. The strength reduction factors for members subjected to fatigue stresses have been found to be different from those for static loads. In some cases, only theoretical stress concentration factors can be obtained. An empirical equation has been proposed[19] for calculating the fatigue strength reduction factor k_f based on the "notch sensitivity" and theoretical static stress concentration factor. That is,

$$k_f = 1 + q(k_t - 1) \tag{4-19}$$

where q = the sensitivity index of the material, called the "notch

---

[19] R. E. Peterson and A. M. Wahl, "Two- and Three-Dimensional Cases of Stress Concentration and Comparison with Fatigue Tests," *A.S.M.E. Applied Mechanics Journal*, 1936, Vol. 58, p. A-15.

sensitivity," and k_t = the geometric (theoretical) or static stress concentration factor equal to

$$\frac{\text{maximum stress at the section}}{\text{average stress for the section based on net area}}$$

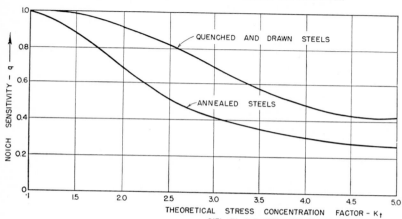

NOTE: CURVES SHOWN ARE AVERAGE CURVES FOR VEE NOTCH TRANSVERSE HOLES, CIRCULAR FILLETS, AND SEMICIRCULAR GROOVES

(a) NOTCH SENSITIVITY OF STEELS

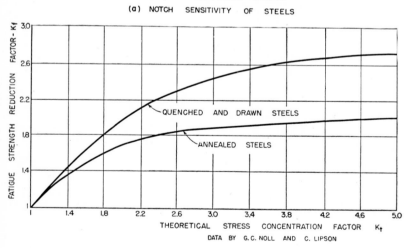

DATA BY G. C. NOLL AND C. LIPSON

(b) RELATION BETWEEN FATIGUE, STRENGTH REDUCTION FACTOR, AND THEORETICAL STRESS CONCENTRATION FACTOR

Fig. 4-13.   (Courtesy Addison-Wesley Press.)

Coarse-grained steels have low values of q, while fine-grained steels have a high value of q. Figure 4-13(a) gives the empirical relationship between q and k_t. That is, Fig. 4-13(a) can be used to determine q. With q known, k_f can be determined from eq. (4-19) or from Fig. 4-13(b) which gives the relation between k_f and k_t.

Rate of Application of Stress. In general, test results show that variation of speed over a range of 200 to 500 cycles per minute has little effect on the fatigue strength. For higher speeds, however, an increase in the fatigue strength of 15 per cent has been reported.

Effect of Understressing and Overstressing. In selecting a metal to resist repeated stress, the effects of repeated stress below the endurance limit and the occasional stress above the endurance limit are important. For a member subjected to a large number of cycles of stress less than the endurance limit of the original material, the endurance limit of this understressed metal will be found to be greater than that of the unstressed metal. This increase appears to be due to the cold-working during the period of understressing. A few

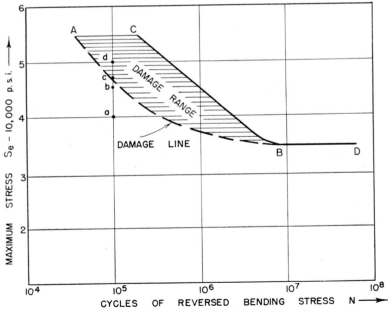

Fig. 4-14.   Determination of probable damage line.

repetitions of stress above the endurance limit give beneficial cold-working without starting a crack. A test that was devised to evaluate the resistance to overstress can be explained by Fig. 4-14. The S-N diagram CBD shown in Fig. 4-14 is obtained in the usual way. Specimens a, b, and c were given a definite number of cycles of stress at different stresses (100,000 cycles at 40,000, 45,000, and 50,000 psi) and removed from the testing machine unfractured. Specimens a and b were then stressed to the endurance limit of the material (36,000 psi) and were found to resist 10^7 cycles of stress without fracture. Apparently the fatigue strengths of the specimens a and b were not lowered by the 100,000 cycles. Specimen d, however, after overstressing at 50,000 psi for 100,000 cycles, fractured under subsequent repeated stressing at 36,000 psi. Evidently the stress that the metal could withstand 100,000 times without reduction of its virgin endurance limit was between 45,000 and 50,000 psi. Estimating this stress at 47,500 psi at point c locates a point on what is called the *probable damage line*. Points similar to point c can be obtained for other values of stress cycles N, and a damage line AB is in this way obtained. The size and shape of the shaded damage area ABC in Fig. 4-14 gives an indication of the resistance of the metal to occasional overstress. A broad area indicates low resistance to overstress, while a narrow area indicates a high resistance.

High and Low Temperatures. Metals subjected to elevated temperatures and fatigue are used in a number of industrial applications, including steam and gas turbines. High temperatures change appreciably the fatigue strength of metals. For example, a wrought aluminum alloy, Alcoa 17-ST showed a decrease of 37 per cent in the fatigue strength at 400° F. and 70 per cent at 500° F., compared to that at room temperature. In some industrial applications, including refrigeration equipment, metals are subjected to fatigue and low temperatures. The fatigue strength is found to increase with decrease in temperature. Other factors influencing the fatigue strength, such as heat treatment, corrosion, variation in amplitude of stress and size of specimen, are discussed in reference (18).

4-8. TYPES OF FATIGUE TEST DATA

The fatigue test results discussed in this chapter have dealt with the material-type test, in which fatigue properties of the material as such are studied.　The factors that influence the results of these tests include:

1. Specimen geometry, including size and shape.
2. Preparation of specimen.
3. Type of testing machine.
4. Testing technique.
5. Type of stress and environment.
6. Speed of testing.

These factors are important in fatigue testing because minor differences may cause appreciable difference in the fatigue strength results. Data from the material-type test is of use in comparing the behavior of different materials and in comparing the effects of various manufacturing practices and processes on the fatigue properties.　These tests are also of use in comparing effects of geometrical factors such as size and shape of notches and of various kinds of surface finishes. Material-type fatigue tests are of value in establishing correlations with other mechanical properties and for checking the quality of different lots of a given material.　The influence of surface treatments such as decarburization, case hardening, shot-peening, plating, and nitriding can also be evaluated by this type of test.　The material-type test on small laboratory specimens, however, cannot in general be applied directly to engineering design in many cases. The reasons that service conditions cannot be predicted quantitatively on the basis of laboratory tests include the differences between actual and assumed loadings, differences between actual and nominal stresses, and differences in the environments of the laboratory versus service conditions.

Structural-type laboratory fatigue tests are sometimes made on such parts as joints, beams, columns, pressure units, bearings, and frames. This type of test is of value when it is used to reveal design or fabrication faults, such as areas of stress concentration.　The structural-type test is also of value in comparing the influence of different materials, designs, or fabricating processes.　Such tests are also useful in developing better design or fabricating procedures.　Structural-type tests may provide a means of predicting service behavior and fatigue life of structural parts.

Service tests of actual complete structures often provide the most satisfactory fatigue test results.　These tests, however, often involve elaborate equipment and the cost of testing complete units may become prohibitive. It should also be realized that the fatigue test results of a service test or structural-type test apply only to that specific design, and the information obtained cannot be used for any other design or modified design.

PROBLEMS

4-1. A circular shaft 4 in. in diameter is subjected to a completely reversed twisting moment. The fatigue strength of the material for complete stress reversal in bending is 42,000 psi at $N = 10^6$ cycles. Determine the twisting moment that will produce fracture in 10^6 cycles. Use a fatigue torsional strength equal to 0.6 the bending fatigue strength.

Ans. 318,000 in. lb.

4-2. What twisting moment can be applied to a shaft with a fillet having a fatigue strength reduction factor of 1.7? The fatigue torsional strength is 24,000 psi and the diameter is 4 in. Use a factor of safety of 3.

4-3. A hollow circular shaft has an outer diameter of 4 in. and an inner diameter of 2 in. The shaft has a fillet with a strength reduction factor of 1.8. The fatigue strength in torsion for complete reversal is 35,000 psi for $N = 10^6$ cycles. What completely reversed twisting moment will produce fracture in 10^6 cycles? What is the allowable torque if the factor of safety is 3?

4-4. A steel cantilever beam is 1 in. wide, 3 in. deep, and 4 ft. long. It is subjected to a completely reversed end-concentrated load. The fatigue strength of the material for complete stress reversal in bending is 50,000 psi for $N = 10^4$ cycles. What is the fluctuating load required to produce fracture in 10^4 cycles?

4-5. A steel cantilever beam is 3 in. wide, 8 in. deep, and 4 ft. long. There is a vertical hole $\frac{1}{4}$ in. in diameter 10 in. from the fixed end. The strength reduction factor produced by this hole is 2.0. Compare the allowable loads with and without the hole. The load is completely reversed and the fatigue strength is 25,000 psi. Use a factor of safety of 3.

Ans. $P_1 = 5550$ lb., $P_2 = 3220$ lb.

4-6. Determine the required diameter of a shaft if it is subjected to a completely reversed bending moment of 2000 ft. lb. The fatigue strength of the material for complete reversal is 40,000 psi. Use a factor of safety of 3.

4-7. A circular shaft has a fillet with a strength reduction factor of 1.5. It is subjected to a completely reversed bending moment of 2000 ft. lb. The allowable fatigue stress is 10,000 psi. Find the shaft diameter.

Ans. $d = 3.32$ in.

4-8. (a) A circular shaft with a 4 in. outside diameter and 2 in. inside diameter is subjected to a completely reversed twisting moment. If the fatigue strength in torsion at $N = 10^5$ cycles is 40,000 psi, determine the fracture torque for 10^5 cycles.

(b) What is the value of the torque in Prob. 4-8(a) if there is a $\frac{1}{8}$-in.-diameter longitudinal hole $1\frac{1}{2}$ in. from the shaft center? The strength reduction factor for the hole is 1.7. Neglect the reduction in cross-sectional area produced by the hole. *Ans.* (a) 472,000 in. lb., (b) 370,000 in. lb.

4-9. What is the allowable reversed bending moment that can be applied to a shaft if the fatigue strength for completely reversed bending is 35,000 psi? The shaft diameter is 4 in. and the factor of safety to be used is 3.

4-10. In a fatigue test of steel under complete stress reversal in bending the following test data were recorded:

Stress (psi)	Cycles to Fracture
92,000	41,000
83,000	128,000
74,000	590,000
67,000	1,620,000
65,000	5,500,000
64,500	8,000,000
64,000	14,000,000
64,100	15,000,000
63,900	specimen did not fracture

Plot the *S-N* semi-log diagram for the foregoing data and obtain the fatigue strengths at $N = 10^5$, $N = 10^6$, and $N = 5 \times 10^6$ cycles.

4-11. A connecting rod of square cross section 2 in. by 2 in. is subjected to a completely reversed bending moment, and a completely reversed axial load of 10,000 lb. The fatigue strength of the material for complete stress reversal and $N = 10^5$ cycles is 50,000 psi. Determine the bending moment value for fracture in 10^5 cycles. Assume that the maximum values occur at the same instant of time.

4-12. (a) A circular rod 2 in. in diameter is subjected to a completely reversed longitudinal load at a distance $\frac{1}{2}$ in. from the center of the rod (Fig. 4-15a). The fatigue strength for complete stress reversal at $N = 10^6$ cycles is 60,000 psi. Determine the load required to fracture the rod in fatigue in 10^6 cycles.

(b) Solve Prob. 4-12(a) if there is a radial hole 8 in. in diameter in the plane of the load and centroidal axis [Fig. 4-15(b)]. The strength reduction factor produced by this hole is 1.5. Neglect the reduction in cross-sectional area resulting from the hole. *Ans.* (a) 62,600 lb., (b) 41,700 lb.

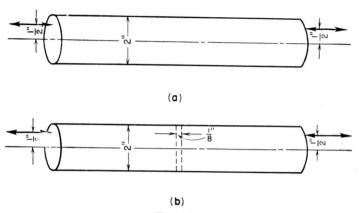

(a)

(b)

Fig. 4-15.

4-13. A threaded steel rod with a 1.5-in. root diameter is subjected to a fluctuating axial tensile load varying from a maximum value of P_{max} to a minimum value of 20,000 lb. The rod material has a tensile yield strength $S_{yp} = 45,000$ psi and a fatigue strength for complete stress reversal $S_e = 40,000$ psi. Determine the value of P_{max} for fracture by fatigue. The fatigue strength reduction factor is 1.5 and the static strength reduction factor is 2.5. Solve using Soderberg's law. *Ans.* 34,100 lb.

4-14. (a) A cantilever beam 10 ft. long is subjected to an end-concentrated load that varies from a value of P to zero. The beam has a section modulus of 42.0 in.^{3}. Use Soderberg's law and determine the value of P, if $S_e = 60,000$ psi and $S_{yp} = 90,000$ psi.

(b) Compare the value obtained in Prob. 4-14(a) with the values obtained using the Goodman modified law and the Gerber law. Use a value of $S_u = 120,000$ psi.

4-15. (a) A member of square cross section 2 in. by 2 in. is subjected to an axial load that fluctuates from a value $P/2$ to P. Determine the allowable value of P if $S_{yp} = 80,000$ psi, $S_e = 60,000$ psi, $N_y = 2$, and $N_e = 3.0$. Solve by Soderberg's law.

(b) Solve Prob. 4-15(a) if the load lies in a plane of symmetry but $\frac{1}{2}$ in. from the neutral axis. *Ans.* (a) 128,000 lb., (b) 51,200 lb.

4-16. A member of circular cross section is subjected to a fluctuating axial load that varies from a value P_{min} to P_{max} and a fluctuating moment that varies from M_{min} to M_{max}. Using Soderberg's law, determine an equation for finding the required diameter. Assume maximum values of stress occur simultaneously.

4-17. A cantilever beam of length L is subjected to plane bending by an end-concentrated load that varies from a maximum value of P_{max} to a minimum value of $P_{min} = \frac{1}{4}P_{max}$. Determine the ratio of the fatigue to static section moduli based on fatigue and static loading. *Given*: $S_e = 40,000$ psi, $S_{yp} = 60,000$ psi, $N_e = 3.0$, and $N_y = 2.0$. Use Soderberg's law.

Ans. $R = 1.47$.

4-18. A circular rotating shaft 4 in. in diameter is subjected to a static twisting moment $T = 10,000$ in. lb. The material has a tensile yield strength of 75,000 psi and a fatigue strength for complete stress reversal of 55,000 psi at $N = 10^6$ cycles. What is the bending moment that will produce fracture in 10^6 cycles? Solve by the distortion energy theory.

4-19. A thin-walled tube 6 in. in diameter and $\frac{1}{4}$ in. wall thickness is closed at the ends and is subjected to a fluctuating internal pressure that varies from a value of 0 to p. The material has a yield stress $S_{yp} = 60,000$ psi and a fatigue strength S_e for 10^5 of 55,000 psi. Determine the value of the pressure p that will produce fracture in 10^5 cycles. Use the distortion energy theory.

Ans. 5550 psi.

4-20. (a) A hub and axle assembly is subjected to a uniform shrink-fit pressure of 5000 psi so that $S_1 = S_2 = -5000$ psi, and a fluctuating bending stress that is completely reversed (Fig. 4-16). By the distortion energy theory what is the value of the bending stress required to produce fracture in 10^6 cycles? The value of $S_{yp} = 50,000$ psi and $S_e = 40,000$ psi for $N = 10^6$ cycles.

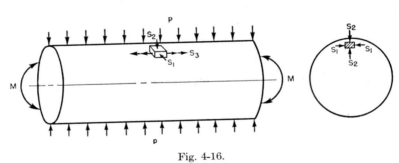

Fig. 4-16.

(b) If the axle in Prob. 4-20(a) has a fillet with a strength reduction factor of 2.0, determine the diameter of the axle for $N_e = N_y = 2$.

4-21. A vertical circular shaft has an internal diameter equal to one-half the external diameter. It is subjected to an axial static tensile load of 50,000 lb. and a fluctuating twisting moment that varies from a value of 10,000 in. lb. to 50,000 in. lb. Determine an equation for finding the diameter. Use values of $S_e = 55,000$ psi, $S_{yp} = 60,000$ psi, $N_y = N_e = 3.0$. Solve by the shear theory.

4-22. A circular shaft is subjected to a twisting moment that varies from a value of 10,000 in. lb. to 50,000 in. lb. and to a fluctuating bending moment that varies from a value 0 to 40,000 in. lb. Determine the required diameter if $S_e = 60,000$ psi, $S_{yp} = 90,000$ psi, and $N_y = N_e = N = 2.0$. Solve by the distortion energy theory. *Ans.* 2.54 in.

4-23. Determine the allowable value of the maximum load P in Fig. 2-11 if the load is fluctuating and the minimum value is zero. The strength $S_e = 65,000$ psi, $S_{yp} = 92,000$ psi, and $N_y = N_e = 2.0$.

BIBLIOGRAPHY

Cazaud, R., *Le Fatigue des Metaux*, Dunod, Paris, 1948.

Freudenthal, A. M., *The Inelastic Behavior of Engineering Materials and Structures*, John Wiley & Sons, Inc., New York, 1950.

Gough, H. J., *The Fatigue of Metals*, Ernest Benn, Ltd., London, 1926.

Jackson, L. R., Grover, H. J., and McMaster, R. C., "Fatigue Properties of Aircraft Materials and Structures," Report OSRD No. 6600, National Defense Research Council, Serial No. M-653, March 1946.

Moore, H. F., and Kommers, J. B., *The Fatigue of Metals*, McGraw-Hill Book Co., Inc., New York, 1927.

Staff of Battelle Memorial Institute, *Prevention of Failure of Metals under Repeated Stress*, John Wiley & Sons, Inc., New York, 1941.

Timoshenko, S., *Strength of Materials*, Part II, D. Van Nostrand Co., Inc., New York, 1941.

Manual on Fatigue Testing, Special Publication No. 91, American Society for Testing Materials, Philadelphia, 1949.

Surface Stressing of Metals, American Society for Metals, 1947.

Symposium on the Failure of Metals by Fatigue, sponsored by the Council for Scientific Research in Australia, Melbourne University Press, 1947.

Chapter 5

Impact Properties

5-1. GENERAL COMMENTS

A load that is suddenly applied to a machine or structure is called an *impact load*. The effect of impact loads differs appreciably from that of static loads because, with a suddenly applied load, both the magnitude of the stresses produced and the resistance properties of the material are affected. Approximate procedures for the determination of stresses in members subjected to impact loads are discussed in Article 5-5. The most important influence of impact loads on the mechanical properties is the reduction in ductility in parts with stress concentration and members subjected to certain combinations of combined stresses.

Two types of impact testing are used to determine the behavior of materials under impact loads. The most common type, made on notched specimens subjected to axial, bending, or torsion loads, will be called *"notched-bar testing."* This type of impact testing is of value in the study of the influence of metallurgical variables. A second type of impact testing, which represents the fundamental type, is used to determine the stress-strain diagrams and mechanical properties for unnotched specimens subjected to impact loads. This latter type of testing will be called *"impact testing."* Before discussing notched-bar testing and impact testing it is desirable to define impact loads more accurately and to indicate the transition from a static to an impact load.

Impact or suddenly applied loads are applied to structures and machines in various ways. Methods by which impact loads are applied include: *rapidly moving loads*, as produced by a locomotive

222

passing over a bridge, *direct impact loads,* as produced by a drop hammer, *sudden application of loads,* as occurs during the explosion stroke in a gasoline engine, and *inertia loads* accompanying high accelerations and producing mechanical shocks.

If the time of application of a load is short compared to the lowest natural period of vibration[1] of the structure or machine, the load is an impact load; whereas if the time of load application is long, the load is considered to be statically applied. For most cases, if the time of load application is less than one-half the fundamental natural period of the structure, the load is definitely considered an impact load. If the time interval is greater than three times the period, the load is considered to be static. The time of loading refers to the time required to increase the load from zero to its maximum value. For dynamic impact loads, the shape of the load-time curve is important, since the impulse, which is equal to the area under the load-time curve, is the significant quantity. On the other hand, for slow loading the shape is not important but the maximum value of the load is significant. The *number of repetitions of the impact load* is of great importance in relation to the fatigue strength. For example, the fatigue strength of a railway car part required to resist many stress cycles of impact stress is of great importance, whereas for a bomb fuse subjected to one impact only, the fatigue strength is of little importance.

5-2. NOTCHED-BAR IMPACT TESTING

Most notched-bar impact tests are made on specimens subjected to bending rather than axial tension. The two main kinds of impact testing machines used in the United States are the Charpy and Izod impact machines. In both these machines an impact load is applied to a specimen by the swinging of a weight from a height h (Fig. 5-1a). The release of the weight W from the height h swings the weight W through the arc of a circle, thereby striking and fracturing the notched specimen and reaching a maximum height h'' after fracture. The energy used in fracturing the specimen is then approximately equal to

$$U_T = Wh - Wh'' \tag{5-1}$$

---

[1] A vibration, in its general sense, is a periodic motion or a motion that repeats itself in all respects after a certain interval of time. This period of time is called the "period of vibration."

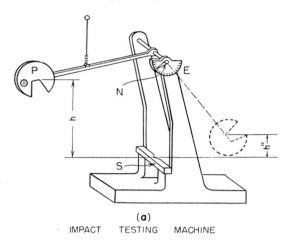

(a)

IMPACT   TESTING   MACHINE

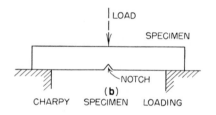

(b)

CHARPY   SPECIMEN   LOADING

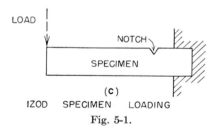

(c)

IZOD   SPECIMEN   LOADING

Fig. 5-1.

where h = the vertical fall of the center of gravity of the pendulum weight W, and h'' = the vertical rise of the center of gravity of the pendulum weight W.

The value of U_T is usually expressed in inch pounds and represents the energy for fracture.   This value of the energy is sometimes called the *impact toughness*.

The Charpy and Izod machines differ mainly in the type of specimen used, as illustrated in Fig. 5-2. The *Charpy impact specimen*
is supported at the ends and struck in the middle, as shown in
Fig. 5-1(b). The specimen is a bar of rectangular cross section,
notched on one side at the mid-point of its length. The blow is
struck on the side opposite the notch at a maximum velocity of
17.4 ft. per sec. The *Izod impact specimen* is supported as a cantilever
beam, as shown in Fig. 5-1(c). For both types of specimens the
notch is placed on the tension side of the beam to insure fracture of
the material. In the operation of the test, using either type of
specimen, the pendulum *P* on dropping and rupturing the specimen
pushes an indicator *N* around a scale *E* as it swings through the

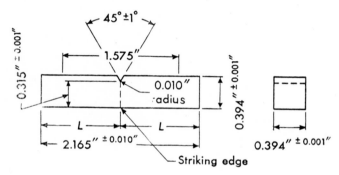

Fig. 5-2(a).   Charpy type specimen.

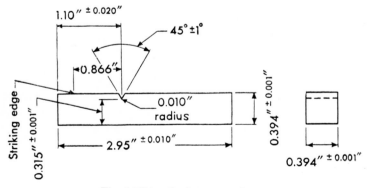

Fig. 5-2(b).   Izod type specimen.

Fig. 5-2(c). Typical brittle and ductile fractures for charpy notched bar impact specimens. (Courtesy R. E. Peterson, *Handbook on Experimental Stress Analysis*, John Wiley and Sons.)

specimen to a height h'' as shown in Fig. 5-1(a). The indicator E does not swing back as the pendulum swings back but remains at the highest point of swing corresponding to h''. Both the Charpy and Izod impact testing machines are sometimes supplied with adapters to determine the energy required to fracture an unnotched tension specimen. In these tests the specimen is secured to the back edge of the pendulum. When the pendulum weight falls, the specimen strikes against two extended anvils, thereby rupturing the specimen as the pendulum passes between the two anvils.

One of the reasons for using a notched specimen is that without the notch and accompanying stress concentration, specimens of ductile materials under impact bending would not fracture. The type of fractured surfaces obtained in notched-bar impact tests is shown in Fig. 5-2(c). There are other types of impact tests and testing machines than the pendulum type discussed. In these machines the impact loads are applied by a dropping weight or a rotating flywheel.

Factors Affecting Test Results. Values obtained for the impact toughness are influenced by a number of factors. The results will vary with different machines because of the difference in energy absorbed by the machine itself. The striking velocity of the pendulum will modify the test values obtained if these velocities are high and above a critical velocity value. The shape and size of the notch are found to influence the impact toughness values. The shape of the bottom of the notch has a marked influence on the test value. The toughness value is found to decrease with sharpness of notch. As discussed in Chapter 6, temperature variation has a much greater effect on the notched-bar impact values than on the static strength.

Notched-bar impact testing is of little value to the design engineer. This is true because at the notch of the specimens used there is a combined state of stress not necessarily present in the member to be designed. The main use of the notched-bar impact test is in the determination of the influence of metallurgical treatments. This usefulness lies in the fact that notched-bar impact values vary considerably with small changes in metallurgical processes such as heat treatments.

Brittleness, or reduced ductility of materials, varies under impact loads depending upon a number of test variables. The presence of a notch in the specimen produces a stress concentration and a combined state of stress that increases the brittleness. The increase in the brittleness is the quantity that is sensitive to metallurgical variables. In addition to studying the influence of heat treatments on the properties of metals, the notched-bar impact test is also of value in studying the influence of alloying elements on the mechanical properties and in evaluating the effect of mechanical treatments of metals.

5-3. IMPACT TESTING

Impact tests, as distinguished from notched-bar impact tests, are made under tension, compression, torsion, or bending loads. For brittle materials, the bending impact test is the most common. In bending, compression, or tension impact tests, the pendulum-type machine used for the notched-bar tests may be used. The load may also be applied by a dropping weight or rotating flywheel. Some tests are made so that the specimen is ruptured by a single blow, while others are fractured by repeated blows. In the repeated-blow test, the blow may be of the same value each time or it may be varied by increasing the height of drop of the weight. A standard flexural impact test for wood is of the increment-drop type where the load is increased in increments and the height of drop at which failure occurs is taken as the measure of toughness. This test has been found useful in applications of wood to aircraft construction. Impact tests in torsion have been found useful as a sensitive method for investigating the optimum heat treatment for products such as drills, taps, and rock-drill parts. Toughness of rock for road-building purposes is determined by an increment-drop compression impact test. Impact tests are also used as an acceptance test for a number of metal products, including rails, car wheels, and axles.

The influence of impact loading on the mechanical properties of materials varies, depending upon the material. Some of the earlier investigations on impact strength were summarized by Davidenkoff.[2] These results show that both the impact yield and ultimate strengths of metals are greater than their static values. These results showed increases in yield strength from 10 to 90 per cent, and increases in the ultimate strength from 2 to 80 per cent. Tension-impact tests were made by Clark and Datwyler[3] on various materials. In these tests, force-elongation diagrams in tension were obtained with an Olsen Izod impact machine using a maximum velocity of 11.3 ft. per sec. A dynamometer measured the force during impact by noting the change in electrical resistance of a wire wrapped around the test bar. The results shown in Table 5-1 give the ratio of the dynamic to the static values for yield strength, maximum load, elongation, reduction in area, and energy required to rupture. The table shows that the percentage increases in the impact yield strengths were found to be greater than the increases in the impact ultimate

[2] N. N. Davidenkoff, "Allowable Working Stresses under Impact," *Trans. A.S.M.E.*, 1934, Vol. 56, pp. 97–108.

[3] D. S. Clark and G. Datwyler, "Stress-Strain Relations under Tension and Impact Loading," *Proc. A.S.T.M.*, 1938, Vol. 38, pp. 98–111.

Table 5-1

Comparison of Strengths and Ductility under Impact and Static Loads

Material	Ratio of impact to static value for:				
	Yield point	Maximum load	Elongation	Reduction of area	Energy
S.A.E. No. 6140*...	....	1.020	2.205	2.940	2.865
S.A.E. No. 1015**..	1.328	1.285	1.418	1.055	1.376
S.A.E. No. 1018....	1.995	1.397	0.992	0.946	0.946
18-8 Alloy.........	1.224	1.212	0.682	0.782	0.600
Duralumin 17S-T...	1.294	1.094	1.000	1.035	0.885
Brass**............	1.387	1.142	1.163	1.136	1.203
Aluminum.........	1.522	1.323	1.628	1.093	1.627
Copper............	1.433	1.390	1.527	0.986	1.597

* Oil-quenched from 1620° F.
** Cold-rolled.

strengths. On the other hand, the elongation, reduction in area, and energy to rupture were either greater or less under dynamic loading than under static loading.

The influence of speed of loading or strain rate on the mechanical properties in tension has been investigated for various metals by Manjoine.[4] In this investigation, tests were made at various temperatures between room temperature and 1000° C. and at rates of strain ranging from 10^{-6} to 10^3 in. per in. per sec. The speed of the conventional tensile test is about 10^{-3} in. per in. per sec.

Figure 5-3(a) shows the stress-strain curves for mild steel at room temperature and illustrates the influence of speed of testing on the shape of the stress-strain curve. For high strain rates the increase in the yield stress with increase in strain rates is best shown by Fig. 5-3(b), which gives the variation in the yield stress, ultimate stress, and total elongation as a function of the strain rate. The elongation increases up to the conventional strain rate of 10^{-3} and remains practically constant for the higher rates. Figure 5-3(b) also shows the variation of the ratio of yield stress to ultimate stress with the strain rate. This stress ratio increases, varying from a

[4] M. J. Manjoine, "Influence of Strain and Temperature on Yield Stresses of Mild Steel," *Jour. App. Mech., Trans. A.S.M.E.*, 1944, Vol. 66, pp. A-211–A-218. See also, *Proc. A.S.T.M.*, 1940, Part I, Vol. 40, pp. 822-837; and Parts II and III, *Jour. App. Mech., Trans. A.S.M.E.*, Vol. 63, pp. A-77–A-91.

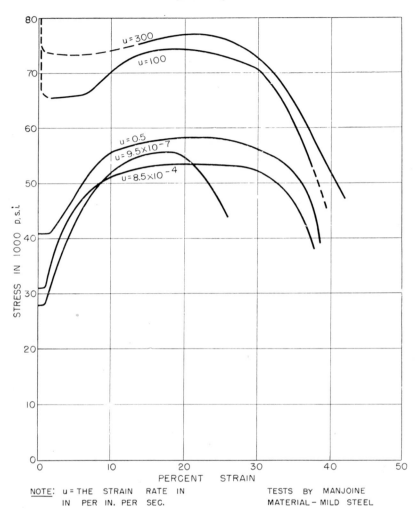

NOTE: u = THE STRAIN RATE IN
IN PER IN. PER SEC.

TESTS BY MANJOINE
MATERIAL – MILD STEEL

(a) INFLUENCE ON STRESS - STRAIN CURVES

Fig. 5-3.　Effect of strain rate on properties in tension.　(Courtesy A.S.M.E.)

value of 0.58 at the conventional strain rate of 10^{-3} to 0.95 at the highest rate.

Of all the properties shown in Fig. 5-3(b), the yield stress is the most responsive to change in strain rate.　From a designer's point

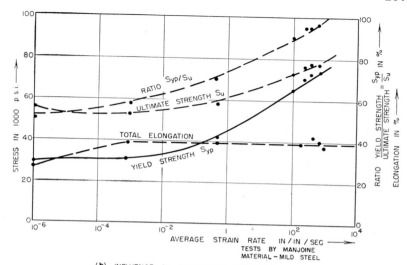

(**b**) INFLUENCE ON MECHANICAL PROPERTIES

Fig. 5-3 (Cont'd).   Effect of strain rate on properties in tension.
(Courtesy A.S.M.E.)

of view this fact is the most important.   Fortunately the change in
yield stress is an increase.   This increase in yield stress with increase
in strain rate cannot be taken advantage of quantitatively in design,
because it is seldom possible to determine the actual strain rate
expected in a given design problem.

From Fig. 5-3(b) it is seen that the stress ratio S_y/S_u is nearly
equal to unity for high strain rates.   This result indicates that for
very great strain rates, mild steel might be expected to behave elas-
tically almost to the ultimate stress.   For metals and alloys other
than mild steel, the ultimate stress was found to increase with higher
strain rates.[4]

5-4. DESIGN IMPACT STRESSES

The increase in yield and ultimate strengths in tension with increasing
strain rates would seem to indicate that an increase in the design
stress for impact loading might be permitted over the values used
for static loading.   There are several considerations, however, that
do not justify this conclusion.   One factor previously mentioned is
that it is difficult to determine the strain rates in an actual application, so that the amount of increase in yield stress or design stress

cannot be determined. Another factor not justifying an increase in design stress is that overloading beyond the yield stress under impact loading is more serious than for static loading, since permanent deformations, produced at the first impact, may increase with continued impact loads. Furthermore, the design load values under impact can be less accurately determined than for static loads. The methods of stress analysis in the case of impact loading involve, in many cases, greater approximations than for static loads. For these reasons it does not seem justified to take advantage of the higher strengths under impact loads. It is recommended, therefore, that the design stresses selected for impact loads be the same as for static loads.

Before the design of members subjected to impact loads can be discussed it will be necessary first to determine expressions for the stresses under various types of loading, as explained in Article 5-5.

5-5. IMPACT STRESSES IN MEMBERS SUBJECTED TO SIMPLE TENSION, BENDING, AND TORSION

Impact Tensile Stresses. A prismatic bar subjected to impact tensile stresses is illustrated in Fig. 5-4. The tensile impact stress is produced in the bar AB by the weight W falling from a height h and striking the flange F with a velocity of $v = \sqrt{2gh}$. An approximate determination of the stresses can be made if the weights of the bar and flange are considered small compared to the weight W and provided it is assumed that the impact is perfectly elastic so that there is no loss in energy during impact. After W strikes the flange the bar elongates and the velocity of the weight will decrease to zero, at which stage of loading the stress in the bar is a maximum. After reaching this position the weight W accelerates upward until it attains its original striking velocity v, but in the opposite direction. At this stage of loading the weight leaves the flange, and the bar becomes unstressed. It is of major interest, however, to determine the maximum stress or the stress when the weight is in its lowest

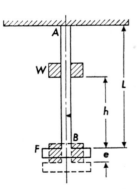

Fig. 5-4. Prismatic bar subjected to a tensile impact load.

position. The magnitude of this stress will be determined on the assumption that the total external work done by W is transformed to energy of strain in the bar. If e is the maximum total elongation of the bar, the external work done by W is $W(h + e)$.

The total internal work or strain energy is equal to the strain energy per unit volume times the volume of the member, or $(S^2AL)/(2E)$, where S is the maximum stress in the bar. That is,

$$W(h + e) = \frac{S^2}{2E} AL \tag{5-2}$$

To determine the stress by eq. (5-2), the value of the total strain $e = \epsilon L = SL/E$ is substituted in eq. (5-2). Then eq. (5-2) becomes a quadratic equation that can be solved for S. The value of the maximum stress S becomes

$$S = \frac{W}{A}\left[1 + \sqrt{1 + 2h\left(\frac{AE}{WL}\right)}\right] \tag{5-3}$$

If the value of the total elongation is required, the value of S in eq. (5-2) can be replaced by $S = \epsilon E = eE/L$, and the resulting quadratic equation solved for e. This gives a total elongation e of magnitude,

$$e = \frac{WL}{AE}\left[1 + \sqrt{1 + 2h\left(\frac{AE}{WL}\right)}\right] \tag{5-4}$$

Equations (5-3) and (5-4) completely define the maximum stress and elongation of the bar in terms of the dimensions A and L, height of drop h of the weight W, and modulus E of the material.

NUMERICAL EXAMPLE. A prismatic bar as shown in Fig. 5-4 is made of steel with a modulus of elasticity $E = 30 \times 10^6$ psi and an impact yield strength of 42,000 psi. The bar is circular in cross section with the diameter $d = 1$ in. and length $L = 4$ ft. It is subjected to an impact load by a weight W dropped from a height $h = 3$ ft. Find (a) the elongation of the bar required to produce yielding and (b) the value of W required to produce yielding.

SOLUTION. *Strain Energy Method.* For a stress of 42,000 psi the elongation of the bar is, by Hooke's law,

$$e = \epsilon L = \frac{S}{E} L = \left(\frac{42,000}{30 \times 10^6}\right) 48 = 0.067 \text{ in.}$$

The external work is equal to the internal strain energy, or

$$W(h + e) = \frac{S^2}{2E} AL$$

or $\quad W(36 + 0.067) = \frac{(42,000)^2}{2 \times 30 \times 10^6} \left(\frac{\pi \times 1^2}{4} \times 48 \right) = 1110$

and $\qquad\qquad W = 30.9 \text{ lb.}$

ALTERNATE SOLUTION. *Equivalent Static Load Method.* The elongation is obtained by Hooke's law as in the preceding solution. The equivalent static load method will be considered to determine W, since it is shorter than the strain energy method in problems where the stresses are not uniform throughout the member, as in torsion and bending of bars.

By the equivalent static load method the member in Fig. 5-4 will be assumed to be subjected to a gradually applied static load P, so that the total elongation and stress in the bar are the same as the values produced by the impact load W. These two loadings are equivalent, since equal work is done in each case. That is,

$$W(h + e) = \frac{Pe}{2}$$

From this equation, since $E = S/\epsilon = SL/e$, or $e = SL/E$ and $P = SA$,

$$W \left(h + \frac{SL}{E} \right) = \left(\frac{SA}{2} \right) \left(\frac{SL}{E} \right) = \frac{S^2 AL}{2E}$$

or $\quad W \left(36 + \frac{42,000 \times 48}{30 \times 10^6} \right) = \frac{42,000^2 \times \pi \times 1^2 \times 48}{2 \times 30 \times 10^6 \times 4}$

and $\qquad\qquad W = 30.9 \text{ lb.}$

Two special cases will next be considered—Case 1 in which the height of drop h is large compared to the deformation e, and Case 2, the other extreme, in which h is zero.

CASE 1: *Height of drop h large compared to e.*

Noting that $WL/(AE) = e_s =$ the elongation of the bar if W were gradually applied, eq. (5-3) and (5-4) can then be written

$$S = \frac{W}{A} \left(1 + \sqrt{1 + \frac{2h}{e_s}} \right) \qquad (5\text{-}5)$$

$$e = e_s \left(1 + \sqrt{1 + \frac{2h}{e_s}} \right) \qquad (5\text{-}6)$$

For the case where the elongation of the bar is small compared to the height of drop h, the magnitude $2h/e_s$ becomes large compared to one, and the second term in eq. (5-5) can be written

$$S = \frac{W}{A}\sqrt{\frac{2h}{e_s}} = \sqrt{\left(\frac{W^2}{A^2}\right)2h\left(\frac{AE}{WL}\right)}$$

or $$S = \sqrt{\left(\frac{2E}{AL}\right)Wh} \qquad (5\text{-}7)$$

From dynamics, $v^2 = 2gh$, where v = the velocity of the weight after a height of drop h, and g is the acceleration of gravity. Placing $h = v^2/(2g)$ in eq. (5-7), an alternate form for eq. (5-7) is

$$S = \sqrt{\left(\frac{2E}{AL}\right)\left(\frac{Wv^2}{2g}\right)} \qquad (5\text{-}8)$$

An examination of eq. (5-7) reveals a very important difference between static and impact loading. In static loading the tensile stress is proportional to the load and indirectly proportional to the area. For impact loading, eq. (5-7) shows that the stress is proportional to the square roots of W, E, and h, and indirectly proportional to the square roots of A and L. That is, the impact stress is now dependent upon the modulus of elasticity E and the volume of the member AL. In other words, the stress can be reduced not only by increasing the area, as in the case of static loading, but also by increasing the length of the bar or by using a material with a smaller value of the modulus of elasticity.

CASE 2: *Height of drop $h = 0$.*

When $h = 0$, or when W is dropped suddenly on the support without initial velocity, the elongation of the bar becomes, from eq. (5-4),

$$e = 2\frac{WL}{AE} = 2e_s \qquad (5\text{-}9)$$

By Hooke's law the corresponding stress in the bar is

$$S = \epsilon E = \frac{eE}{L} = \frac{2e_sE}{L} = 2S_{st} \qquad (5\text{-}10)$$

where $S_{st} = e_sE/L$ = the stress if W were gradually applied. Equation (5-10) shows that a suddenly applied load dropped from a height $h = 0$ onto the flange produces a stress equal to twice the stress produced by the same load gradually applied.

It is of interest to relate the impact stress and strain to the natural frequency of vibration of the bar. A consideration of the natural frequency of vibration of the bar f_n shows that it can be expressed in terms of the elongation e_s,[5] or

$$f_n = 3.13\sqrt{\frac{1}{e_s}} \tag{5-11}$$

Placing the value of e_s from eq. (5-11) in eq. (5-6),

$$e = e_s(1 + \sqrt{1 + 0.204f_n^2h}) \tag{5-12}$$

The magnification factor in the brackets of eq. (5-12) depends both on the height of drop of the weight W and the natural frequency of vibration of the bar. Hooke's law will be assumed to determine the maximum stress produced in the bar.

If the weight of the bar is considered, it can be shown that the stress produced is[6]

$$S = \frac{Ee_s}{L}\left\{1 + \sqrt{1 + \left(\frac{2h}{e_s}\right)\left[\frac{1}{1 + (qL/3W)}\right]}\right\} \tag{5-13}$$

where q is the weight of the bar per unit length.

The stress as determined by eq. (5-13) is a good approximation provided the weight of the bar is small compared to W. If this is not the case, the longitudinal vibrations of the bar must be considered.

This analysis also applies for the case in which the weight W is attached to the flange and is then given a sudden downward velocity v, the bar being initially unstressed. Then in eq. (5-5), $h = v^2/(2g)$ and

$$S = \frac{Ee_s}{L}\left[1 + \sqrt{1 + \frac{v_2}{e_sg}}\right] \tag{5-14}$$

The *time of contact between the weight and flange*, in the case where the weight is dropped from a height h, can be calculated if it is assumed that h is greater than e_s. The weight strikes the flange and the system goes through approximately one-half a cycle of free vibration before the weight becomes clear again from the flange. Then the time of contact is approximately equal to one-half the natural period of vibration or, by eq. (5-11), the time of contact in seconds is

$$t = \frac{1}{2f_n} = 0.160\sqrt{e_s} \tag{5-15}$$

The foregoing equations for calculating the stress are adequate provided the stresses remain below the proportional limit. Beyond this stress value

[5] See, for example, J. P. DenHartog, *Mechanical Vibrations*, McGraw-Hill Book Co., Inc., New York, 1947.

[6] See S. Timoshenko, *Strength of Materials*, D. Van Nostrand Co., Inc., 1942, Part I.

the problem becomes more complicated, since the elongation of the bar is no longer proportional to the stress. If the stress-strain curve under static load is assumed for impact loads, then fracture of the bar will occur when the external work done $W(h + e)$ equals the internal strain energy. This strain energy is approximately equal to the volume of the bar multiplied by the strain energy per unit volume, or AL times the area under the stress-strain curve to rupture. The area under the stress-strain curve to rupture is approximately equal to $(S_{yp} + S_u)\epsilon_f/2$, where ϵ_f is the strain at fracture. That is,

$$W(h + e) = \frac{S_{yp} + S_u}{2} \epsilon_f AL$$

or

$$W = \frac{S_{yp} + S_u}{2(h + e)} \epsilon_f AL$$

But since the average value of e is $\epsilon_f L$,

$$W = \frac{(S_{yp} + S_u)(\epsilon_f AL)}{2(h + \epsilon_f L)} \tag{5-16}$$

Equation (5-16) gives a rough approximation for the load W required to fracture a prismatic bar in tension when it is dropped from a height h.

NUMERICAL EXAMPLE. *Comparison of the Impact Load Required to Produce Yielding in Two Bars with Different Moduli of Elasticity.* Two prismatic bars are as shown in Fig. 5-4. They are made of a steel alloy having a value of $E = 30 \times 10^6$ psi and an aluminum alloy with $E = 10.6 \times 10^6$ psi. The yield stresses for both materials are equal to 40,000 psi and the cross-sectional areas for both bars are equal to 2 sq. in. The weights in each case are dropped from a height of 10 in. The length of the steel and aluminum bars is 20 in. Compare the loads W required to produce yielding.

SOLUTION. Equating the external work to the internal strain energy, the weight required to produce yielding in the steel bar is defined by the equation

$$W(h + e) = \frac{S^2}{2E} AL$$

For the *steel bar*, $e = \epsilon L = SL/E = 40,000 \times 20/(30 \times 10^6) = 0.0267$ in., and

$$W(10 + 0.0267) = \left(\frac{40,000^2}{2 \times 30 \times 10^6} \right) (2 \times 20)$$

or

$$W = \frac{1065}{10.0267} = 106.5 \text{ lb.}$$

For the *aluminum bar*,

$$e = \epsilon L = SL/E = 40,000 \times 20/(10.6 \times 10^6) = 0.0755 \text{ in.,}$$

and

$$W(10 + 0.0755) = \left(\frac{40{,}000^2}{2 \times 10.6 \times 10^6} \right) (2 \times 20)$$

or
$$W = \frac{3020}{10.0755} = 302.0 \text{ lb.}$$

Impact Bending Stresses. An "exact" method of solution using the equation of vibration for a vibrating beam can be used to determine impact stresses in bending.[7] It has been shown, however, that this procedure does not give values of stress that agree with

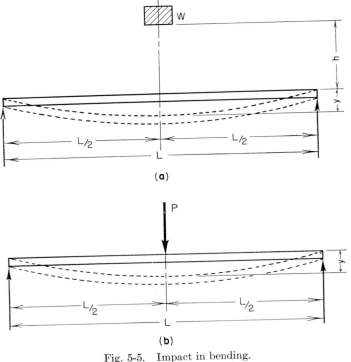

Fig. 5-5.   Impact in bending.

[7] See John Prescott, *Applied Elasticity*, Longmans, Green & Co., London, 1924, Chaps. IX and X; E. G. Fischer, "Lateral Vibrations and Stress in a Beam under Shock Machine Loading," *Proc. S.E.S.A.*, 1947, Vol. 5, No. 1; and R. D. Mindlin, "Influence of Damping on the Response to Shock of Distributed Mass Systems," *Proc. S.E.S.A.*, 1947, Vol. 5, No. 2.

the experimental results, and internal damping[8] must be considered to obtain approximately correct results.

In the approximate method it is assumed that the shape of the deflection curve under static and impact loads is the same. The assumptions made in the solution of the tension-impact problem also apply in the following analysis. For example, Fig. 5-5(a) shows a simply supported beam subjected to an impact load by a weight W falling from a height h. To determine the deflections and stresses produced it will be assumed that the external work done by W is completely transformed into strain energy of bending of the beam. If y is the maximum deflection produced at the mid-span of the beam under the load W, then the work done is $W(h + y)$. There is an *equivalent static load* P, as shown in Fig. 5-5(b), that would produce the same deflection y. The work done by this load is $Py/2$. Equating the work done by W to the work done by P,

$$W(h + y) = \frac{Py}{2} \qquad (5\text{-}17)$$

For a simply supported beam subjected to a center load the deflection is

$$y = \frac{PL^3}{48EI} \quad \text{or} \quad P = \frac{48EI}{L^3} y \qquad (5\text{-}18)$$

Placing the value of P from eq. (5-18) in eq. (5-17),

$$W(h + y) = \left(\frac{24EI}{L^3}\right) y^2$$

or

$$y = y_s \left(1 + \sqrt{1 + \frac{2h}{y_s}}\right) \qquad (5\text{-}19)$$

or

$$y = y_s \left(1 + \sqrt{1 + \frac{v^2}{gy_s}}\right) \qquad (5\text{-}20)$$

where $y_s = WL^3/(48EI)$, for the case considered, is the static deflection produced by the weight W.

When h is large compared to y_s, eq. (5-19) can be written as

$$y = \sqrt{2y_s h} = \sqrt{\frac{y_s v^2}{g}} \qquad (5\text{-}21)$$

---

[8] Internal damping is defined as the energy dissipated in heat per cycle of vibration.

The maximum stress produced can be obtained from the beam formula

$$S = \frac{M_{\max}c}{I} = \frac{(PL/4)c}{I} = \left(\frac{48EIy}{L^3}\right)\left(\frac{L}{4}\right)\left(\frac{c}{I}\right) = \frac{12Eyc}{L^2} \quad (5\text{-}22)$$

Substituting the value of y from eq. (5-21) in eq. (5-22) and noting that $y_s = WL^3/(48EI)$, the maximum stress for cases in which h is large compared to y_s becomes

$$S = \sqrt{(Wh)\left(\frac{6c^2E}{IL}\right)} = \sqrt{\left(\frac{Wv^2}{2g}\right)\left(\frac{6c^2E}{IL}\right)} \quad (5\text{-}23)$$

Equation (5-23) shows that in impact bending the stress is proportional to the outer fiber distance c and the square root of the modulus of elasticity, and is inversely proportional to the square root of the moment of inertia I and the span length L.

In cases where the weight of the beam is not small compared to the weight W, an approximate solution can be obtained by assuming the shape of the deflection curve under impact and static loads to be the same. An equivalent beam weight W_e referred to the point of impact is then calculated. If the velocity of the weight W and equivalent beam weight W_e is v_a, then v_a is

$$v_a = \left(\frac{W}{W + W_e}\right)v \quad (5\text{-}24)$$

where v = the actual striking velocity of the weight W. Then the total kinetic energy of the new system $(W + W_e)$ is

$$\left(\frac{W + W_e}{2g}\right)v_a^2 = \left[\frac{1}{1 + (W_e/W)}\right]\frac{Wv^2}{2g}$$

or

$$v_a = \frac{v}{1 + (W_e/W)} \quad (5\text{-}25)$$

Placing the velocity v_a from eq. (5-25) in eq. (5-20) for the velocity v, the maximum deflection becomes

$$y = y_s\left\{1 + \sqrt{1 + \left[\frac{1}{1 + (W_e/W)}\right]\left(\frac{v^2}{gy_s}\right)}\right\} \quad (5\text{-}26)$$

The value of W_e for a simply supported beam with a center load is $17qL/35$, where q is the weight of the beam per unit length. For a cantilever beam with an end load, $W_e = 33qL/140$. Results obtained by Mason and Arnold[9] indicate that stresses obtained using eq. (5-26) are approximately correct. Arnold found that calculated stresses were about 20 per cent less than the measured stresses.

NUMERICAL EXAMPLE. *Cantilever Beam Subjected to an End-concentrated Impact Load.* A weight W is dropped from a height $h = 40$ in. on the end of a cantilever beam of length $L = 5$ ft. The beam is made of steel and has a rectangular cross section with $b = 1$ in. and $d = 3$ in. Determine the value of W that will produce yielding if the yield stress of the material is 40,000 psi and $E = 30 \times 10^6$ psi. Neglect the weight of the beam.

SOLUTION. For an equivalent end static load P, the external work is $Py/2$ for an end deflection y. Equating this to the work done by the impact load W,

$$W(h + y) = \frac{Py}{2}$$

This equation can now be used to find the weight W that will produce yielding. The load P is first determined from the yield stress relation

$$S_{yp} = \frac{Mc}{I} = PL\frac{c}{I}$$

or

$$P = \frac{S_{yp}I}{Lc} = \frac{40,000 \times 1 \times 3^3/12}{60 \times 1.5} = 1000 \text{ lb.}$$

For $P = 1000$ lb., the deflection y becomes

$$y = \frac{PL^3}{3EI} = \frac{1000 \times 60^3}{3 \times 30 \times 10^6 \times 1 \times 3^3/12} = 1.07 \text{ in.}$$

With y and P known, the load W can be obtained from the above equation, or

$$W(40 + 1.07) = \frac{1000 \times 1.07}{2}$$

or

$$W = 13 \text{ lb.}$$

Impact Torsional Stresses. To determine the deformations and stresses in members subjected to torsion and impact loads, the approximate procedure used for axial tension and bending can be used. Figure 5-6 shows a bar of circular cross section subjected to

---

[9] H. L. Mason, "Impact on Beams," *Trans. A.S.M.E.*, 1935, pp. A-55–61; and R. N. Arnold, "Impact Stresses in a Freely Supported Beam," *Proc. Inst. Mech. Engrs.*, London, 1937, Vol. 137, pp. 217-283.

an impact torque loading by weights W striking the bar AB at A and B with velocities of v and kinetic energies of $Wv^2/(2g)$. To find the stresses produced, let P be the equivalent static load applied at A and B that will produce the same angle of twist θ or displacement y. Then the work done by the equivalent static loads is $2Py/2 = Py$. The work done by the impact loads can be considered as the kinetic energies $Wv^2/(2g)$ of each weight W, equivalent to $2Wh$ plus the work done by the weights W in moving the distance y. Then

$$Py = 2W(h + y) \qquad (5\text{-}27)$$

where $h = v^2/2g$.

The displacement y can be expressed in terms of the angle of twist, since for small angles, $\theta = y/(a/2)$ or $y = a\theta/2$. Placing this value of y in eq. (5-27),

$$\frac{Pa\theta}{2} = 2W\left(h + \frac{a\theta}{2}\right) \qquad (5\text{-}28)$$

But $Pa = T$, the equivalent static torque, and $Wa = T_s$, the static torque produced by W applied statically. Placing $Pa = T$ and $Wa = T_s$ in eq. (5-28),

$$T\theta = 4Wh + 2T_s\theta \qquad (5\text{-}29)$$

From *Strength of Materials*,

$$T = \frac{E_sJ}{L}\theta \text{ and } T_s = \frac{E_sJ}{L}\theta_s$$

so that eq. (5-29) can be written as

$$\left(\frac{E_sJ}{L}\right)\theta^2 = 4Wh + 2\left(\frac{E_sJ\theta_s}{L}\right)\theta$$

Solving this equation for θ,

$$\theta = \theta_s\left[1 + \sqrt{1 + \frac{4h}{\theta_s a}}\right] \qquad (5\text{-}30)$$

where $\theta_s = (T_sL)/(E_sJ) = $ the angle of twist if the load were gradually applied.

Equation (5-30) gives the angle of twist for a length L in terms of the angle of twist θ_s.

When the kinetic energy $= Wv^2/(2g)$ and the striking velocity v applied at A and B are known, the value of $W = KE \times 2g/v^2$ and the value of $h = v^2/2g$. The shear stress can be obtained from eq. (5-30) by replacing θ with its value $TL/(E_sJ) = S_sL/(E_sr)$ and θ_s by its value $T_sL/(E_sJ) = WaL/(E_sJ)$. Then,

$$\frac{S_sL}{E_sr} = \frac{WaL}{E_sJ}\left[1 + \sqrt{1 + \frac{4hE_sJ}{Wa^2L}}\right]$$

$$S_s = \frac{War}{J}\left[1 + \sqrt{1 + \frac{4hE_sJ}{Wa^2L}}\right] \qquad (5\text{-}31)$$

If the equivalent height of drop h is large compared to y, eq. (5-31) can be written approximately as

$$S_s = \sqrt{\left(\frac{4E_sr^2}{JL}\right)Wh} \qquad (5\text{-}32)$$

or
$$S_s = \sqrt{\left(\frac{8E_s}{AL}\right)\left(\frac{Wv^2}{2g}\right)} \qquad (5\text{-}33)$$

where A = the cross-sectional area πr^2 and $Wv^2/2g$ = the kinetic energy of the weights applied at A and B.

Equations (5-32) and (5-33) give results similar to those for axial tension and bending. That is, the shear impact stress produced is proportional to the square root of the modulus of elasticity in shear and the square root of the kinetic energy applied. The stress is also inversely proportional to the square root of the volume AL of the bar.

5-6. UTILIZATION OF IMPACT PROPERTIES IN DESIGN

In the design of members subjected to impact it is important to realize that the design of a member for impact loads is different from the design for static loads. In the case of impact loading the structure or machine member is required to absorb a certain amount of kinetic energy, which is temporarily stored in the form of potential energy. This is different from the case of static loading where the part must be designed to resist a given load. It has been noted, as given by eq. (5-8), that the stress is inversely proportional to the square root of the volume AL of the member. That is, to reduce the stress in a given case, the volume is changed. In other words, the stress can be modified by changing either the area or the length and not just the area as in the case of static tension. In the same way for a beam, the impact stress can be changed not only by changing the cross-sectional dimensions, but also by changing the length.

That is, the impact stress, as given by eq. (5-23), can be decreased by increasing the beam length.

The following numerical examples are intended to illustrate the design of some simple stress members.

NUMERICAL EXAMPLE. *Design of a Member Subjected to Impact Tensile Stresses.* A steel rod of circular cross section is subjected to an impact load produced by a weight $W = 20$ lb. falling through a height $h = 60$ in. Determine the required diameter of the rod if the length is 48 in. The design stress is to be $S_w = 20,000$ psi and $E = 30 \times 10^6$ psi. What is the diameter required using an aluminum alloy, if the design stress to be used is the same but $E = 10.6 \times 10^6$ psi?

SOLUTION. Equating the external work to the internal strain energy,

$$W(h + e) = \frac{S^2}{2E} AL$$

For the *steel rod*, the stress $S = 20,000$ psi and

$$e = \epsilon L = SL/E = 20,000 \times 48/(30 \times 10^6) = 0.0320 \text{ in.}$$

Then by the foregoing equation,

$$(20)(60 + 0.032) = \left(\frac{20,000^2}{2 \times 30 \times 10^6}\right)\left(\frac{\pi d^2}{4}\right)(48)$$

or
$$d^2 = 4.78 \quad \text{and} \quad d = 2.2 \text{ in.}$$

For the *aluminum rod*, the stress $S = 20,000$ psi, and

$$e = \epsilon L = SL/E = 20,000 \times 48/(10.6 \times 10^6) = 0.0905 \text{ in.}$$

Then by the foregoing equation,

$$(20)(60 \times 0.0905) = \left(\frac{20,000^2}{2 \times 10.6 \times 10^6}\right)\left(\frac{\pi d^2}{4}\right)(48)$$

or
$$d^2 = 1.69 \quad \text{and} \quad d = 1.3 \text{ in.}$$

NUMERICAL EXAMPLE. *Design of a Beam Subjected to Impact Loading.* A beam of square cross section is simply supported at the ends and is subjected to a center-concentrated load. Determine the optimum values of the depth and span length if it is to resist either a load of 5 lb. dropped from a height $h = 10$ in. or a gradually applied static load of 500 lb. Both loads are to be applied at the center of the beam. The design stress is $S_w = 30,000$ psi and the beam is made of an aluminum alloy with $E = 10.6 \times 10^6$ psi.

SOLUTION. For static loading the required depth of the beam is obtained from the equation

$$S_w = \frac{M_{\max}c}{I} = \left(\frac{WL}{4}\right)\left(\frac{6}{b^3}\right)$$

or

$$\frac{b^3}{L} = \frac{3}{2}\frac{W}{S_w} = \frac{3}{2} \times \frac{500}{30{,}000} = 0.025$$

and

$$L = 40b^3$$

Equating the external work done by the weight $W = 5$ lb. to the work done by the equivalent static load P,

$$W(h + y) = \frac{P}{2} y$$

The equivalent load P is determined from the working stress relation $S_w = Mc/I = (PL/4)(c/I)$, or

$$P = \frac{4S_w I}{Lc} = \frac{4 \times 30{,}000 \times (b^4/12)}{Lb/2} = \frac{20{,}000b^3}{L}$$

and

$$y = \frac{PL^3}{48EI} = \left(\frac{20{,}000b^3}{L}\right)L^3\left[\frac{1}{48 \times 10.6 \times 10^6 \times (b^4/12)}\right]$$

$$= \frac{0.000472L^2}{b}$$

Placing these values of P and y in the above equation and values of W and h as given,

$$5\left(10 + \frac{0.000472L^2}{b}\right) = \left(\frac{20{,}000b^3}{L}\right)\left(\frac{0.000472L^2}{2b}\right)$$

Substituting $L = 40b^3$, as obtained for the static condition in this equation,

$$5(10 + 0.755b^5) = 4.72 \times 40b^5$$

$$b^5 = 0.260$$

or

$$b = 0.767 \text{ in.} \quad \text{and} \quad L = 180 \text{ in.}$$

NUMERICAL EXAMPLE. *Design of a Circular Shaft Subjected to Impact Torsion Loading.* A solid circular shaft of length L and diameter d is subjected to an impact twisting moment produced by weights $W = 5$ lb. dropped from distances of 10 in. (Fig. 5-6). During other periods of time it is also subjected to a completely reversed fatigue load $W = 50$ lb. The torque arm $a = 50$ in. and $E_s = 6.2 \times 10^6$ psi. Determine the optimum values of the length L

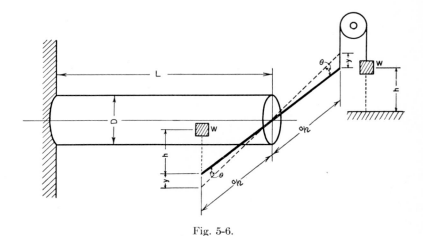

Fig. 5-6.

and diameter d if the design fatigue shear stress is 20,000 psi and the design static shear stress is 40,000 psi.

SOLUTION. Based on the fatigue stress condition, the required diameter is obtained from $S_s = Tr/J = (Td/2)/(\pi d^4/32)$, or

$$d = \sqrt[3]{\frac{16T}{\pi S_s}} = \sqrt[3]{\frac{16 \times 50 \times 50}{\pi \times 20,000}} = 0.86 \text{ in.}$$

The required length can be determined based on the impact loading condition. Equating the work done by W to the work done by the equivalent static load, $2W(h + y) = 2(Py/2) = Py$. But

$$y = \theta \frac{a}{2} = \frac{TL}{E_s J} \frac{a}{2} = \left(\frac{JS_s}{r}\right)\left(\frac{L}{E_s J}\right)\left(\frac{a}{2}\right) = \frac{S_s La}{2E_s r}$$

and $P = T/a = JS_s/ra$. Then

$$2W\left(h + \frac{S_s La}{2E_s r}\right) = \left(\frac{JS_s}{ra}\right)\left(\frac{S_s La}{2E_s r}\right) = \frac{S_s^2 LJ}{2E_s r^2}$$

and

$$(2 \times 5)\left(10 + \frac{40,000 \times L}{2 \times 6.2 \times 10^6 \times 0.43}\right)$$
$$= \frac{40,000^2 \times L \times \pi \times (0.43^4/2)}{2 \times 6.2 \times 10^6 \times 0.43^2}$$

or $(10)(10 + 0.0075L) = 37.4L$

Thus $L = 2.67$ in.

PROBLEMS

5-1. (a) An aluminum-alloy rod of circular cross section 4 ft. long is subjected to an axial impact tensile load by means of a weight of 30 lb. dropped from a height of 3 ft. onto the lower end of the rod. What must the rod diameter be to prevent yielding? The impact yield stress of the material is 40,000 psi and $E = 10.3 \times 10^6$ psi.

(b) Solve Prob. 5-1(a) if the load is statically applied, and the static yield stress is 40,000 psi.

(c) Solve Prob. 5-1(a) if the bar has a stress concentration factor of 2.0.
Ans. (a) $d = 0.62$ in.; (b) $d = 0.031$ in.; (c) $d = 1.24$ in.

5-2. A metal rod of circular cross section and of length equal to 5 ft. is subjected to an impact load by dropping a load of 50 lb. from a height of 3 ft. Two materials are to be considered—a steel alloy with $S_{yp} = 40,000$ psi and $E = 30 \times 10^6$ psi, and an aluminum alloy with $S_{yp} = 40,000$ psi and $E = 10.3 \times 10^6$ psi. The densities of the steel and aluminum alloys are, respectively, 0.284 and 0.102 lb. per cu. in. What material should be selected if the aluminum costs twice as much per pound as the steel?
Ans. Aluminum.

5-3. Two rods of steel are subjected to an impact tensile load by a weight of 4000 lb. dropping from a height of 2 ft. If one rod is 2 ft. long and the other is 4 ft. long, compare the diameters required to prevent yielding. The yield stress of the steel is 45,000 psi and $E = 30 \times 10^6$ psi.
Ans. $d_1 = 12.3$ in., $d_2 = 8.72$ in.

5-4. A steel rod 2 in. in diameter and 10 in. long is subjected to an impact axial tensile load by a weight dropping from a height $h = \frac{1}{4}$ in. (Fig. 5-4). Determine (a) the load value to produce yielding if $E = 30 \times 10^6$ psi and $S_{yp} = 35,000$ psi, (b) the elongation of the bar, (c) the time of contact of the load, and (d) the allowable load if the factor of safety is 2.5. What is the total elongation of the bar corresponding to this load?

5-5. A connecting rod is subjected to a fluctuating axial load varying from an axial force of 5000 lb. to 2000 lb. At other times the rod is also subjected to an impact axial tensile force produced by a weight of 50 lb. dropped from a height of 10 in. on the end of the rod. Determine the optimum diameter and length if the design impact stress is 20,000 psi, the fatigue strength $S_e = 40,000$ psi, $S_{yp} = 50,000$ psi, and $E = 10.6 \times 10^6$ psi. Use Soderberg's law for fatigue strength and a factor of safety $N = 2$ for both the static and variable stress. *Ans.* $L = 30$ in., $d = 1$ in.

5-7. A simply supported beam is 60 in. long and is subjected to an impact load at the midspan by a weight of 30 lb. dropped from a height h. The beam has a width of 2 in., depth 8 in., and the yield stress of the material is 60,000 psi. Determine the height of drop required to produce yielding if the beam is made of (a) steel with $E = 30 \times 10^6$ psi, and (b) an aluminum alloy with $E = 10.6 \times 10^6$ psi.

5-8. (a) A cantilever beam of length $L = 48$ in. is subjected to an end impact load produced by a weight of 50 lb. dropped from a height of 20 in. The beam has a width equal to $\frac{1}{2}$ the depth. Determine the required depth if the design impact stress is 20,000 psi and $E = 6.0 \times 10^6$ psi.

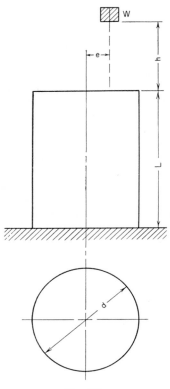

(b) If the length of the beam is halved, what is the required beam depth in Prob. 5-8(a)?

(c) What is the end deflection produced in Prob. 5-8(a)?

Ans. (a) $d = 3.46$ in.;
(b) $d = 4.89$ in.; (c) $y = 1.44$ in.

5-9. A cantilever beam of circular cross section and length L is subjected to an impact load produced by a load of 40 lb. dropped from a height of 25 in. What are the optimum values of the diameter and length if the design stress is 20,000 psi, the modulus of elasticity $E = 30 \times 10^6$ psi, and the maximum deflection is not to exceed $\frac{1}{360}$ of the beam length?

5-10. (a) A circular rod of diameter d and length L is subjected to an eccentric impact load at an eccentricity e, as shown in Fig. 5-7. The impact load is produced by a load W dropped from a height h. Determine an expression for the maximum stress.

(b) What is the maximum stress in Prob. 5-10(a) if $d = 2$ in., $L = 20$ in., $W = 50$ lb., $e = 0.5$, $h = 30$ in., and $E = 6 \times 10^6$ psi?

5-11. A circular shaft of diameter equal to 2 in. is subjected to an impact twisting moment produced by weights of $W = 20$ lb. dropped from distances of 5 in. (Fig. 5-6). If $a = 20$ in., $S_{sy} = 30,000$ psi, and $E_s = 12 \times 10^6$ psi, what is the length required to prevent yielding? Solve by both the exact and approximate methods. *Ans.* $L = 3.44$ in.

5-12. A circular shaft is subjected to an impact twisting moment (Fig. 5-6). If $W = 15$ lb., $h = 10$ in., $a = 20$ in., $S_{sw} = 15,000$ psi, $E = 6 \times 10^6$

Fig. 5-7.

psi, and the allowable angle of twist is to be less than one degree in 20 diameters of length, determine the optimum values of the diameter and length.

BIBLIOGRAPHY

Davidenkoff, N. N., "Allowable Working Stresses under Impact," *Trans. A.S.M.E.*, 1934, Vol. 56, pp. 97-108.

Manjoine, M. J., "Influence of Strain and Temperature on Yield Stresses of Mild Steel," *Journal of App. Mech., Trans. A.S.M.E.*, 1944, Vol. 66, pp. A-211 to A-218.

Salmon, E. H., *Materials and Structures*, Longmans, Green and Co., New York, 1931, Vol. 1.

Teed, P. L., *The Properties of Metallic Materials at Low Temperatures*, John Wiley & Sons, Inc., New York, 1950.

Timoshenko, S., *Strength of Materials*, D. Van Nostrand Co., Inc., New York, 1930, Part I.

Metals Handbook, published by the American Society for Metals, 1948.

"Symposium on Impact Testing," *Proc. A.S.T.M.*, 1922, Part II, Vol. 22, p. 5.

"Symposium on Impact Testing," *Proc. A.S.T.M.*, 1938, Vol. 38, p. 21.

Chapter 6

Creep and Temperature Properties

6-1. INTRODUCTORY COMMENTS

Materials are frequently used in engineering applications under operating conditions of either high or low temperatures. Elevated temperatures occur in parts of steam and gas turbines, oil refining and other chemical equipment, and in automotive parts. Low temperatures are encountered in refrigeration equipment and in machines or structures in geographic locations where cold weather occurs. The designer must consider the influence of low and high temperatures on the mechanical properties of the material selected. High and low temperatures may influence appreciably the strength, ductility, and toughness of the material used, so that design based on mechanical property values determined for normal temperatures is no longer adequate. In addition to its effect on the ordinary mechanical properties, an elevated temperature will usually produce creep or "time-flow" of the material. Creep may be defined as the time-dependent deformation produced in solids subjected to stress. It is a deformation that occurs under constant stress and, for some materials, at normal temperatures.

Creep of materials when subjected to stress is of great importance in a number of applications where the deformations of the part must be maintained within prescribed limits. Creep at elevated temperatures is an important consideration in steam or gas turbine design and in equipment used for oil refining or other chemical processes. The increased use of plastics in applications where deformations must be kept small requires a consideration of the creep properties.

6-2. TEMPERATURE PROPERTIES

There are two effects of temperature on the properties of metals. Changes in temperature modify not only the shape of the stress-strain curve or mechanical properties, but also the structure of the material. In steel, for example, between 70° F. and 400° F. a precipitation occurs which alters the structure of the steel. At high temperatures, recrystallization also occurs with stressing above the elastic limit. Lowering of the temperature below 70° F., however, influences only the values of the mechanical properties.

Properties of Metals at Low Temperatures. In selecting metals for low-temperature applications it is important to consider the toughness and ductility, since these properties may be appreciably reduced with decrease in temperature.

Metals are used at low temperatures in many products and machines. Many processes in the chemical industries utilize equipment operating at temperatures as low as −150° F. Refrigeration equipment requires metals operating at temperatures as low as −75° F. The petroleum industry uses metal equipment operating at low temperatures for refining of oil products, as, for example, in the dewaxing process. The aircraft, railroad, automotive, and marine industries use metals at low temperatures during the winter months in many locations. Equipment used for the production of oxygen is an important example of metals used under low-temperature conditions.

One important characteristic of ferrous metals at low temperatures is the sudden loss in toughness when a certain low temperature is reached. This temperature is called the "transition temperature" and is illustrated in Fig. 6-1. While all ferrous metals have a transition temperature, most of the nonferrous metals such as copper, nickel, and alloys of these metals are relatively free from this behavior. The brittle behavior in some metals at low temperature is accentuated by using specimens with notches. The notched-bar impact test conducted at various temperatures is commonly used to obtain the "transition temperature." At this temperature the toughness value, as obtained from the notched-bar standard impact test, is suddenly reduced in magnitude. This brittle behavior at the "transition temperature" is accompanied by a coarse-grained fracture. Standard bending or tensile tests do not reveal the "transition temperature."

A number of investigations have been conducted to show how

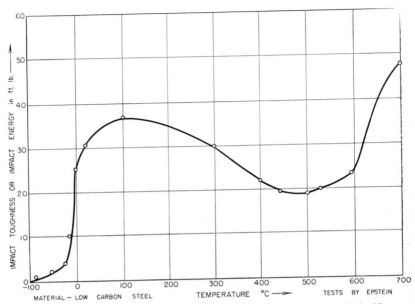

Fig. 6-1. Transition temperature curve. (*Proc. A.S.T.M.* Vol. 32, 1932. Courtesy A.S.T.M.)

low temperatures influence the properties of thermal expansion, thermal conductivity, and the modulus of elasticity.[1] Test results show that the coefficient of thermal expansion decreases with decrease in temperature but that the coefficient of thermal conductivity and the modulus of elasticity increase with a decrease in temperature. It is possible that there are exceptions to this behavior. It can be noted, however, that for most metals exposed to subatmospheric temperatures the influence of low temperature is as noted in the foregoing statements.   The changes produced in the properties at low

[1] Values of these and other properties of metals at low temperatures are tabulated in the *Metals Handbook*, published by the American Society for Metals, 1948, pp. 205-215. See also, "Mechanical Properties of Metals and Alloys," by J. L. Everhart *et al.*, *Circular C-447*, published by the U. S. Department of Commerce, National Bureau of Standards, 1943; *Literature Survey on the Low-Temperature Properties of Metals*, by A. E. White and C. A. Siebert, Edwards Bros., Ann Arbor, Mich., 1947, 558 pp.; "Mechanical Properties of Metals at Low Temperature," *Trans. A.S.M.*, 1948, Vol. 40, pp. 813-861, by L. Seigle and R. M. Brock; and P. L. Teed, *The Properties of Metallic Materials at Low Temperatures*, John Wiley & Sons, Inc., 1950.

temperatures are undoubtedly related to the metallurgical changes accompanying reduction in temperature.

Test results[1] show that the tensile strength of carbon steels is greatly increased with little change in ductility as the temperature is reduced to minus 150° F. However, the toughness of plain carbon steels at this temperature is appreciably reduced. Increase in carbon content of steel greatly decreases the ductility at low temperatures but increases the strength (Fig. 6-2). Toughness of fine-grained

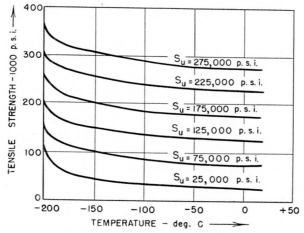

Fig. 6-2. Influence of low temperature on tensile strength of steels at various strength levels. (*Note:* Curves shown are obtained from the empirical relation $S'_u = C/S_u^{\frac{1}{2}}$, where S_u = ultimate tensile strength at normal temperature (20° C), C = a constant and S'_u = tensile strength for particular temperature considered.) (After Hollomon and Jaffe, *Ferrous Metallurgical Design*, 1947. Courtesy John Wiley & Sons.)

alloy steels is superior to that of coarse-grained steels at low temperatures.

Results of tension tests at low temperatures for aluminum alloys[1] show that neither the strength nor the ductility changes greatly with decrease in temperature to as low as −112° F. Copper and most copper alloys possess remarkable toughness when exposed to extremely low temperatures. The tensile strength of copper alloys increases without a decrease in ductility as the temperature is re-

duced.   Magnesium alloys have little toughness at normal temperatures but a reduction in temperature does not influence the toughness.   The tensile strength of wrought magnesium alloys, however,
is appreciably increased with temperature decrease.   Cast magnesium alloys, on the other hand, show no change in tensile strength
at low temperature.   Nickel-base alloys, known as Monel or Inconel,
have about the same toughness and ductility at low temperatures
but exhibit an appreciable increase in strength.

There is some doubt as to the quantitative significance of the
transition temperature that is found for some metals in using the
notched-bar impact test.   The reason for questioning the value of
the transition temperature is that, when a notched bar is used, a
complicated state of triaxial stress exists.   Furthermore, a specimen
with stress variations makes it impossible to interpret accurately
the results obtained.   Tests by MacGregor and Grossman[2] show
that there is general correlation between transition temperatures
obtained with a notched bar and with specimens having various ratios
of biaxial combined stresses.   That is, although the transition temperatures are not the same in the two types of tests, the relative
values for various materials are similar.

A discussion of the effect of low temperature on properties of both
metals and nonmetals is given in a Symposium of the American
Society for Testing Materials.[3]

Properties of Metals at Elevated Temperatures.   One important influence of elevated temperature on the properties of stressed
metals is the occurrence of continuous deformation of the material
with time.   This deformation with time is called "creep," and will
be discussed in subsequent articles.   Elevated temperatures may
have a marked effect on both the static and dynamic mechanical
properties of materials.   Elevated temperature tests are conducted
with standard testing equipment.   Provision must be made, however, for applying the elevated temperature to the specimen.   This
is usually done by enclosing the specimen in an electrically heated
furnace with temperature controls and temperature-measuring de-

---

[2] C. W. MacGregor and N. Grossman, "The Effect of Combined Stresses on
the Transition Temperature for Brittle Fracture," *The Welding Journal Research
Supplement*, January 1948.

[3] See "Symposium on Effect of Low Temperatures on Materials," *Special
Technical Publication No. 78*, published by the A.S.T.M., 1948.

vices, usually in the form of thermocouples.   A mechanical or optical strain gage is used for obtaining strain readings during loading. The test procedure and method of recording and reporting test data for high-temperature tests have been specified by the American Society for Testing Materials.[4]

Many investigations have been conducted to study the influence

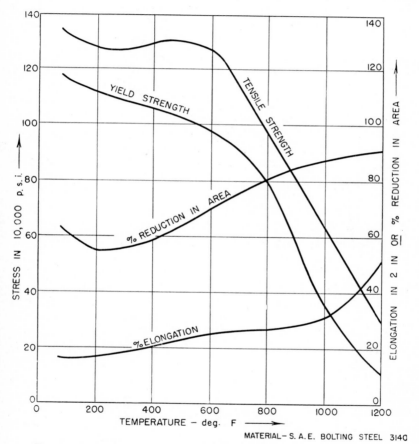

MATERIAL— S. A. E. BOLTING STEEL 3140

Fig. 6-3.   Influence of elevated temperatures on mechanical properties in tension.

[4] See "Short-Time Elevated Temperature Tension Tests of Metallic Materials," *A.S.T.M. Standards Designation E 21-43*, 1944.

of elevated temperatures on the properties of materials. The influence of elevated temperatures on the impact toughness as well as the yield strength, ultimate strength, elongation, and creep in ten-

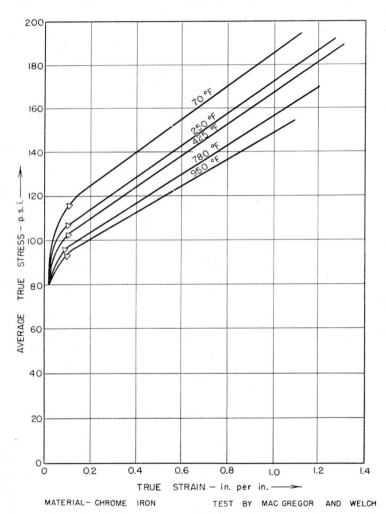

MATERIAL— CHROME IRON   TEST BY MAC GREGOR AND WELCH

Fig. 6-4. True stress-strain curves in tension at various temperatures. (Data from A.I.M.M.E.)

sion has been determined for many metals and alloys.[5] Some of the earlier investigations on the influence of elevated temperatures on the properties of metals are given in the *Symposium on the Effect of Temperature on the Properties of Metals.*[6]

The influence of elevated temperature for the initial range of temperature increase differs depending on the metal or alloy considered. For some of the ferrous metals such as mild steels, the tensile strength and ductility increase up to certain temperatures. Beyond

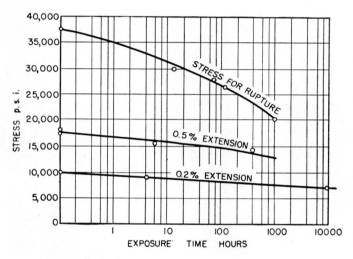

MATERIAL – MAGNESIUM BASE ALLOY   A Z 63

Fig. 6-5.   Stress for rupture and for 0.5%, and 0.2% extension at 200° F.   (Tests by J. C. McDonald; *Proc. A.S.T.M.*, Vol. 48, 1948.   Courtesy A.S.T.M.)

this elevated temperature the tensile strength decreases, while the ductility continues to increase. The yield strength, however, continues to decrease with increase in temperature. An example of such behavior is illustrated in Fig. 6-3. In general, aluminum and magnesium alloys show a decrease in the yield and ultimate strengths

---

[5] "Mechanical Properties of Metals and Alloys," by John L. Everhart *et al.*, Bureau of Standards, *Circular C-447*, Dec. 1943. See also, *Properties of Metals at Elevated Temperatures*, by B. V. Smith. McGraw-Hill Book Co., Inc., 1950.

[6] Published by the A.S.T.M. and A.S.M.E., June, 1931, 620 pp.

and an increase in ductility for tension with an increase in temperature.

True stress-strain relations in tension at elevated temperatures have been obtained using the "two-load method"[7] described in

    1   2   3

Fig. 6-6(a). Comparison of fracture of Cr–Mo–W steel for short- and long-time tension loadings: 1, short-time test at room temperature. 2, short-time test at 1000° F. 3, long-time test at 1000° F, 60,000 psi, 18.4 hr. (From R. E. Peterson, *Handbook on Experimental Stress Analysis*. Courtesy John Wiley & Sons.)

Chapter 1. Figure 6-4 illustrates the true stress-strain diagrams obtained for chrome iron at various temperatures.

There are applications of metals, such as in gas turbines, jet aircraft engines, and turbosuperchargers, that require operation under ex-

[7] "True Stress-Strain Relations at High Temperatures by the Two-Load Method," by C. W. MacGregor and L. E. Welch, *Tech. Pub. No. 1507*, Metals Technology, Sept. 1942.

treme conditions of high temperature. In many of these applications the permissible creep deformation is high, and the only requirement is that rupture of the metal does not take place during the life of the part. To determine the properties of metals for this relatively short-time service, the *stress-rupture test* rather than the long-time creep test is used. Tension stress-rupture tests are made by subjecting a series of specimens to the same temperature, but each specimen to a different stress value. The time required to produce failure by rupture is then determined and a graph is plotted giving

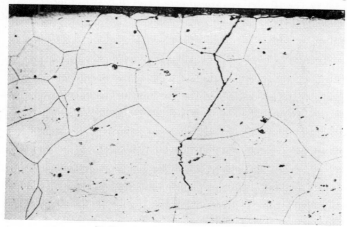

Fatigue failure (trans-crystalline)

Creep-rupture failure (inter-crystalline)

Fig. 6-6(b). Comparison of microstructure showing characteristic cracks for creep-rupture and fatigue failures. (From R. E. Peterson, *Handbook on Experimental Stress Analysis*. Courtesy John Wiley & Sons.)

a relation between the time for rupture and the stress (Fig. 6-5). Figure 6-5 shows that as the stress is increased the time required for rupture is reduced. A plot of the stresses versus the log time to rupture usually shows a straight-line relation. Stress-rupture test results are often reported in terms of the stresses that produce rupture in 10, 100, and 1000 hours. Stress-time relations corresponding to specific values of elongation are also given in Fig. 6-5.

Other forms of creep tests are the *constant-strain-rate* test and the *stress-relaxation test*. In the constant-strain-rate test the quantity measured is the stress reaction produced by applying a constant strain rate to the specimen. The relaxation test is usually made by maintaining a constant value of the elastic plus the creep strain with time by decreasing the stress. A stress-relaxation-time relation is plotted to represent the behavior in this type of test. Relaxation creep-stress relations are discussed in more detail in Article 6-4. The type of fracture obtained for metals in creep tests at elevated temperatures compared to other loading conditions is shown in Fig. 6-6.

6-3. LONG-TIME CREEP PROPERTIES IN TENSION

In the foregoing discussion, failure of materials at elevated temperatures has been defined by the yield or ultimate strength for a particular operating temperature. Strength is a satisfactory measure for specifying failure if the elevated temperature occurs for relatively short periods of time compared to the life of the member, or if the creep or continuous change in deformation that occurs is permissible and does not interfere with the successful operation of the construction.

In some industrial applications operating at elevated temperatures, such as steam or gas turbines, the creep deformations are an important consideration. The elevated temperature in these cases is present over long periods of time and the creep deformations must be kept small in order to maintain clearances between the moving and stationary parts of the turbine. It becomes necessary, in the design of some members, to determine the allowable stress on the basis of a permissible creep deformation. The working stress is then defined as the stress that will not produce a unit creep deformation greater than a specified amount during the estimated life of the construction and for a particular operating temperature. The creep deformation allowed for a given member is often specified by the creep rate, which represents the amount of creep per unit of time. For example, in the design of a turbine cylinder, a working stress was selected so that the creep rate was less than 0.01 per cent per year over a period of 25 years. The creep requirements for various types of applications are given in the *Symposium on the Effect of Temperature on the Properties of Metals.*[6]

Creep occurs for most metals at stresses below the yield stress and only if the temperature is elevated. For some metals such as lead and some nonferrous alloys, creep occurs at low stresses and room temperature. Creep occurs also at low stresses and room temperature in nonmetallic materials such as plastics and concrete.

Determination of Creep Test Data.   Most of the information on creep properties of materials has been obtained from observation of specimens subjected to constant tensile loads and constant temperature. In the tension-creep test, specimens are usually subjected to constant loads by a lever system of loading, as shown in Fig. 11-15, Chapter 11. Provision is made for obtaining the creep deformations at various time intervals covering the entire duration of the tests. The creep deformations are usually measured by micrometer microscopes. For room-temperature creep tests as, for example, in creep tests of plastics, electric strain gages are sometimes used for measurement of the creep strains. In creep tests at elevated temperatures, electric furnaces with thermocouple temperature controls are used to apply elevated temperatures to the specimens.

The procedure for creep testing has been standardized to some extent by the American Society for Testing Materials.[8] These standards specify dimensions of test specimens, methods of measuring loads, deformations, and temperature, and the method of reporting the test results.

In conducting creep tests it is desirable to use several testing units simultaneously, as illustrated in Fig. 11-15, Chapter 11. The reason for testing a number of specimens simultaneously is that creep tests cover relatively long periods of time and, furthermore, it is necessary to test specimens at different stress values in order to obtain the necessary data. In creep tests, measurements of load, temperature,

---

[8] "Conducting of Long-Time High-Temperature Tension Tests of Metallic Materials," *A.S.T.M. Standards, Part I, Metals.*

creep deformation, and time are recorded.   Creep tests for metals are usually made for a period of 1000 hours, or about 42 days, as specified by the A.S.T.M. Standards.[8]   From the measurements made, values can be calculated of the creep deformations ϵ, usually measured in in. per in., and the time, usually measured in hours. Creep-time relations for a specific stress and temperature can then be plotted as illustrated in Fig. 6-7.   Usually the plotted values of

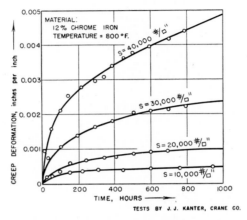

Fig. 6-7.   Creep time curves for 12% chrome iron.

the creep strains include the initial elastic strain produced by the load in addition to the creep strain.   The shape of the creep-time curves depends upon a number of factors, including the material tested, the stress value, and the temperature.

For metals at higher values of stress or temperature, four stages in the creep-time relation can be distinguished, as indicated in Fig. 6-8.   These stages are: (1) an initial stage in which the total deformation is partly elastic and partly plastic; (2) a second stage where the rate of creep deformation decreases with time, indicating the influence of strain-hardening; (3) a third stage where the effect of strain-hardening is counteracted by an annealing influence, which results in a stage of constant minimum creep rate; and (4) a final stage where the reduction in the cross section of the specimens leads to higher stress, a greater creep rate, and eventual fracture.   For

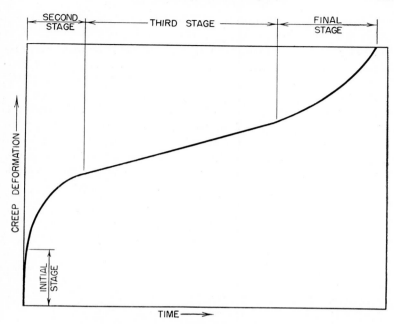

Fig. 6-8.   Creep-time relation showing various stages of creep.

the lower stresses and temperatures the fourth and final stage of creep is not obtained during the usual times covered by the tests. The shapes of creep-time curves for particular metals are also influenced by such factors as crystal grain size, age hardening, oxidization, and corrosion.   Creep-time relations for plastics are found to be similar to those for metals.   For the lower stresses, however, the third stage of constant creep rate may be one in which the creep rate gradually decreases with time.

With creep-time relations available, as shown in Fig. 6-7, it is now possible to select an allowable value of stress or a limiting creep stress based on a limiting value of creep strain.   In evaluating this allowable stress there is the difficulty that the test data usually cover a period of time much less than the estimated service life of the member to be designed.   Industrial progress usually cannot wait for the results of long-time tests covering periods of time approaching those of the life span of the machine.   It becomes necessary, therefore, to extrapolate test data in order that the data will apply for times equal to the estimated service life. Various methods of interpretation have been proposed for extrapolating test data.

Methods of Interpretation of Creep Test Data. Methods of interpretation of tension creep test data are of two types. One type attempts to determine an empirical equation to fit a particular creep-time curve at a given stress. The other type of interpretation, which is of much greater use to the designer, includes those methods that attempt to relate the creep strain or creep rate and the stress for a given temperature and material. A relation between the creep strain, time, and stress is required by the designer since it is necessary for him to select an allowable creep stress based on an allowable

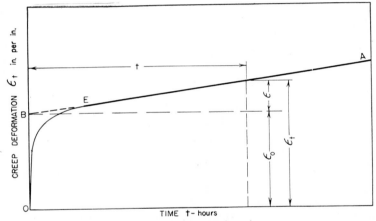

Fig. 6-9. Creep-time relation.

creep deformation for the estimated life of the part. Various methods of interpretation for defining creep-strain-stress-time relations for the purpose of obtaining allowable creep-stress values are discussed later in this article. A method will be considered first that has been found to be in satisfactory agreement with test data for many engineering materials. This method is designated as the *Modified Log-Log Method.*

By the *modified log-log method* the creep strain ϵ_t at a time t is considered to be made up of two parts, an intercept strain ϵ_0 equal approximately to the elastic plus the initial creep strains, and the time-dependent strain ϵ (Fig. 6-9). That is,

$$\epsilon_t = \epsilon_0 + \epsilon \tag{6-1}$$

In using eq. (6-1), the creep-time curve OEA, made up of the initial curved part OE and the assumed straight portion EA, is replaced by the two straight lines OB and BA. This substitution is satisfactory provided creep strains for short intervals of time are not required. In using eq. (6-1) it is necessary to express both ϵ_0 and ϵ as functions of stress and time. Tests on some metals and plastics have shown that the intercept ϵ_0 is approximately related to the stress by the equation

$$\epsilon_0 = D \left(\frac{S}{S_0} \right)^p \tag{6-2}$$

where D, S_0 and p are experimental constants whose values depend upon the material and temperature.

It has also been found that the time-dependent creep strain ϵ is approximately related to the stress and time by the equation

$$\epsilon = Bt \left(\frac{S}{S_0} \right)^n \tag{6-3}$$

where B, S_0 and n are experimental constants whose values depend upon the material and temperature. Placing the values of ϵ_0 and ϵ from eqs. (6-2) and (6-3) in eq. (6-1), the strain ϵ_t becomes

$$\epsilon_t = D \left(\frac{S}{S_0} \right)^p + Bt \left(\frac{S}{S_0} \right)^n \tag{6-4}$$

In many applications the strains for long periods of time, such as five or ten years, are the basis for design. Under these circumstances the creep strain ϵ_0 is small compared to ϵ and can be neglected. Then, by eqs. (6-1) and (6-3),

$$\epsilon_t = \epsilon = Bt \left(\frac{S}{S_0} \right)^n$$

Thus $$\frac{\epsilon}{t} = B \left(\frac{S}{S_0} \right)^n \quad \text{or} \quad C = B \left(\frac{S}{S_0} \right)^n \tag{6-5}$$

where $C = \epsilon/t =$ the creep rate or the slope of the line EA in Fig. 6-9.

If the logarithms of both sides of eq. (6-5) are taken,

$$\log_{10} C = n \log_{10} S + \log_{10} \left(\frac{B}{S_0{}^n} \right) \tag{6-6}$$

Equation (6-6) represents a straight line on a log-log plot since it can be expressed by

$$y = nx + b \qquad (6\text{-}7)$$

where $y = \log_{10} C$ and $x = \log_{10} S$.

The agreement between the empirical relation expressed by eqs. (6-5) or (6-6) and test data is indicated in Fig. 6-10 for a carbon steel, at various temperatures. Figure 6-10 shows that the test points are close to the straight lines and that eq. (6-5) or (6-6) gives

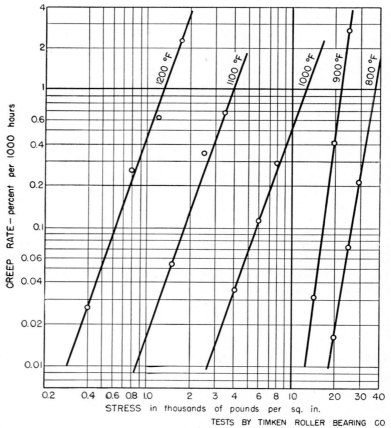

TESTS BY TIMKEN ROLLER BEARING CO

Fig. 6-10.   Creep rate-stress relation for "killed" carbon steel in tension.

a good approximation.[9] The value of n represents the slope of straight lines in Fig. 6-10, as can be seen from eq. (6-7), while $b = \log_{10} (B/S_0{}^n)$ is the intercept on the y-axis where $x = \log_{10} S = 0$ or $S = 1$. The constant S_0 is arbitrarily selected, a value of 1000 psi being commonly used.

The creep rate-stress relation expressed by eq. (6-5) is often referred to as the *log-log relation*. Among the empirical relations that have been proposed to express the variation between the creep strain and time are those represented in Table 6-1 and proposed by McVetty,[10] Weaver,[11] Sturm,[12] and Findley.[13]

Other Methods of Interpretation for Creep-Time Stress Relations.
The log-log creep rate-stress relation given by eq. (6-5) has an advantage over other methods because it is a simple relation and at the same time is a good approximation of the test data. Other methods have been proposed that, in some cases, may give better agreement with the test data but at the expense of considerable complication in the resulting relations. Some of these other methods will now be discussed.

Soderberg's method[14] assumes that the creep-time relations for various stress values and a constant temperature are geometrically similar. Mathematically this means that the creep deformation ϵ can be written as

$$\epsilon = F'T' \tag{a}$$

where F' is a function of the stress only and T' is a function of the time only.

In determining the values of F' and T' it is assumed that the creep curves approach asymptotically a minimum creep rate and that the arithmetical increments of stress produce geometrical increments in the creep rate. Based on these assumed conditions, the functions F' and T' become

$$F' = k_1 \left[\text{antilog} \left(\frac{S}{k_2} \right) - 1 \right] \tag{b}$$

---

[9] Many test results on metals collected in *Compilation of Available High-Temperature Creep Characteristics of Metals and Alloys*, published by the A.S.T.M. and A.S.M.E., March 1938, show that this log-log relation is in good agreement with many of the test results.

[10] "Factors Affecting the Choice of Working Stresses for High Temperature Service," by P. G. McVetty, *Trans. A.S.M.E.*, 1933, Vol. 55, p. 99.

[11] "The Creep Curve and Stability of Steels at Constant Stress and Temperature," *Trans. A.S.M.E.*, Nov. 1936, Vol. 58, No. 8, p. 745.

[12] "A Method of Analyzing Creep Data," by R. G. Sturm, C. Dumont, and F. M. Howell, *Trans. A.S.M.E.*, 1936, Vol. 58, pp. 62-67

[13] "Short-Time Static Tests and Creep Tests of a Paper Laminated Plastic," by W. N. Findley and W. J. Worley, *Proc. A.S.T.M.*, 1944, Vol. 44, pp. 949-969.

[14] "The Interpretation of Creep Tests for Machine Design," by C. R. Soderberg, *Trans. A.S.M.E.*, Nov. 1936, Vol. 58, No. 8, p. 733.

$$T' = t + k_3 \left[1 - \text{antilog} \left(\frac{t}{k_4} \right) \right] \qquad (c)$$

where k_1, k_2, k_3, and k_4 are experimental constants.

Substituting the values of F' and T' from eqs. (b) and (c) in eq. (a), the creep deformation ϵ in terms of the stress S and time t is defined by

$$\epsilon = k_1 \left[\text{antilog} \left(\frac{S}{k_2} \right) - 1 \right] \left\{ t + k_3 \left[1 - \text{antilog} \left(\frac{t}{k_4} \right) \right] \right\} \qquad (6\text{-}11)$$

Equation (6-11) defines the creep strain ϵ for a stress S at a time t in terms of the experimental constants k_1, k_2, k_3, and k_4.

For interpretation of creep test results of plastics in tension, Findley[13] proposed the creep rate-stress-time relation

$$C = k_1(\text{antilog } k_2 S - 1)t^{k_3} \qquad (6\text{-}12)$$

where C is the creep rate, S is the stress, t is the time, and k_1, k_2, and k_3 are experimental constants.

The Findley method of interpretation given by eq. (6-12) defines a creep rate for a given stress at a particular value of t. There are a number of methods of interpretation that assume that after the initial creep the creep rate becomes a constant. The hyperbolic sine, log, and log-log methods are of this type.

A hyperbolic sine-creep relation was proposed by Nadai.[15] By this relation the constant and minimum creep rate C in terms of the stress S is defined by the equation

$$C = k_1 \sinh \left(\frac{S}{k_2} \right) \qquad (6\text{-}13)$$

where k_1 and k_2 are constants.

The *log method of interpretation* of creep test results assumes that there is a linear relation between the logarithm of the constant minimum creep rate and the stress. That is, the relation between the constant creep rate C and the stress S is defined by

$$\log C = k_1 + k_2 S \qquad (6\text{-}14)$$

where k_1 and k_2 are experimental constants. Some test data on metals at high stresses and temperature have been found to agree with eq. (6-14).

The various equations outlined in the foregoing paragraphs for defining creep strain-stress-time relations are summarized in Table 6-1. In the various empirical relations that have been proposed, attempts are made to

---

[15] *The Influence of Time upon Creep—The Hyperbolic Sine Creep Law,* by A. Nadai, Stephen Timoshenko 60th Anniversary Volume, The Macmillan Co., New York, 1938, pp. 155-171.

Table 6-1

Creep-Time and Creep-Time-Stress Relations

Method	Creep-Time Relations	Eq. No.
McVetty's:	$\epsilon = k_1 + Ct - (k_1/k_2)$ antilog $(k_2 t)$	(6-8)
Weaver's:	$\epsilon = k_1 \log t - k_2 + Ct$	(6-9)
Sturm's or Findley's:	$\epsilon = k_1 t^{k_2}$	(6-10)

Method	Creep-Time-Stress Relations	Eq. No.
Log-Log:	$C = B(S/S_0)^n$	(6-5)
Modified Log-Log:	$\epsilon = D(S/S_0)^p + B(S/S_0)^n t$	(6-4)
Soderberg's:	$\epsilon = k_1(\text{antilog } S/k_2 - 1)$ $\{t + k_3[1 - \text{antilog } (t/k_4)]\}$	(6-11)
Findley's:	$C = k_1 [\text{antilog } k_2 S - 1]t^{k_3}$	(6-12)
Nadai's:	$C = k_1 \sinh S/k_2$	(6-13)
Log:	$\log C = k_1 + k_2 S$	(6-14)

Note: ϵ = creep strain, S = stress, C = creep rate, and t = time. The other symbols denote experimental constants whose values depend upon the material and the temperature. The same symbol in two different relations does not denote that the values of these constants are the same.

determine equations that fit the test data for periods of time covered by the tests. The time usually covered by the tests is 1000 hours. However, when the empirical equations determined on the basis of 1000-hour tests are used in design, they are extrapolated for periods of time not covered by the tests. In some instances these periods of time may be several years. It should be realized, therefore, that even if a method of interpretation fits the test data well, it may only approximately represent the actual situation when the results are extrapolated. A comparison of some of the methods of interpretation of test data[16] shows that there may be considerable difference in the allowable stress value depending on the method selected for extrapolating the test data. It is desirable, therefore, to obtain test data covering as long a period of time as possible. In this connection the A.S.T.M. Standards state: "Test periods of less than one per cent of the expected life are not deemed to give significant results. Tests extending to ten per cent of the expected life are preferable where feasible."

---

[16] "A Comparison of Methods used for Interpreting Creep Test Data," by J. Marin, *Proc. A.S.T.M.*, 1937, pp. 258-265.

Not all the methods of interpreting creep test results have been given, but the number that have been presented show that materials and test conditions vary to such an extent that one method of fitting the test data by a particular type of empirical equation is not suitable. Considerable data for both metals and plastics, however, appear to agree best with the log-log method of interpretation as given by eqs. (6-5). Because of the amount of supporting test data, and since the resulting equations are simple, the log-log method is recommended. Further support for this conclusion, at least for metals, is given in a recommendation made in the A.S.T.M. Standards: "For a particular temperature, log-log plots of stress versus rate of creep are desirable. Such plots are useful within the limits of determined values." Another advantage of the log-log method is that it leads to simpler mathematical treatment of the stress analysis of members subjected to creep and other types of stress such as bending, torsion, and combined states of stress.

Whatever method of interpretation of creep data is used, it is desirable, for purpose of design, to present design stress-creep strain relations as shown in Fig. 6-11. From these graphs a design stress can be selected for a given

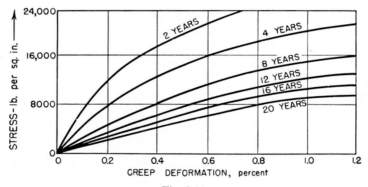

Fig. 6-11.

allowable creep deformation in a specified time or estimated life of the part. Figure 6-11 represents plots of empirical equations such as eqs. (6-5) for a given temperature.

It is sometimes desirable to plot a working stress diagram covering a range of possible operating temperatures. Figure 6-12 shows such a plot. For a specified temperature, and using Fig. 6-12, an allowable stress can be selected that will produce a creep strain less than a certain percentage in ten years. Attempts have been made to express empirical relations for

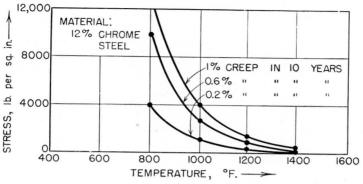

Fig. 6-12.

the allowable creep stress in terms of the temperature. Bailey[17] proposed the following relation between the constant minimum creep rate C, the stress S, and the temperature T:

$$C = (a_1 S^n)(\text{antilog } b_1 T) \tag{6-15}$$

where a_1, b_1, and n are experimental constants.

NUMERICAL EXAMPLE.   A steel member 10 ft. long is subjected to an axial tensile load of 10,000 lb. and an operating temperature of 400° C.   Find the cross-sectional area required for an estimated life of twenty years based on (a) a yield stress of 20,000 psi at 400° C., and a factor of safety of 2.0; (b) an estimated rupture stress of 24,000 psi at 400° C. at the end of twenty years, using a factor of safety of 3.0; and (c) an allowable creep rate of 0.001 in. per in. per year.   Based on creep, determine the area using the log-log relation $C = B(S/S_0)^n$, where $n = 7.0$, $S_0 = 1000$ psi, and $B = 5.2 \times 10^{-12}$ in. per in. per day.

SOLUTION.   (a) Based on a yield stress $S_{yp} = 20,000$ and a factor of safety $F = 2.0$, the required area is obtained from

$$A_1 = \frac{P}{S_w} = \frac{10,000}{(20,000/2)} = 1.0 \text{ sq. in.}$$

---

[17] "The Utilization of Creep-Test Data in Engineering Design," by R. W. Bailey, *Proc. Inst. of Mech. Engrs.*, London, Nov. 1935, Vol. 131.

(b) Using the rupture stress of 24,000 psi, the required area is obtained from

$$A_2 = \frac{P}{S_w} = \frac{10,000}{(24,000/3)} = 1.25 \text{ sq. in.}$$

(c) For an allowable creep rate of 0.001 in. per in. per year the design stress is

$$S_w = \left(\frac{C}{B}\right)^{1/n} S_0 = \left(\frac{0.001}{365 \times 5.2 \times 10^{-12}}\right)^{1/7.0} (1000) = 6570 \text{ psi}$$

The required area for an allowable creep stress of 6570 psi is

$$A_3 = \frac{P}{S_w} = \frac{10,000}{6570} = 1.50 \text{ sq. in.}$$

The governing area will be the largest of the three values A_1, A_2, and A_3, or 1.50 sq. in.

6-4. CREEP STRESS-RELAXATION IN TENSION

In the discussion of creep in tension, bending, and torsion, the condition in which applied loads and stresses remained unchanged with time was considered. There are a number of important engineering applications in which creep deformations take place with diminishing stress values. Such creep stress-relaxation conditions are encountered in bolted joints and assemblies with shrink- or press-fits. In a bolted flange connection used in a pipeline operating at elevated temperatures, the creep deformations produced with time in the bolts and flange produce a reduction or relaxation of the stress in the bolts. If the initial tension in the bolts is not the correct amount, the bolt will elongate and the flange will rotate. This leads to the reduction or relaxation of stress in the bolts. Loosening of the joint may eventually take place, with leakage at the connection occurring if it is not tightened. Bailey[17] and Baumann[18] have made theoretical investigations of stress relaxation. In these analyses the creep deformations of component parts are considered and stress-time relations are obtained.

Creep stress-relaxation properties of materials are usually determined by subjecting tensile specimens to constant temperature under

[18] "Some Considerations Affecting the Future Development of the Steam Cycle," by K. Baumann, *Engineering*, 1930, Vol. 130, p. 597. See also *Mechanical Properties of Materials and Design*, by J. Marin, McGraw-Hill Book Company, Inc., 1942, Chap. VI.

a decreasing load so that the specimen length remains fixed in value for the duration of the test.[19] In other words, a constant length means that the elastic plus the creep deformation remains constant. For this to be possible the increase in creep deformation must be balanced by a reduction in elastic deformation and, hence, by a reduc-

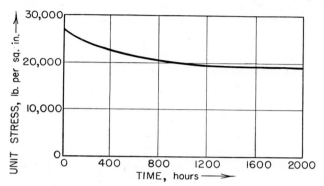

Fig. 6-13. Stress relaxation curve for SAE 4140 steel at 850° F.

tion in the stress. Figure 6-13 shows a stress-relaxation curve giving the variation in the stress with time for a fixed gage length or zero resultant deformation.

Various methods have been used to interpret stress-relaxation test results. Efforts have been made to predict stress-relaxation curves based on the constant-stress creep test results. The most common basis for predicting the stress-relaxation relation is to use the log-log stress-creep rate relation as given in eq. (6-5). Methods for predicting creep-stress relaxation using eq. (6-5) have been developed by Bailey,[17] Robinson,[20] and others. A modification of this theory for simple tension and constant deformation will now be developed.

Consider a test member in tension with provision for maintaining

[19] A review of investigations of this type are given in the A.S.M.E.-A.S.T.M. Joint Research Committee Report by E. L. Robinson, "The Resistance to Relaxation of Materials at High Temperatures," *Trans. A.S.M.E.*, 1938, Vol. 60, pp. 543-554.
[20] "A Relaxation Test on 0.35 C. Steel at 350° F.," by E. L. Robinson, *Trans. A.S.M.E.*, 1937, Vol. 59, p. 451. See also "A New Automatic Relaxation Machine," by A. Nadai and J. Boyd, *Trans. A.S.M.E.*, 1938, Vol. 60, p. A-118.

the length equal to the initially deformed length and let S_i = the initial tensile stress, ϵ_i = the initial elastic strain, C_i = the initial creep rate, S = the tensile stress at a time t, ϵ_e = the tensile elastic strain at a time t, ϵ = the tensile creep strain at a time t, and C = the creep rate at a time $t = d\epsilon/dt$.

If the deformation is to remain constant, then the initial elastic strain equals the sum of the elastic strain at a time t and the creep strain at a time t, or

$$\epsilon_i = \epsilon_e + \epsilon \tag{a}$$

The elastic stresses and strains are proportional by Hooke's law, so that

$$\frac{\epsilon_e}{\epsilon_i} = \frac{S}{S_i} \quad \text{or} \quad \epsilon_e = \frac{S}{S_i}\,\epsilon_i \tag{b}$$

Substituting the value of ϵ_e from eq. (b) in eq. (a),

$$\epsilon_i - \left(\frac{S}{S_i}\right)\epsilon_i - \epsilon = 0 \quad \text{or} \quad \epsilon + \epsilon_i\left(\frac{S}{S_i} - 1\right) = 0 \tag{c}$$

The creep deformation ϵ is defined by eq. (c) in terms of the initial elastic strain and the stresses S and S_i. Differentiating eq. (c) gives the equation

$$\left(\frac{d\epsilon}{dt}\right) + \left(\frac{\epsilon_i}{S_i}\right)\left(\frac{dS}{dt}\right) = 0$$

or

$$C + \left(\frac{\epsilon_i}{S_i}\right)\left(\frac{dS}{dt}\right) = 0 \tag{d}$$

Assuming the log-log creep-rate stress relation given by eq. (6-5),

$$C = B\left(\frac{S}{S_0}\right)^n \tag{e}$$

Placing the value of C from eq. (e) in eq. (d),

$$B\left(\frac{S}{S_0}\right)^n + \left(\frac{\epsilon_i}{S_i}\right)\left(\frac{dS}{dt}\right) = 0 \tag{f}$$

Separating the variables in eq. (f) and noting that $\epsilon_i = S_i/E$,

$$B\left(\frac{S}{S_0}\right)^n + \frac{1}{E}\left(\frac{dS}{dt}\right) = 0$$

or

$$dt = -\left(\frac{S_0{}^n}{EB}\right)\left(\frac{dS}{S^n}\right) \tag{g}$$

By integrating eq. (g),

$$t = \int_0^t dt = -\left(\frac{S_0^n}{EB}\right)\int_{S_i}^S \left(\frac{dS}{S^n}\right) = -\frac{S_0^n}{EB}\left[\frac{S^{1-n}}{1-n}\right]_{S_i}^S$$

$$= \left[\frac{S_0^n}{(n-1)BES^{n-1}}\right]\left[1 - \left(\frac{S}{S_i}\right)^{n-1}\right] \tag{6-16}$$

Equation (6-16) gives the stress-time relaxation relation. That is, the time t required for the stress to decrease from an initial value S_i to a value S is defined in terms of experimental constants S_0, n, B, and E for the material. Figure 6-14 shows a stress-relaxation curve for a medium carbon steel as obtained by eq. (6-16). A comparison

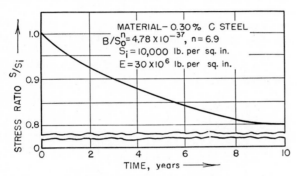

Fig. 6-14.   Stress-relaxation curve.

of Figs. 6-13 and 6-14 shows that the theoretical stress-relaxation curve is of the same shape as the actual curve. Both figures show that with increase in time the rate of decrease in stress is reduced, so that after a long period of time there is little change in the stress.

NUMERICAL EXAMPLE. A bolt is subjected to tension and is attached rigidly to two plates at its ends. Determine the value of the initial stress S_i so that the stress S at the end of two years is 80 per cent of the initial stress S_i. The bolt is subjected to an elevated temperature with $n = 7.0$, $B = 4.8 \times 10^{-9}$ in. per in. per day, $S_0 = 1000$ psi, and $E = 30 \times 10^6$ psi.

SOLUTION. From eq. (6-16) the value of $(S/S_i)^{n-1}$ is

$$\left(\frac{S}{S_i}\right)^{n-1} = 1 - \frac{(n-1)BES^{n-1}t}{S_0^n}$$

Hence $\left(\dfrac{0.8S_i}{S_i}\right)^6 = 1 - \dfrac{6 \times 4.8 \times 10^{-9} \times 3 \times 10^7 (0.8S_i)^6 \times 730}{10^{21}}$

$0.262 = 1 - 6.30 \times 10^{-19} \times 0.262 (S_i)^6$

and $S_i = 1280$ psi.

6-5. CREEP STRAINS AND STRESSES IN SIMPLE BENDING

The stresses and deflections in members subjected to creep in bending can be determined by making certain assumptions as in the elastic analysis. Three assumptions will be made; namely,

(1) A transverse cross section of the member remains plane after bending.

(2) For any fiber, the relation between the creep rate and stress is the same as for simple tension and is assumed to be given by the log-log relation between creep rate and stress, as defined by eq. (6-5).

(3) The creep rate-stress relation is the same for tension and compression.

Creep deflection rates in members subjected to bending, determined by tests, agree with values obtained theoretically based on the foregoing assumptions.[21]   The case considered in this analysis is a prismatic beam subjected to pure bending creep, as illustrated in Fig. 6-15.

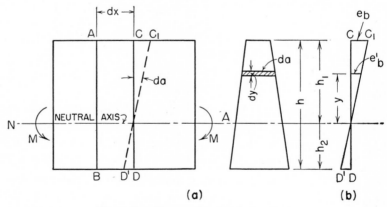

Fig. 6-15.   Beam subjected to bending.

[21] See "An Experimental and Analytical Investigation of Creep in Bending," by G. H. McCullough, *Trans. A.S.M.E.*, 1935, Vol. 55; "An Investigation of the Nature of Creep under Stresses Produced by Pure Flexure," by H. J. Tapsell, *Journ. Inst. of Metals*, August 1935, pp. 387-407; "Creep of Aluminum Subjected to Bending at Normal Temperatures," by J. Marin and L. Zwissler, *Proc. A.S.T.M.*, 1940; "Static and Dynamic Creep Properties of Laminated Plastics for Various Types of Stress," by J. Marin, *N.A.C.A. Tech. Note 1105*, April 1946, pp. 1-67.

In addition to the foregoing assumptions it is necessary that two conditions of equilibrium be satisfied as in the elastic theory. That is: (1) the summation of the stresses perpendicular to any cross section of the beam and at right angles to the longitudinal axis is zero, or $\Sigma F = 0$; and (2), the internal resisting moment produced by these stresses is equal to the external moment, or $\Sigma M = M$.

With the above assumptions and conditions of equilibrium the creep stress and deflection equations in bending can be determined. For this purpose let ϵ_b, C_b, and S_b be the creep deformation, creep rate, and stress respectively for the outer fiber, and ϵ_b', C_b', and S_b' be the corresponding values for any fiber at a distance y from the neutral axis. The moment M produces stresses that vary in magnitude over the cross section so that there is a line, the neutral axis, where the stress is zero (Fig. 6-15).

By assumption (1), or for plane sections to remain plane,

$$\frac{\epsilon_b}{\epsilon_b'} = \frac{h_1}{y} \tag{a}$$

Experiments show[21] that the creep rate becomes constant and a minimum creep rate is reached soon after the application of the load. If the creep strain intercept is neglected, then

$$\frac{C_b}{C_b'} = \frac{\epsilon_b}{\epsilon_b'} \tag{b}$$

By eqs. (a) and (b) the ratio of the creep rates is

$$\frac{C_b}{C_b'} = \frac{h_1}{y} \tag{c}$$

Using assumption (2), the relations between the creep rates and stresses are

$$C_b = B\left(\frac{S_b}{S_0}\right)^n \quad \text{and} \quad C_b' = B\left(\frac{S_b'}{S_0}\right)^n \tag{d}$$

The variation in the stress over the beam cross section can now be found from eqs. (c) and (d) by substituting values of C_b and C_b' from eqs. (d) in eq. (c), or

$$\frac{S_b}{S_b'} = \left(\frac{h_1}{y}\right)^{1/n} \tag{e}$$

Equation (e) shows that the stress variation is no longer linear as in the elastic case. In the elastic case the stress variation is linear because the strain variation is linear and the stress is proportional to the strain. For creep, however, the stress variation is not linear because although the strain variation is linear, the stress is not proportional to the creep strain. For $n = 1$, however, eq. (e) gives a variation in stress as in the elastic theory.

In combining eqs. (c) and (d) it is assumed that creep rate-stress relations for tension and compression are identical.

The position of the neutral axis can be found by using the first condition of equilibrium given above. That is, for the summation of the stresses over a cross section to be zero,

$$\int_{-h_2}^{h_1} S_b' \, da = 0 \tag{f}$$

where da is an element of the area as shown in Fig. 6-15.

For a rectangular cross section, $da = b\,dy$ and, by eqs. (e) and (f),

$$bS_b \left(\frac{1}{h_1}\right)^{1/n} \int_{-h_2}^{h_1} y^{1/n} \, dy = 0 \tag{g}$$

For eq. (g) to be satisfied, the integral must be zero, since the remaining terms are not zero. That is,

$$\int_{-h_2}^{h_1} y^{1/n} \, dy = 0 \qquad \text{or} \qquad \int_{0}^{h_1} y^{1/n} \, dy = \int_{0}^{h_2} y^{1/n} \, dy$$

or $h_1 = h_2 = h/2$. Then, for a rectangular cross section, the neutral axis coincides with the centroidal axis.

The actual stress distribution is obtained by the second condition of equilibrium. In other words, the resisting moment produced by the stresses must equal the external bending moment M, or for a rectangular cross section,

$$\int_{-h/2}^{h/2} yS_b' \, da = M \tag{h}$$

Substituting the value of S_b' from eq. (e) in eq. (h) and integrating, the stress on the outer fiber becomes

$$S_b = \left(\frac{Mh}{2I}\right)\left(\frac{2n+1}{3n}\right) \tag{6-17}$$

where $I = bh^3/12 =$ the moment of inertia of the cross section about the neutral axis.

Since the stress on the outer fiber, by the elastic theory, is $S_e = Mh/(2I)$, eq. (6-17) can be written as

$$S_b = S_e \left(\frac{2n+1}{3n}\right) \tag{6-18}$$

By eqs. (6-18) and (e), the stress for any fiber is

$$S_b' = S_e \left[\left(\frac{2y}{h}\right)^{1/n}\left(\frac{2n+1}{3n}\right)\right] \tag{6-19}$$

A comparison of the stress variation over the beam cross section for the case of creep compared to the elastic case can be obtained by using eq. (6-19). Values of the stress ratio S_b'/S_e versus the relative distance from the neutral axis, equal to $y/(h/2)$, are shown in Fig. 6-16 for two typical values of n used for steel. The linear stress variation for the elastic case is also shown in Fig. 6-16. An examination of the creep-stress variation in Fig. 6-16 shows

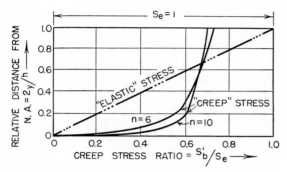

Fig. 6-16.   Stress distribution in bending accompanied by creep.

that it is more favorable than the elastic case for the same moment M, since the maximum creep stress is about $\frac{2}{3}$ the value of the maximum elastic stress for the values of n considered. The foregoing theory for the creep bending stress is essentially that presented by Tapsell[21] and Bailey.[17]

In the design of members subjected to creep in bending it appears from Fig. 6-16 that the design based on the elastic theory, with the appropriate design stress value, would be on the safe side. However, the design may

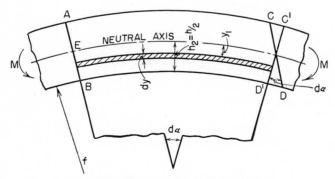

Fig. 6-17.   Member subjected to bending.

be governed by the allowable creep deflection. A theory based on the assumption made in obtaining the creep stress given by eq. (6-5) can be obtained for evaluating creep deflections in bending. To obtain the differential equation for creep deflection, consider Fig. 6-17. Assuming plane sections remain plane after bending, a cross section CD that is originally parallel to AB after bending relative to section AB, rotates to $C'D'$ so that the strains at distances h_2 and y are, respectively,

$$\epsilon_b = \frac{DD'}{BD} = \frac{h_2\,d\alpha}{f\,d\alpha} = \frac{h_2}{f}$$

and
$$\epsilon_b' = \frac{y}{h_2}\,\epsilon_b = \frac{y}{f} = C_b't \tag{i}$$

where f = the curvature due to creep and t = the time.

From the second of eqs. (i), $C_b' = y/(tf)$. The relation between the stress and the curvature can be found by placing this value of C_b' in eq. (d). Making this substitution, the stress S_b' becomes

$$S_b' = \left(\frac{y}{tfB}\right)^{1/n} S_0 \tag{j}$$

For equilibrium, the internal resisting moment equals the applied moment M, or

$$\int_{-h_2}^{h_1} y S_b'\,da = \left(\frac{1}{Bft}\right)^{1/n}(S_0)\int_{-h_2}^{h_1} y^{(1/n)+1}\,da = M \tag{k}$$

Also for equilibrium, the summation of the stresses must equal zero. For a rectangular cross section it was shown above that this condition gives $h_1 = h_2 = h/2$. Then by eq. (k),

$$M = \left(\frac{1}{Btf}\right)^{1/n}(S_0)\int_{-h/2}^{h/2} y^{(1/n)+1}b\,dy$$

$$= 2\left(\frac{1}{Btf}\right)^{1/n}(bS_0)\left[\frac{y^{(1/n)+2}}{1/n+2}\right]_0^{h/2}$$

$$= \left(\frac{1}{Btf}\right)^{1/n}(S_0)\left[\frac{2b(h/2)^{(1/n)+2}}{2+1/n}\right]$$

or
$$\left(\frac{D}{t}\right)\left(\frac{1}{f}\right) = M^n \tag{6-20}$$

where
$$D = \left(\frac{S_0}{B}\right)^n\left[\frac{(2b)^n(h/2)^{2n+1}}{(2+1/n)^n}\right] \tag{6-21}$$

For small deflections the curvature $1/f$ can be replaced by its value d^2y_c/dx^2 where y_c is the creep deflection. Then eq. (6-20) becomes

$$\left(\frac{D}{t}\right)\left(\frac{d^2y_c}{dx^2}\right) = M^n \tag{6-22}$$

Equation (6-22) is analogous to the equation $EI\ d^2y/dx^2 = M$ for the elastic case. The solution of eq. (6-22) for the creep deflection y_c depends upon the beam loading and the boundary conditions.

EXAMPLE. Determine an expression for the maximum creep deflection in a cantilever beam of rectangular cross section and length L subjected to an end-concentrated load. Use eq. (6-22).

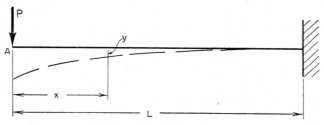

Fig. 6-18.

SOLUTION. If the origin of the beam is selected at the loaded end A, as shown in Fig. 6-18, the moment at a distance x from A is

$$M = Px \tag{1}$$

Placing the value of M from eq. (1) in eq. (6-22),

$$\left(\frac{D}{t}\right)\left(\frac{d^2y_c}{dx^2}\right) = P^n x^n \tag{m}$$

Integrating eq. (m) twice,

$$\left(\frac{D}{t}\right)\left(\frac{dy_c}{dx}\right) = \frac{P^n x^{n+1}}{n+1} + c_1 \tag{n}$$

$$\left(\frac{D}{t}\right) y_c = \frac{P^n x^{n+2}}{(n+1)(n+2)} + c_1 x + c_2 \tag{o}$$

For $x = L$, the slope $dy_c/(dx) = 0$ and the deflection $y_c = 0$, so by eqs. (n) and (o),

$$c_1 = \frac{-P^n L^{n+1}}{n+1} \tag{p}$$

and

$$c_2 = \frac{P^n L^{n+2}}{n+2} \tag{q}$$

The creep deflection y_c can now be found by substituting c_1 and c_2 from eqs. (p) and (q) in eq. (o), or

$$\left(\frac{D}{t}\right) y_c = \frac{P^n x^{n+2}}{(n+1)(n+2)} - \frac{P^n L^{n+1} x}{n+1} + \frac{P^n L^{n+2}}{n+2} \tag{r}$$

The maximum creep deflection occurs at $x = 0$, or by eq. (r),

$$(y_c)_{max} = \frac{t}{D}\left(\frac{P^n L^{n+2}}{n+2}\right) \tag{s}$$

6-6. CREEP STRAINS AND STRESSES IN TORSION

The theory for the shear creep stresses and strains in the torsion of a member of circular cross section can be obtained in a manner similar to that used in Article 6-5 for bending. To determine the stress distribution for the bar of circular cross section in Fig. 6-19 it will be assumed, as in the elas-

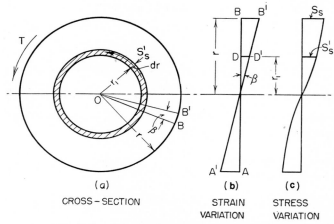

(a)
CROSS – SECTION

(b)
STRAIN
VARIATION

(c)
STRESS
VARIATION

Fig. 6-19.   Circular shaft subjected to torsion.

tic theory, that there is no distortion of the cross section in the longitudinal direction. That is, a plane cross section remains plane after loading. It will be assumed also that a radius OB remains a straight line and moves to the position OB' after loading Fig. 6-19. Then a point D moves to D' and

$$\frac{DD'}{BB'} = \frac{r_1}{r} \tag{a}$$

It will be assumed that the creep strains for the individual fibers in torsion vary with time as for creep in simple tension. Then if C_s' and C_s are the constant minimum creep rates respectively for the fibers at D and B,

$$\frac{C_s'}{C_s} = \frac{DD'}{BB'} \tag{b}$$

By eqs. (a) and (b) the creep rates vary as the distance from O, or,

$$\frac{C_s'}{C_s} = \frac{r_1}{r} \tag{c}$$

Some torsion tests on tubes of steel, by Everett,[22] show that the constant minimum creep rates can be expressed in terms of the shear stress by the relation

$$C_s = B_s \left(\frac{S_s}{S_{os}}\right)^n \tag{d}$$

where B_s, S_{os} and n are constants.

Figure 6-20 shows that eq. (d) is a good approximation.   By eq. (d) the

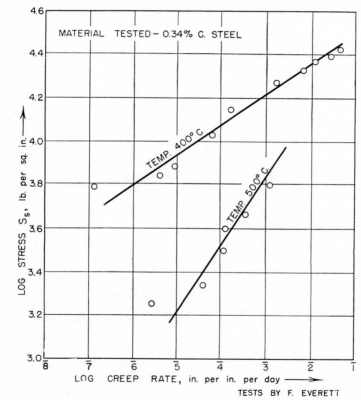

Fig. 6-20.   Creep rate stress relations for torsion.

[22] "The Strength of Materials Subjected to Shear at High Temperatures," by F. L. Everett, *Trans. A.S.M.E.*, 1931, Vol. 53, p. 117.

creep rates for the fibers at D and B are

$$C_s' = B_s \left(\frac{S_s'}{S_{os}}\right)^n \quad \text{and} \quad C_s = B_s \left(\frac{S_s}{S_{os}}\right)^n$$

Then the ratio of the creep rates is $C_s'/C_s = (S_s'/S_s)^n$, and by eq. (c),

$$S_s' = \left(\frac{r_1}{r}\right)^{1/n} S_s \tag{e}$$

The shear stress S_s' at any point on the cross section in terms of the twisting moment can now be determined by the condition of equilibrium that the summation of the internal twisting moments produced by the shear stresses equals the applied twisting moment. That is,

$$T = \int_0^r r_1 S_s' \, da \tag{f}$$

Noting that $da = 2\pi r_1 \, dr_1$ and placing the value of S_s from eq. (e) in eq. (f), it is possible to integrate eq. (f). Then

$$T = \int_0^r r_1 \left(\frac{r_1}{r}\right)^{1/n} S_s (2\pi r_1) \, dr_1$$

or

$$S_s = \left(\frac{Tr}{J}\right)\left(\frac{3n+1}{4n}\right) \tag{6-23}$$

That is, the maximum shear stress on the outer fiber equals the maximum shear stress by the elastic theory $S_{se} = Tr/J$ times the factor $(3n+1)/(4n)$, where n is an experimental constant. For purposes of comparing the shear stress distribution in creep with the elastic case, the value of $S_s = S_{se}(3n+1)/(4n)$ will be substituted in eq. (e). Then

$$S_s' = S_{se}\left[\left(\frac{3n+1}{4n}\right)\left(\frac{r_1}{r}\right)^{1/n}\right] \tag{g}$$

The shear stress distribution in creep, represented by eq. (g), is plotted in Fig. 6-21. In Fig. 6-21 the stress ratio S_s'/S_{se} is plotted versus the relative distance ratio (r_1/r) from the center of the section. A value of $n = 6$, representative of a medium-carbon steel, was used in plotting eq. (g). The elastic stress distribution is indicated by the straight-line variation shown in Fig. 6-21. A comparison of the creep and elastic shear stress distribution shows that the maximum shear stress in creep is less than the maximum in the elastic case. That is, the shear stress distribution in creep is more favorable than the elastic case, as was also found for pure bending. Since values of n are greater than one, the foregoing conclusion applies for all values of n, as can be shown by eq. (g).

In addition to the maximum shear stress it is necessary to consider the

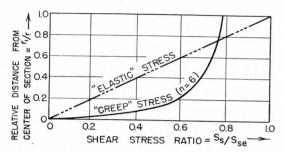

Fig. 6-21.   Stress distribution in torsion accompanied by creep.

allowable creep angle of twist in designing a torsion member.   If $\gamma = \beta/t$, is the minimum angular creep rate for a unit length where β is the creep angle per unit length, then the shear creep rate for the outer fiber is

$$C_s = r\gamma = \frac{r\beta}{t} \tag{h}$$

By eq. (d), $C_s = B_s(S_s/S_{os})^n$, and

$$(S_s)^n = \left(\frac{r}{B_s} \cdot \frac{\beta}{t}\right)(S_{os})^n \tag{i}$$

Substituting the value of S_s from eq. (6-23) in eq. (i),

$$\beta = \left[\frac{B_s t}{r(S_{os})^n}\right]\left(\frac{Tr}{J}\right)^n\left(\frac{3n+1}{4n}\right)^n \tag{6-24}$$

The angle of twist β per unit length of the member is defined in eq. (6-24) in terms of the twisting moment T, the radius of the cross section r, the polar moment of inertia of the cross section $J = \pi r^4/2$, the time t, and the material constants B_s, S_{os}, and n.   Since β is equal to the angular creep rate ($C_s r$) times the time, the initial creep is neglected in using eq. (6-24).   For long periods of time this initial creep is negligible.   With the foregoing expressions for the shear stress and angle of twist it is possible to design members of circular cross section subjected to twisting moments.

NUMERICAL EXAMPLE.   A steel shaft of circular cross section is 4 ft. long and is subjected to a twisting moment of 12,000 in. lb.   The shaft is to operate at a temperature of 400° C.   Determine the required shaft diameter if (a) the yield shear stress of the material at 400° C. is 30,000 psi and a factor of safety of 3 is to be used.   Solve by eq. (6-23) and use a value of $n = 9$. (b) The allowable angle of twist in twenty years is two degrees in twenty diameters of length.   Use values of $B_s = 1.60 \times 10^{-2}$ in. per in. per day, $S_{os} = 1000$ psi, $n = 9.0$, and eq. (6-24).

SOLUTION. The required diameter of the shaft based on the yield stress is obtained by eq. (6-23) if S_s is replaced by the allowable value $30,000/3 = 10,000$. Then

$$S_s = \left(\frac{Tr}{J}\right)\left(\frac{3n+1}{4n}\right) = \frac{(Td/2)}{(\pi d^4/32)}\left(\frac{3n+1}{4n}\right) = 10,000$$

or

$$d = \sqrt[3]{\frac{4T(3n+1)}{10,000\pi \times n}}$$

$$= \sqrt[3]{\frac{4 \times 12,000 \times 28}{10,000 \times \pi \times 9}} = \sqrt[3]{4.75} = 1.68 \text{ in.}$$

When eq. (6-24) is used, the required diameter based on the allowable angle of twist can be found by noting that $\beta = 2\pi/(180 \times 20d)$ radians per inch length, $t = 20$ years $= 20 \times 365$ days, $n = 9$, $r = d/2$, and $J = \pi d^4/32$. That is, by eq. (6-24),

$$\frac{\pi}{1800d} = \frac{B_s}{(S_{os})^n}\left(\frac{t}{r}\right)\left(\frac{Tr}{J}\right)^n\left(\frac{3n+1}{4n}\right)^n$$

$$= \left(\frac{1.60 \times 10^{-2} \times 7300 \times 2}{1000^9 \times d}\right)\left(\frac{12,000 \times d/2}{\pi d^4/32}\right)^9\left(\frac{7}{9}\right)^9$$

and

$$d^{27} = \left(\frac{1.60 \times 10^{-29} \times 7300 \times 2}{\pi^{10}}\right)\left(\frac{12,000 \times 16 \times 7}{9}\right)^9 (1800)$$

or $d = 5.60$ in.

The required diameter will therefore be the larger of the two values, or 5.60 in.

6-7. CREEP STRAINS FOR COMBINED STRESSES

There are a number of important applications in machine design, such as pipe lines, pressure vessels, turbine disks, and rotors, where the members are subjected to combined stresses and an elevated temperature. The elevated temperature in some cases is large enough so that it is necessary to consider the creep deformations. That is, the part must be designed so that the maximum creep strain shall not exceed some permissible value. It is desirable to formulate a theory whereby the creep strains in the case of combined stresses can be predicted based on creep constants of the material in simple tension.

There have been several theories proposed for predicting creep rates for combined states of stress in terms of the material creep constants in simple tension. Bailey,[17] Soderberg,[23] Odquist,[24] and others have proposed such

---

[23] "The Interpretation of Creep Tests for Machine Design," by C. R. Soderberg, *Trans. A.S.M.E.*, Nov. 1936, Vol. 58, No. 8, p. 733. See also *Plasticity and Creep in Machine Design*, by C. R. Soderberg, Stephen Timoshenko 60th Anniversary Volume, The Macmillan Co., 1938, pp. 197-210.

theories. A theory for predicting creep rates under combined stresses, that agrees approximately with the few experimental results available, will be presented. This theory, called the "Modified St. Venant Theory," was first presented by Soderberg.[23]

In 1870, St. Venant proposed the basic equations of plasticity, which are still used. A modification of these plasticity equations can be made so that they may be used for formulating the creep rates under combined stresses. To determine values of the principal creep rates C_1, C_2, and C_3, in the directions of the principal stresses S_1, S_2, and S_3, three assumptions will be made as follows:

(1) The directions of the principal creep strains coincide with the directions of the principal stresses at all times.

(2) The volume of the material remains constant. If ϵ_1, ϵ_2, and ϵ_3 are the creep strains in the principal stress directions, then for the volume to remain constant,

$$\epsilon_1 + \epsilon_2 + \epsilon_3 = 0 \tag{a}$$

(3) The principal shear creep strains are proportional to the principal shear stresses. To formulate the third assumption it is first necessary to express the values of the principal shear creep strains and stresses. These are

$$\gamma_1 = \epsilon_1 - \epsilon_2, \quad \gamma_2 = \epsilon_2 - \epsilon_3, \quad \gamma_3 = \epsilon_3 - \epsilon_1 \tag{b}$$

and the principal shear stresses are

$$S_{s1} = \frac{(S_1 - S_2)}{2}, \quad S_{s2} = \frac{(S_2 - S_3)}{2}, \quad S_{s3} = \frac{(S_3 - S_1)}{2} \tag{c}$$

By the third assumption that the principal shear stresses and strains are proportional,

$$\frac{\gamma_1}{S_{s1}} = \frac{\gamma_2}{S_{s2}} = \frac{\gamma_3}{S_{s3}} = k_1'$$

or

$$\frac{\epsilon_1 - \epsilon_2}{S_1 - S_2} = \frac{\epsilon_2 - \epsilon_3}{S_2 - S_3} = \frac{\epsilon_3 - \epsilon_1}{S_3 - S_1} = \frac{k_1'}{2} = k_1 \tag{d}$$

Equations (a) and (d) can be solved to determine the strains in terms of the stresses. Doing this we get

$$\left.\begin{aligned}
\epsilon_1 &= \frac{k_1}{3}\left[(S_1 - S_2) - (S_3 - S_1)\right] \\[6pt]
\epsilon_2 &= \frac{k_1}{3}\left[(S_2 - S_3) - (S_1 - S_2)\right] \\[6pt]
\epsilon_3 &= \frac{k_1}{3}\left[(S_3 - S_1) - (S_2 - S_3)\right]
\end{aligned}\right\} \tag{e}$$

---

[24] "A Theory of Creep under Combined Stresses," by F. Odquist, Royal Swedish Institute for Engineering Research, Stockholm, 1934. See also *Proc. 4th International Congress on Applied Mechanics*, 1934, p. 228.

If the creep rates are assumed to be constant and the initial creep is neglected, then $C_1 = \epsilon_1/t$, $C_2 = \epsilon_2/t$, and $C_3 = \epsilon_3/t$ and eqs. (e) can be written

$$C_1 = \frac{k_2}{3}\left[(S_1 - S_2) - (S_3 - S_1)\right]$$

$$C_2 = \frac{k_2}{3}\left[(S_2 - S_3) - (S_1 - S_2)\right] \qquad \left.\right\} \qquad \text{(f)}$$

$$C_3 = \frac{k_2}{3}\left[(S_3 - S_1) - (S_2 - S_3)\right]$$

where $k_2 = k_1 t$ may be considered as a creep modulus of the material.

To be correct, eqs. (f) must apply for the case of simple tension. For simple tension, $C_1 = C$, $S_2 = S_3 = 0$, and $S_1 = S$. Then by eq. (f),

$$C = \frac{2}{3}k_2 S = \frac{2}{3}\frac{k_1 S}{t} \qquad \text{(g)}$$

Since the creep rate is not linearly related to the stress S, the quantity k_2 cannot be a constant but is some function of the stress. In the case of combined stresses, k_1 would be some function of the combined stresses. It will be assumed that there is an equivalent stress S_e in simple tension such that the rate of dissipation of shear energy per unit time is the same as under combined stresses. The rate of dissipation of distortion energy is

$$\frac{du_d}{dt} = \frac{d}{dt}(u - u_v) \qquad \text{(h)}$$

where u = the total strain energy = the sum of the distortion energy u_d and the energy to change volume u_v. But

$$u = S_1\epsilon_1 + S_2\epsilon_2 + S_3\epsilon_3 \qquad \text{(i)}$$

and, since there is no volume change,

$$u_v = 0 \qquad \text{(j)}$$

Placing the values of ϵ_1, ϵ_2, and ϵ_3 from eqs. (e) in eq. (i),

$$u = \frac{k_1}{3}\left[(S_1 - S_2)^2 + (S_2 - S_3)^2 + (S_3 - S_1)^2\right] \qquad \text{(k)}$$

From eqs. (h), (j), and (k),

$$\frac{du_d}{dt} = \frac{d}{dt}\left\{\frac{k_1}{3}\left[(S_1 - S_2)^2 + (S_2 - S_3)^2 + (S_3 - S_1)^2\right]\right\} \qquad \text{(l)}$$

The rate of dissipation of distortion energy for the equivalent tensile stress is obtained from eq. (l) by noting that for tension, $S_1 = S_e$, $S_2 = S_3 = 0$, or

$$\frac{dV}{dt} = \frac{d}{dt}\left[\left(\frac{2k_1}{3}\right)(S_e^2)\right] \tag{m}$$

By eqs. (l) and (m), since the rates of dissipation of distortion energy are assumed to be equal for the case of combined stresses and for the equivalent simple tension case, by equating the right-hand sides of eqs. (l) and (m) and solving for S_e,

$$S_e = \frac{1}{\sqrt{2}}\sqrt{(S_1 - S_2)^2 + (S_2 - S_3)^2 + (S_3 - S_1)^2} \tag{n}$$

The creep rate corresponding to this stress is, by eq. (g),

$$C_e = \frac{2}{3}k_2 S_e \tag{o}$$

For simple tension it will be assumed that the log-log creep rate-stress relation applies. That is,

$$C_e = B\left(\frac{S_e}{S_0}\right)^n \tag{p}$$

Equating the values of C_e from eqs. (o) and (p),

$$k_2 = \frac{3}{2}\left(\frac{B}{S_0^n}\right)S_e^{n-1} \tag{q}$$

Substituting the value of S_e from eq. (n) in eq. (q) the value of k_2 becomes

$$k_2 = \left(\frac{3B}{S_0^n}\right)\left(\frac{1}{2^{\frac{n+1}{2}}}\right)[(S_1 - S_2)^2 + (S_2 - S_3)^2 + (S_3 - S_1)^2]^{\frac{n-1}{2}} \tag{r}$$

The value of k_2 is now determined, and by eqs. (f) the principal creep rates are

$$
\left.
\begin{aligned}
C_1 &= \left(\frac{B}{S_0^n}\right)\left(\frac{1}{2^{\frac{n+1}{2}}}\right)[(S_1 - S_2)^2 + (S_2 - S_3)^2 + (S_3 - S_1)^2]^{\frac{n-1}{2}} \\
&\qquad\qquad (2S_1 - S_2 - S_3) \\
C_2 &= \left(\frac{B}{S_0^n}\right)\left(\frac{1}{2^{\frac{n+1}{2}}}\right)[(S_1 - S_2)^2 + (S_2 - S_3)^2 + (S_3 - S_1)^2]^{\frac{n-1}{2}} \\
&\qquad\qquad (2S_2 - S_3 - S_1) \\
C_3 &= \left(\frac{B}{S_0^n}\right)\left(\frac{1}{2^{\frac{n+1}{2}}}\right)[(S_1 - S_2)^2 + (S_2 - S_3)^2 + (S_3 - S_1)^2]^{\frac{n-1}{2}} \\
&\qquad\qquad (2S_3 - S_1 - S_2)
\end{aligned}
\right\} \tag{6-25}
$$

Equations (6-25) define the principal creep rates in the direction of the principal stresses S_1, S_2, and S_3, and the creep constants for tension B, S_0, and n. The application of these equations in design will be illustrated by the following example.

EXAMPLE. Determine the required wall thickness of a thin-walled cylindrical vessel subjected to creep due to an internal pressure p. The internal diameter is d and the wall thickness is t. Assume that the ends of the vessel are closed. Determine the allowable wall thickness if the allowable creep rate C_w and the Modified St. Venant Theory, defined by eqs. (6-25), are used.

SOLUTION. For a thin-walled cylindrical vessel subjected to internal pressure the stresses are

$$S_1 = \frac{pd}{2t}, \quad S_2 = \frac{pd}{4t}, \quad S_3 = 0 \tag{s}$$

Placing the values of the stresses from eqs. (s) in eqs. (6-25) and equating the creep rates to the allowable value C_w, the equations for t are found. By the first of eqs. (6-25),

$$C_1 = C_w = \left(\frac{B}{S_0^n}\right)\left(\frac{1}{2^{\frac{n+1}{2}}}\right)\left[\left(\frac{pd}{2t_1} - \frac{pd}{4t_1}\right)^2 + \left(\frac{pd}{4t_1}\right)^2 + \left(\frac{pd}{2t_1}\right)^2\right]^{\frac{n-1}{2}}\left(2\frac{pd}{2t_1} - \frac{pd}{4t_1}\right)$$

$$= \left(\frac{B}{S_0^n 2^{\frac{n+1}{2}}}\right)\left(\frac{pd}{4t_1}\right)^n (6)^{\frac{n-1}{2}} (3) = \left(\frac{B}{S_0^n}\right)\left(\frac{pd}{4t_1}\right)^n \left(\frac{3^{\frac{n+1}{2}}}{2}\right)$$

or

$$t_1 = \left(\frac{3^{\frac{n+1}{2}}B}{2C_w}\right)^{1/n}\left(\frac{pd}{4S_0}\right) \tag{t}$$

Similarly, the second and third of eqs. (6-25) give $t_2 = 0$,

and

$$t_3 = \left(\frac{3^{\frac{n+1}{2}}B}{2C_w}\right)^{1/n}\left(\frac{pd}{4S_0}\right) \tag{u}$$

A comparison of eqs. (t) and (u) shows that t_1 is equal to t_3. That is, the required wall thickness t is given by eq. (t) or (u) in terms of the pressure p, the diameter d, the material constants B, n, and S_0, and the allowable creep rate C_w.

Figure 6-22 shows the variation in the working creep stress for two-dimensional stresses. The graphs shown are determined from eqs. (6-25) by placing $S_3 = 0$ and equating the creep rates C_1, C_2, and C_3 to their allowable values of $C_w = BS_w^n/S_0^n$, where S_w = the working stress in simple tension. That is, by the first of eqs. (6-25),

$$S_w^n = \tfrac{1}{2}(S_1^2 - S_1 S_2 + S_2^2)^{\frac{n-1}{2}}(2S_1 - S_2) \tag{v}$$

Then the allowable value of S_1 can be obtained from eq. (n) by rewriting this equation as follows:

$$S_w{}^n = \tfrac{1}{2}(S_1)^{n-1}(1 - R + R^2)^{\frac{n-1}{2}}(S_1)(1 - R)$$

or
$$S_1 = \frac{S_w}{[\tfrac{1}{2}(1 - R + R^2)^{\frac{n-1}{2}}(2 - R)]^{1/n}} \qquad \text{(w)}$$

where R = the stress ratio S_2/S_1 and is less than one, since S_1 is considered the larger of the two stresses S_1 and S_2.

Similarly for the creep rates C_2 and C_3,

$$S_1 = \frac{S_w}{[\tfrac{1}{2}(1 - R + R^2)^{\frac{n-1}{2}}(2R - 1)]^{1/n}} \qquad \text{(x)}$$

and
$$S_1 = \frac{S_w}{[\tfrac{1}{2}(1 - R + R^2)^{\frac{n-1}{2}}(-R - 1)]^{1/n}} \qquad \text{(y)}$$

The governing value of S_1 is the maximum of the values given by eqs. (w), (x) and (y). The value to be selected is best illustrated by plotting the values of S_1/S_w versus $R = S_2/S_1$ for each of equations (w), (x) and (y), as shown in Fig. 6-22. In Figure 6-22 the governing values of the working stress S_1 are represented by the ordinates to the solid curves for a given stress ratio $R = S_2/S_1$, since the ordinates to the dotted curves are greater and, hence, do not give the governing working stress. For example, for a

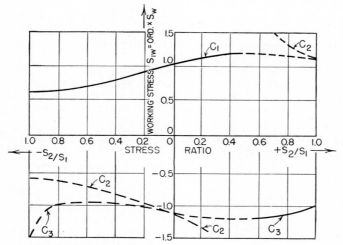

Fig. 6-22.   Working-stress values for two-dimensional stress for $n = 6$.

stress ratio $R = S_2/S_1 = 0.2$, the values of S_1/S_w, or ordinates to the curves, are about 1.1, -1.3, and -1.2, so that the value selected for $S_1/S_w = 1.1$, or $S_1 = 1.1S_w$.

Applications of combined stresses including rotating disks and thick-walled cylinders subjected to internal pressure and creep are given in the references indicated in Footnotes 17, 23, and 24. A comparison of combined creep test results and theories is summarized in the reference given in Footnote 25. The physical theory of creep, the mechanism of creep, and the influence of metallurgical variables on creep are discussed in the references given in Footnotes 26 and 27.

PROBLEMS

6-1. In tension creep tests of a steel alloy the following unit creep strains were obtained:

Time (hours)	Tensile stresses in psi			
	3000	5000	8000	11,000
0	0	0	0	0
50	0.020	0.045	0.099	0.135
200	0.028	0.053	0.140	0.238
400	0.030	0.055	0.149	0.305
600	0.031	0.058	0.155	0.368
800	0.033	0.062	0.164	0.433
1000	0.035	0.065	0.173	0.520

(a) Plot the creep-time curves for each stress, using the foregoing data. Use Cartesian coordinates. (b) Determine minimum creep rates in Prob. 6-1(a) using the average slope between 500 and 1000 hours. (c) With the data obtained in Prob. 6-1(b), determine the creep constants B and n in the equation $C = B(S/S_0)^n$, where $S_0 = 1000$ psi.

6-2. Determine the constants k_1 and k_2 in Prob. 6-1, using the semi-log relation given by eq. (6-14).

6-3. From tension creep tests of a canvas-base laminated plastic the following creep strains were obtained:

[25] *Mechanical Properties of Materials and Design*, by J. Marin, McGraw-Hill Book Co., Inc., New York, 1942.

[26] *Metallic Creep*, by A. H. Sully, Interscience Publishers, Inc., New York, 1949.

[27] *The Creep of Metals and Alloys*, by E. G. Sanford, Temple Press Ltd., London, 1949.

Time (hours)	Tensile stresses in psi			
	2680	4000	5270	6380
0	0	0	0	0
0.02	0.0021	0.0026	0.0035	0.00575
20	0.0027	0.0034	0.0042	0.0088
40	0.0030	0.00355	0.0045	0.00985
60	0.0032	0.0037	0.0047	0.01035
100	0.00335	0.0038	0.0051	0.0109
150	0.0034	0.0039	0.0053	0.0113
200	0.00345	0.0040	0.0054	0.0115
400	0.0035	0.0042	0.0056	0.0117
600	0.0036	0.00425	0.0058	0.0119
800	0.0037	0.00435	0.00595	0.0121

(a) Plot the creep strain-time curves for each of the stresses using the foregoing data. (b) Using the data in Prob. 6-3(a), obtain the minimum creep rates C and the material creep constants B and n in the empirical relation $C = B(S/S_0)^n$ if $S_0 = 1000$ psi.

6-4. Determine the material creep constants in Prob. 6-3, using the semi-log method in place of the log-log method.

6-5. A steel member 10 ft. long is subjected to an axial tensile load of 10,000 lb. and an operating temperature of 400° C. The creep constants in the relation $C = B(S/S_0)^n$ for the material at 400° C. are $B = 4.52 \times 10^{-16}$ in. per in. per day, and $n = 6.80$. Find the cross-sectional area required based on (a) A yield stress of 25,000 psi at 400° C. and a factor of safety of 2.0. (b) An allowable creep of 0.020 in. per in. in twenty years. (c) A rupture stress of 20,000 psi at 400° C. in twenty years, using a factor of safety of 2.5. (Given: $S_0 = 1000$ psi.)

6-6. A member is 4 ft. long and is subjected to an axial tensile load of 3000 lb. What is the total creep strain in ten years using the log-log relation $C = B(S/S_0)^n$ with $B = 3 \times 10^{-10}$ in. per in. per day, and $n = 4.2$? The cross-sectional area of the member is 1.2 sq. in. (Given: $S_0 = 1000$ psi.)

6-7. A steel member 10 ft. long is subjected to an axial tensile load at an operating temperature of 400° C. The creep constants in the creep rate-stress relation $C = BS^n/S_0^n$ are $B = 4 \times 10^{-12}$ in. per in. per day, $n = 7.0$, and $S_0 = 1000$ psi. The cross-sectional area of the member is 1.0 sq. in. Determine the allowable tensile load based on (a) a yield stress of 25,000 psi at 400° C., using a factor of safety of 2.0, and (b) an allowable creep rate of 0.001 in. per in. per year. *Ans.* 6810 lb.

6-8. A steel bolt is subjected to an axial tensile load between two rigid plates so that the length of the bolt remains constant. The bolt is subjected to an elevated temperature so that creep is produced. What must be the initial stress so that 70 per cent of the stress is retained after ten years? Use the relaxation relation based on the log-log method, with values of $n = 6.0$, $B = 4.2 \times 10^{-8}$ in. per in. per day, $S_0 = 1000$ psi, and $E = 30 \times 10^6$ psi.

6-9. A member is subjected to an initial tension of 2000 psi and relaxation of the stress occurs since it is subjected to an elevated temperature and the length of the member is maintained constant. Find the time required for the stress to become 1800 psi if the log-log method is used, with $n = 8.0$, $B = 7.2 \times 10^{-9}$ in. per in. per day, $S_0 = 1000$ psi, and $E = 30 \times 10^6$ psi.

6-10. Determine an expression for the maximum creep deflection in a beam simply supported and subjected to a center-concentrated load. Use eq. (6-22).

6-11. A cantilever beam of length L is subjected to a triangular loading that varies from zero at the free end to w lb. per ft. at the fixed end. Using eq. (6-22), determine an expression for the maximum creep deflection.

6-12. A cantilever beam of square cross section and length $L = 4$ ft. is subjected to an end-concentrated load $P = 2000$ lb. Determine the cross-sectional dimensions if (a) the creep stress is not to exceed 10,000 psi and $n = 6$ [use eq. (6-17)], and the creep deflection is to be less than $\frac{1}{30}$ of the beam length in five years. Use eq. (s) in Article 6-5 and values of $B = 8 \times 10^{-6}$ in. per in. per day, $S_0 = 1000$ psi, and $n = 6$.

Ans. $b = 0.27$ in., $h = 3.46$ in.

6-13. Using the semi-log creep rate-stress in place of the log-log relation, determine expressions for the maximum creep stress and angle of twist for a member of circular cross section subjected to twisting.

6-14. A steel shaft 4 ft. long and of circular cross section with a diameter $d = 4$ in. is subjected to a twisting moment at 500° C. Determine the allowable twisting moment if (a) the yield shear stress of the material is 20,000 psi at 300° C. and a safety factor of 2.5 is used. Solve by eq. (6-23) and use a value of $n = 6$. (b) The allowable angle of twist in ten years is 2 degrees in 20 diameters of length. Use values of $B_s = 8 \times 10^{-12}$ in. per in. per day, $S_{os} = 1000$ psi, and $n = 6$. Solve by eq. (6-24). *Ans.* 88,500 in. lb.

6-15. A bolt is subjected to a tensile load and is rigidly attached at its ends. Determine the time required for the stress to relax 20 per cent if the bolt is subjected to an elevated temperature. Use values of $n = 7.0$, $B = 6.8 \times 10^{-12}$ in. per in. per day, $S_0 = 1000$ psi, and $E = 30 \times 10^6$ psi. An initial load of 20,000 lb. was applied to the bolt and the cross-sectional area is 2 sq. in. Use eq. (6-16). *Ans.* 2.3 days.

6-16. Obtain an expression similar to eq. (6-16) based on the semi-log creep-rate stress relation given by eq. (6-14).

6-17. A thin-walled pressure vessel of circular cross section is subjected to an internal pressure at an elevated temperature. It has a diameter of 20 in. and a wall thickness of 1 in. What is the allowable pressure using (a) the shear theory and an allowable stress in simple tension of 10,000 psi; (b) an allowable creep strain of 0.005 in. per in. in two years. Use the Modified St. Venant Theory and values of $B = 5.8 \times 10^{-12}$ in. per in. per day, $n = 8$, and $S_0 = 1000$ psi. *Ans.* (a) 1000 psi, (b) 675 psi.

6-18. Determine expressions for the creep rates in a closed circular tube subjected to creep and to both an internal pressure and an axial tensile load, using the Modified St. Venant Theory.

6-19. A thin-walled spherical shell is subjected to internal pressure at an elevated temperature so that creep is produced. Obtain expressions for the creep rates using the St. Venant Theory.

BIBLIOGRAPHY

Bailey, R. W., "The Utilization of Creep-Test Data in Engineering Design," *Proc. Inst. of Mech. Engrs.*, London, 1935, Vol. 131, pp. 131-349.

Clark, F. H., *Metals at High Temperatures*, Reinhold Publishing Corp., New York, 1950.

Freudenthal, A. M., *The Inelastic Behavior of Engineering Materials and Structures*, John Wiley & Sons, Inc., New York, 1950.

Rotherham, L., *Creep of Metals*, Institute of Physics, London, 1951.

Smith, G. V., *Properties of Metals at Elevated Temperatures*, McGraw-Hill Book Co., Inc., New York, 1950.

Soderberg, C. R., "The Interpretation of Creep Tests for Machine Design," *Trans. A.S.M.E.*, Nov. 1936. See also "Plastic Flow and Creep in Polycrystalline Metals," *Proc. 5th Int. Congress on Applied Mechanics*, 1938; and *Plasticity and Creep in Machine Design*, Stephen Timoshenko 60th Anniversary Volume, The Macmillan Co., New York, 1938.

Stanford, E. G., *The Creep of Metals and Alloys*, Temple Press Ltd., London, 1949.

Sully, A. H., *Metallic Creep*, Interscience Publishers, Inc., New York, 1949.

PART TWO

Specific Materials

Chapter 7

Structure of Materials;

Control of Their Properties

7-1. INTRODUCTION

An important consideration in the design of structures and machines is the selection of the material most suitable for the given application. In selecting the material the engineer not only must consider the various possible materials that can be used, but also should evaluate the potential properties of each material. The possible properties in a finished part are dependent on both the chemical composition and the methods of fabrication. The properties may therefore be controlled by both chemical and mechanical means.

The mechanical properties of materials are affected by chemical and mechanical changes because these changes influence the structure of materials. Members of machines and structures are made up of numerous crystals, fibers, grains, or similar units arranged in some geometrical pattern. For a metal, the unit is the grain or crystal, which consists of a large number of atoms arranged in a definite manner, called a space lattice, as explained in Chapter 1. The characteristics of the space lattice are determined by the chemical composition, whereas the shape, size, and relative orientation of the grains are controlled by mechanical or physical operations. In the case of a nonmetallic material, the unit is usually a long chain molecule of fiber. A simple view of the structure of matter, sufficient for engineering purposes, is presented below.

7-2. STRUCTURE OF MATTER

Whereas the smallest aggregate of matter is the molecule or crystal, the smallest unit of an element itself is the atom. All atoms, in turn, consist of varying numbers of still smaller particles called electrons, protons, and neutrons. The electron has a negative charge of 4.8×10^{-14} ESU (electrostatic units) and a mass of 9.1×10^{-28} grams. Each element differs in the number of electrons in its outer shell. The electron is thus a basic component of the atom of the element, which consists of both outer-shell rotating electrons and a central nucleus.

In the case of the simplest element, hydrogen, the nucleus consists of a single particle called the proton, which has a positive charge equal in value to that of the electron, but has a mass of 1.67×10^{-24} grams, or 1840 times that of the electron. Other elements differ from hydrogen in having a greater number of protons in the nucleus and also in having in the nucleus various numbers of neutrons. The number of protons in the nucleus controls the chemical properties of the substance and is known as the atomic number of the element. A neutron, as its name implies, has no charge; it has a mass approximately the same as that of the proton. The simplest element containing both protons and neutrons would be an isotope of hydrogen called *heavy hydrogen*, from which *heavy water* is made. This element contains one proton and one neutron in its center nucleus, and one electron rotating about this nucleus. Since the number of protons in heavy hydrogen is the same as that for ordinary hydrogen, the chemical properties of the two substances are alike even though their masses are different.

All of the elements in the periodic table may be considered to be built from these three basic units. Oxygen, for example, consists of 8 electrons rotating about a nucleus containing 8 protons and 8 neutrons. It thus has an atomic weight of 16 and an atomic number of 8. As another example, mercury has a nucleus consisting of 80 protons and 120 neutrons, and has in its outer shell orbit 80 electrons. Since, as already mentioned, the chemical properties of the substance are governed by the number of protons in the nucleus, the addition of an extra neutron would not affect the chemical activity of the substance but would produce what is known as an isotope of the element in question. For example, heavy hydrogen, or deuterium, is an isotope of hydrogen of mass 2, whereas tritium, containing one proton and two neutrons in the nucleus, is a hydrogen isotope of mass 3. The addition or subtraction of an electron from the outer orbit produces what is known as a negative or positive *ion*, depending on whether the electron is added or subtracted.

The atoms of the various elements differ somewhat in size but, in general, they are of the order of 1 angstrom, namely, 10^{-8} centimeters. For example, copper has an atomic radius of 1.0 angstrom units; gold, 1.4 angstrom units; hydrogen, 2.1 angstrom units.

The smallest aggregates of the element (rather than the smallest units) are known as molecules. Molecular dimensions are not a great deal larger than atomic dimensions. For example, hydrogen gas, H_2, has a molecular radius of about 2.4 angstroms, and oxygen gas, O_2, about 3.0 angstroms. The number of molecules in a gram molecule, that is, in an amount of the substance in grams equal to its molecular weight, is the same for all elements, namely, 6.2×10^{23}, and is known as Avogadro's number.

Many substances, of course, are not gaseous at room temperatures, but may exist in either the liquid or the solid state. Sodium chloride, for instance, is crystalline in nature and is held together by the ionic bonds between the positive sodium and the negative chlorine ion. Whether an element exists at room temperature as a gas, as a liquid, or as a solid depends entirely on the nature of the forces or bonds holding the various units of the element together. These forces may be valence, electrostatic, or dipole forces, but they are governed entirely by the nature of the constituent parts of the atom and their interactions. Most of the elements that we know as metals tend at room temperature to form a so-called *lattice structure*. Again depending on the nature of the force between the units of the element, the lattice structure may be simple cubic, face-centered cubic, body-centered cubic, hexagonal, etc. In all instances, however, the atoms are in definite locations and the crystal, as a whole, is highly ordered compared, say, to the same crystal when heated above its melting temperature. Nonmetallic materials, such as wood and plastics, on the other hand, do not possess definite lattice structure. Here, the individual atoms tend to form in terms of fibers, or of long-chain molecules. The particular formation is again dependent on the nature of the material in question and on how it has been produced.

In general, we are interested in the atomic and molecular structure of matter because of the fact that this structure vitally affects the mechanical properties. It does so, in general, in two ways: first, through the nature of the chemical composition itself and, secondly, through the nature of the physical arrangement of the constituent atoms. For example, aluminum and copper are both crystalline at room temperatures and both possess the same type of lattice structure. Yet, their properties are vastly different because the elements themselves are different and the nature of the bonding forces is different. On the other hand, marble and limestone are examples of materials having the same chemical composition ($CaCO_3$), and yet they, too, have vastly different properties because, in this case, the physical or geometrical arrangement of the units is different. The potential properties of any element or group of elements that form an alloy are thus governed by its chemical composition, which controls its basic structure lattice type, and by the physical arrangement of the individual crystals or grains, which is governed largely by the nature of the fabrication process.

7-3. INFLUENCE OF CHEMICAL COMPOSITION AND MECHANICAL TREATMENT ON PROPERTIES

It has been noted that the properties of a material may be changed by modifying the constituents themselves or their geometrical structural arrangement. The modifications in the crystals are produced by physical and chemical means, and each method affects the continuity of the slip planes, thereby altering the resistance to slipping.

There are two ways in which chemical composition influences the mechanical properties. One method is the addition of a second material to a base material where a homogeneous assembly of crystals results, having a uniform composition and containing atoms of both materials. The disruption of the symmetry of the slip plane of the base material by addition of atoms of the second material sets up forces that tend to increase the resistance to shear and, hence, the strength is increased. A second method by which chemical composition affects mechanical properties is the case of mixtures of crystals of two or more typical compositions, with each composition having different properties. The properties of the whole will then depend on the properties of each component and their relative abundance. For example, steel consists of brittle crystals of iron carbide (Fe_3C) interspersed among relatively ductile iron crystals. The hard crystals greatly increase the strength of the resultant material. As shown in Fig. 8-9, one per cent carbon in steel gives a tensile strength more than twice as great as 0.1 per cent carbon.

Mechanical properties can be changed by physical methods in two ways, either by a change in the orientation of the slip planes, or by a change in the size of crystals. Properties of crystals are not isotropic and differ in different directions, so that by controlling the orientation of the crystals the properties of a material can be changed.

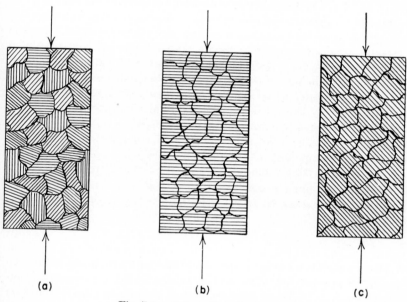

Fig. 7-1.   Orientation of crystals.

If the crystals in a given metal are not in a random orientation, as in Fig. 7-1(a), but are oriented as in Fig. 7-1(b) so that the applied load has a zero component in the direction of slip, then the strength is increased. The worst orientation, offering the least resistance to slip, is that shown in Fig. 7-1(c), where the slip planes for all the crystals are at 45° to the direction of the applied compressive load. If the crystals in a metallic member are arranged with slip planes and glide directions parallel, the properties of the mass will be approximately the same as the properties of the single crystals. With random orientation, which is the more usual case, it is to be expected that the properties of the mass will tend to be the average of the properties of individual crystals oriented in different possible directions. Shaping operations, as forging and rolling, produce orientation of crystals and different properties in one direction compared to another.

In addition to orientation of crystals, a change in their size will change the material's properties. It is well known that a material made up of many small crystals or grains is much stronger than the same material made of large crystals. With a fine-grained material the amount of slip possible along the slip planes is limited by the restraint produced by the adjacent grains that have slip planes in other directions, or by the amorphous nature of the grain boundaries themselves. The size of crystals may be changed either by changing the rate of cooling while the material goes from the liquid to the solid state or by the application of mechanical treatments.

It has been pointed out that the properties of materials can be controlled through (1) control of chemical composition, (2) control in rate of cooling, and (3) control in fabrication operations. The changes produced by cooling will be considered by a study of cooling curves and equilibrium diagrams. This will be followed by a summary of the influence on properties produced by various fabrication operations.

7-4. COOLING CURVES

A large number of engineering materials in their manufacture go through a process of heating and melting with subsequent reduction in temperature. The procedure used in cooling has been found to have a marked effect on the properties of the material produced. In metallurgy, many principles have been discovered that make possible the control of properties by proper temperature changes. In the manufacture of glass and clay products, properties may also be modified by a control of temperature changes.

When a molten metal cools to a solid state the temperature does not usually fall in a uniform manner, but changes by stages brought about by the state of the metal and the type of alloy. Cooling curves can be obtained if the temperatures are measured at equal intervals of time and the data plotted on temperature-time diagrams as shown in Fig. 7-2.

Graph (a) in Fig. 7-2 shows a cooling curve of a pure metal. The

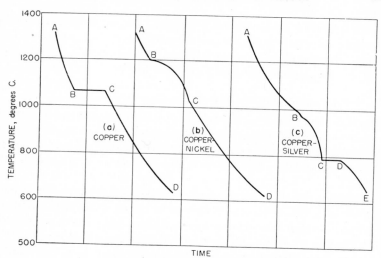

Fig. 7-2. Typical cooling curves.

cooling of a pure metal proceeds at a decreasing rate from a temperature at A to that at B, remaining entirely liquid to B. At B it solidifies and as freezing continues, heat is liberated in such amounts that the temperature remains constant from B to C until the mass has entirely solidified. The solid then cools along the line CD.

For two metals that form a solid solution, a cooling curve such as curve (b) in Fig. 7-2 is obtained. In this type of cooling the liquid cools along the line AB to a temperature B when the liquid begins to solidify, not as two separate metals but as a solid solution of the two metals dissolved in each other. With continued freezing the temperature drops along the line BC until the entire mass has solidified, after which the solid cools along the line CD.

Curve (c) in Fig. 7-2 is the cooling curve for two metals that dissolve in each other while liquid but do not remain dissolved in each other while solid. The liquid cools along the line AB until the temperature B is reached, at which point some crystallization takes place. When the temperature has dropped to C, a stable composition (the eutectic mixture) is reached, and freezing continues along line CD. After point D is reached, the solid cools along the line DE. The mass is molten in region AB, partly liquid from B to D, and entirely solid from D to E.

The foregoing three curves are typical of most cooling curves, although complex alloys may have several critical points on the curves. Equilibrium diagrams for any alloy can be constructed with the use of cooling curves.

7-5. EQUILIBRIUM DIAGRAMS

With data from the cooling curves obtained for different compositions, curves representing equilibrium diagrams can be constructed. These diagrams show graphically the behavior of a mixture of metals on cooling, and are sometimes called composition or constitution diagrams.

There are three main types of diagrams, namely, the *layer type*, the *solid-solution type*, and the *eutectic type*. Although there are various combinations, these three represent three characteristic actions that may occur when two liquids are mixed and cooled.

Layer-Type Diagram. The layer-type diagram is the simplest and is obtained when the two materials are mutually insoluble and form neither chemical compounds nor solutions. Lead and aluminum are metals that give this type of diagram, as shown in Fig. 7-3. These metals are mutually insoluble. In Fig. 7-3 the temperatures in degrees are plotted as ordinates and the compositions as abscissas.

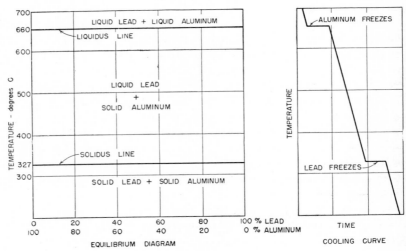

Fig. 7-3.   Layer-type diagram.

The left boundary of the figure represents pure aluminum, while the right is pure lead. The line at 660° F. represents the boundary between a liquid mixture and a mixture of solid aluminum in liquid lead. This line where a solid begins to form is called the *liquidus*. At the horizontal line of 327° C. all the lead becomes solid, so that below this line, called the *solidus*, there exists a solid mixture of lead and aluminum. For materials with the layer-type diagram, when cooled from a liquid state, regardless of the percentage of the two elements, one solidifies at a particular temperature and, with further cooling, the other solidifies as indicated in Fig. 7-3. For purposes of correlation with time, the cooling curve showing the temperature-time relation is also given in Fig. 7-3.

Solid-Solution-Type Diagram. This type of diagram is obtained when the two materials are soluble in each other. This is possible if both constituents have the same type of lattice and have approximately the same size atoms. Gold and silver are two such materials. Figure 7-4 shows their equilibrium diagram, the left boundary representing pure gold and the right pure silver. The upper of the two curves, the *liquidus*, represents the temperature at

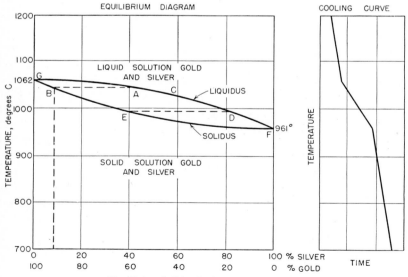

Fig. 7-4.   Solid-solution-type diagram.

which solidification begins. That is, it represents a change from a completely liquid state to a combination of liquid and solid. The lower curve, or *solidus*, indicates the temperature at which solidification is complete, or is the boundary between the solid state and the combined liquid-and-solid state. Changes of state can be predicted from the diagram after the boundary lines are established. For example, a mixture of 40 per cent silver and 60 per cent gold when cooled from 1500° C. will reach a temperature indicated by point A. Crystallization then begins and the crystals formed have the composition indicated by point B. The formation of the crystals increases the proportion of silver present in the remaining liquid so that freezing of more crystals will not take place until the temperature is lowered to a point designated, for example, by C. The crystals formed at the temperature A will not be in equilibrium with the liquid at C. To reach a state of equilibrium, the crystals will absorb more silver. This process continues with reduction in temperature. At point D the precipitating crystals have the composition as indicated by point E, or 40 per cent silver and 60 per cent gold. The process continues until all the liquid solidifies. Diffusion between the crystals of varying composition continues to take place even after complete solidification. This diffusion, if the cooling is sufficiently slow, will cause the final crystals at room temperature to have the same composition as the initial composition of 40 per cent silver and 60 per cent gold. When adequate time is not permitted for cooling, equilibrium will not be established. Then as freezing continues, the liquid will become richer in silver. With continued decrease in temperature, the last crystal to form at F will be silver and, therefore, variation in the composition of the solid results. Little diffusion will now take place because of the rapid rate of cooling and, hence, the final product at room temperature will consist of crystals of widely varying composition.

The properties and structure of solid solutions can be explained by considering their space lattices. A solid solution of two metals will be formed in all proportions if the atoms of one can replace atoms in the space lattice of the other. The replacement, in general, occurs in a random manner, as indicated in Fig. 7-5(a). For certain combinations of materials, a definite pattern known as an *ordered lattice* or *super lattice* is formed. An ordered lattice is shown in Fig. 7-5(b), where the atoms of one metal occupy the corners of the lattice and the atoms of the other metal occupy the center position. An ordered lattice is possible only when the atoms of the two metals are present in the proper proportions.

The super lattice pattern of atoms represents a more stable condition, with higher strength and hardness than with the random arrangement. Usually, for each composition, there is a particular temperature above which a super lattice cannot exist. When a

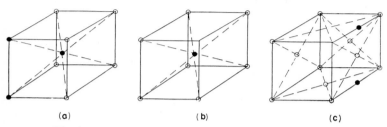

(a)   (b)   (c)

Fig. 7-5.   Types of lattice structures for solid solutions.

material is cooled rapidly or quenched from the critical temperature range to room temperature, the formation of the super lattice is retarded. Acceleration in the formation of the super lattice structure may be produced, however, by annealing or reheating the material to a temperature below the critical temperature and allowing the slow cooling of the alloy.

If the lattices of two metals are not approximately the same in size and if they are not of the same type, they will not be mutually soluble. The reason for this is that in order for the replaced atom to be in equilibrium, the forces that the neighboring atoms exert on a given atom must remain approximately the same for the two metals. It is found that for metals with the same type of lattice and for differences in atom size of less than 8 per cent the metals are mutually soluble in all proportions and the liquidus tends to be convex upward. For a difference of atom size between 8 and 15 per cent, however, the metals are still mutually soluble but the liquidus is convex downward and tends to become tangent to the solidus at a temperature lower than the freezing point of either metal, approaching the behavior of the eutectic shown in Fig. 7-6.

Finally, if the difference in atom size between the two metals exceeds 15 per cent, the metals are not usually mutually soluble in all proportions.   The structure for this case is shown in Fig. 7-5(c) and is known as an *interstitial solid solution*.   This structure can occur only if the atoms of one metal are small enough to fit into the spaces between the atoms of the other.   Hydrogen, nitrogen, and carbon combine with some metals in this way.   The introduction of the atoms of one element into the space lattice of a second produces a local disturbance of the slip planes resulting in an increase in the strength of the new material.

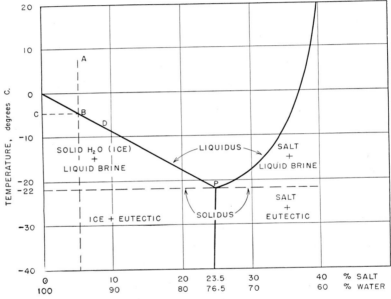

Fig. 7-6.   Eutectic-type equilibrium diagram.

Eutectic-Type Equilibrium Diagram.   The type of equilibrium diagram obtained when two materials form a eutectic is shown in Fig. 7-6.   The eutectic corresponds to point *P* in Fig. 7-6 and is that mechanical mixture of two materials which has the lowest possible freezing point of any combination of the two materials. A eutectic has a definite freezing point and chemical composition but it is not a chemical compound.   Each grain is a mixture of particles of one constituent with particles of the other.   A characteristic of eutectics is that they possess high strength and hardness in addition to the lowest possible melting point.

Referring to the equilibrium diagram in Fig. 7-6, if a liquid mixture of salt and water, at a temperature and of composition indicated by point A, is slowly cooled, freezing begins when point B is reached, with crystals of ice being formed (corresponding to point C obtained by projecting the horizontal line from the liquidus to the solidus). The formation of ice increases the percentage of salt in the liquid, hence lowering the freezing point to point D. The selective freezing continues until point P, the eutectic, is reached. Then all the remaining liquid freezes in the form of the eutectic, the entire mass on the average still having the composition indicated by point A. The term eutectic refers to the formation of a solid solution from a liquid. When the mixture is formed from a solid solution the term eutectoid is used. Both a eutectic and a eutectoid are shown in Fig. 7-7.

There are also *combination types* of equilibrium diagrams representing combinations of the foregoing three basic types. Figure 7-7 shows an equilibrium diagram of two materials that exist as a solid solution in one range of temperature but undergo a transformation

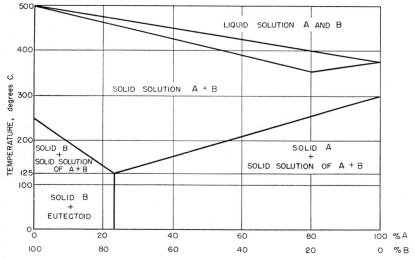

Fig. 7-7. Equilibrium diagram for solid solution and eutectoid.

with decrease in temperature—the lower part of the diagram yielding the eutectic-type and the upper part the solid-solution-type diagram.

The equilibrium diagrams discussed above are for the condition of slow cooling and are, in general, reversible. That is, if a solid solution is heated it will begin to liquefy at the solidus line and will be completely liquefied when the liquidus line is reached.

With rapid cooling the transformations indicated are only partially fulfilled and the high-temperature characteristics may be retained at room temperatures. When the eutectoid properties are not desired, quenching is used, since with quenching there is not sufficient time for the formation of the eutectoid.

Equilibrium diagrams are important because they show the nature of the material formed during cooling. The properties of many materials depend upon the treatment they receive during cooling and the treatment desired can be determined by a study of the equilibrium diagram. For example, if the solid solution of two materials A and B in Fig. 7-7 is different from the mixture of the eutectoid and material A, and if the properties of the solid plus the eutectoid are desired, then from an examination of the equilibrium diagram we know that the material cannot be used above 125° C. This is because the material would be changed from the solid plus the eutectoid with the desired properties to the solid solution with the undesirable properties. On the other hand, if the properties of the solid solution are desired, means are considered to prevent the formation of the eutectoid on cooling. This may be done by adding a third element or by altering the cooling rate from slow to fast. Rapid cooling will prevent the formation of the eutectoid, thus yielding the desired solid solution.

7-6. INFLUENCE OF FABRICATION METHODS ON PROPERTIES

A complete study of the many fabrication methods used to form materials into commercial shapes is beyond the scope of this text.[1] For this reason only the influence of fabrication methods on the mechanical properties of the finished product will be the main concern of this article. This is an important consideration when it is realized that the mechanical properties of materials as obtained from

---

[1] For a complete treatment see J. F. Young, *Materials and Processes*, John Wiley & Sons, Inc., 1944; and W. H. Clapp and D. S. Clark, *Engineering Materials and Processes*, International Textbook Co., 1938.

specimens may be quite different from those of the material in the finished product, as a result of the changes produced by the fabrication process.

Methods of fabrication involve operations that may be classified into four groups: (1) casting, (2) cold and hot working, (3) fastening, and (4) finishing. *Casting* consists of pouring the material in a liquid form into a mold of the shape required and allowing the liquid to become solid. *Cold and hot working* involve operations such as rolling, forging, extruding, and drawing, where the material is hammered or pressed into the desired shape while it is in a plastic though solid condition. *Fastening* together of parts involves the attachment together of members by welding, brazing, and riveting. Parts are also combined by pressing together materials to form laminated constructions. *Finishing* includes many operations that serve to improve the appearance and surface properties or reduce the part to the desired dimensions.

Casting. Materials that are difficult to shape in the solid state, except by grinding, are formed into shape by casting in molds. Many alloys of both the ferrous and nonferrous types have been developed for casting. When many parts of either simple or complex shape are to be made, casting is a suitable method of production. Sand casting, as shown in Fig. 7-8, is used for a large part of metal

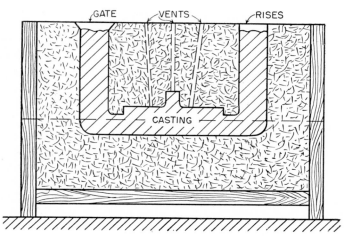

Fig. 7-8.   Mold for steel casting.

production. When smooth finishes are desired, plaster-of-Paris molds are used in place of sand. When accuracy of the dimensions is important, hardened alloy-steel molds are employed and the metal is cast under a high pressure. The casting produced is called a *die casting*. Concrete structures and ceramic products are formed to the desired shapes by casting in molds. Plastics of various kinds and glass may also be fabricated by casting.

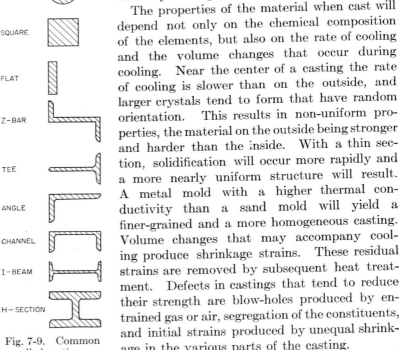

ROUND

SQUARE

FLAT

Z-BAR

TEE

ANGLE

CHANNEL

I-BEAM

H—SECTION

Fig. 7-9. Common rolled sections.

The properties of the material when cast will depend not only on the chemical composition of the elements, but also on the rate of cooling and the volume changes that occur during cooling. Near the center of a casting the rate of cooling is slower than on the outside, and larger crystals tend to form that have random orientation. This results in non-uniform properties, the material on the outside being stronger and harder than the inside. With a thin section, solidification will occur more rapidly and a more nearly uniform structure will result. A metal mold with a higher thermal conductivity than a sand mold will yield a finer-grained and a more homogeneous casting. Volume changes that may accompany cooling produce shrinkage strains. These residual strains are removed by subsequent heat treatment. Defects in castings that tend to reduce their strength are blow-holes produced by entrained gas or air, segregation of the constituents, and initial strains produced by unequal shrinkage in the various parts of the casting.

Rolling. Rolling is used to produce most structural alloy shapes as, for example, angles, channels, and rail sections (Fig. 7-9). Sheet material, plates, and round, square, and other shaped bars are also manufactured by rolling. Rolling may be done at elevated temperatures, when it is known as *hot-rolling*, or close to room temperatures and below the recrystallization temperature, when it is known as *cold-rolling*.

In hot rolling the coarse grain structure of castings or ingots is refined, orientation of crystals is changed, the metal becomes more homogeneous, and both strength and ductility are increased. By comparison, the cold-working operation produces a grain distortion (Fig. 7-10) with a resulting large increase in yield strength and hardness, a reduction in the ductility, and a better finish. This change

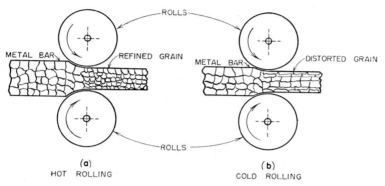

Fig. 7-10.   Rolling of metal.

occurs because the crystal form imposed by rolling below the critical temperature is maintained and the properties thereby altered. When rolling is done just above the critical temperature the crystals are reduced in size, producing an increase in strength but not a decrease in ductility. This is possible because there is not sufficient time on cooling to the critical temperature for readjustment of crystal boundaries, so that a fine-grained structure giving both strength and ductility is retained. Compared to cold-rolling, however, the strength increase is not as great.

Forging.   Small and large metal parts are produced by forging. Usually forging is done by placing a billet or slab of the material in a die of proper shape and pressing or hammering the metal into place (Fig. 7-11). Sheet-metal parts, as used in aircraft and automobiles are made by a modification of the forging process, known as *press-forming* or *stamping*.

Forging has the same general effects on the properties as are produced by rolling. When a metal is forged into shape, refinement of the grain or strain-hardening is produced. A grain-like appearance of the material results that is due to the elongation of the crystals.

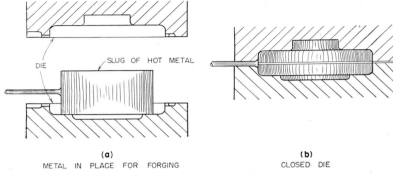

(a)

METAL IN PLACE FOR FORGING

(b)

CLOSED DIE

Fig. 7-11.   Flow of metal in a forging die.

When forging is conducted at the correct temperatures, grain size is reduced by the mechanical working and an increase in strength results with no reduction in ductility.

Extrusions.   Extrusions are produced by applying pressure to a rod so as to force it through a die or opening—the cross section of

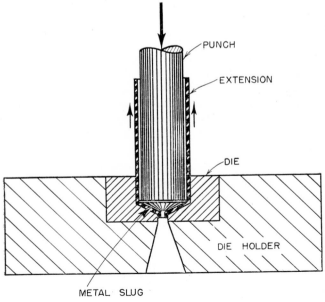

Fig. 7-12.   Impact extruding of tubing.

the die forming the outline of the piece being shaped, as shown in Fig. 7-12. Many metals and alloys, clay products such as brick and tile, as well as plastics and textile fibers, are formed by extruding.

Metal extrusions as a result of their method of manufacture have directional properties. In forcing the metal through the dies, stresses well above the elastic limit are produced. This results in refinement of the grain structure and in strain-hardening.

Other methods of forming include *drawing*, used to produce wire and tubing, *piercing*, for the manufacture of seamless tubing, and *spinning*, used for the fabricating of thin-walled pressure vessels.

Riveting. The fabrication of many complicated constructions can be achieved by using simple members and connecting them in different ways. Common types of connections are bolts, rivets, nails, screws, and other fasteners. The advantage of these is that complicated constructions can be made by using simple rolled or extruded parts; the disadvantage is that bulky connections often result.

Welding and Brazing. Welding is defined as the intimate joining or consolidating of metals, through application of heat or through application of heat and pressure combined. Brazing differs from welding in that a molten nonferrous filler metal, with a melting point below that of the metals being joined, is used.

Welded connections may have defects including incomplete joining of parts with resulting seams; oxide inclusions produced by overheating during welding; and cooling strains. However, under properly controlled conditions, these defects may be considerably reduced and a welded joint may have a strength that exceeds that of the base metal.

Laminated Constructions are used so that a nonisotropic material can be made to produce a product that is essentially isotropic. For example, in plywood the grain in any one layer is at right angles to the adjacent layer, resulting in a more nearly isotropic sheet. Laminated constructions are used in safety glass and in the manufacture of many plastic products.

Powder Metallurgy has been developed commercially only in recent years although the technique has been known for over a century. The process consists of placing the material to be shaped, which is in the form of a fine powder, into a die of the desired form. Pressure is applied to consolidate the mass. The compact mass is then removed from the die and placed in a furnace for a short time at a temperature less than the melting point of the material. The part is finally heat-treated. The properties of the product resulting from this procedure depend upon the composition of the powder used, the size, shape, and gradation of the particles, the pressure used during consolidation, and on the heat-treatment used.

Selection of Materials and Processes. The choice of the best material and process to be used for a given construction or product is not always a simple matter. It is necessary first to decide what the main property requirements are and then to consider the materials that have these properties. Often strength and other mechanical properties are not the most important consideration, and the appearance, resistance to corrosion, weight, method of fabrication, or cost may be the deciding factor in the selection of a material.

PROBLEMS

7-1. Metal A, with a freezing point of 1750° C., and metal B, with a freezing point of 1050° C., form a solid solution in all proportions. For a mixture having 50 per cent of metal A and 50 per cent of metal B, freezing begins at 1530° C. and the mixture becomes entirely solid at 1180° C. Draw the equilibrium diagram and designate the areas in this diagram.

7-2. Lead forms a eutectic with silver at 300° C. This eutectic contains 5 per cent silver and 95 per cent lead. Construct the equilibrium diagram.

7-3. Tin and lead, with freezing points of 232° C. and 327° C. respectively, form a eutectic containing 65 per cent tin and 35 per cent lead. Construct the equilibrium diagram and label the areas.

7-4. Two metals A and B are mutually insoluble in any proportions. The freezing points for A and B are 620° C. and 320° C. respectively. Draw the equilibrium diagram and label the areas.

7-5. Copper and nickel form a solid solution in all proportions. The freezing points of copper and nickel are 1090° C. and 1450° C. respectively. A mixture containing 50 per cent of each begins to freeze at 1300° C. and becomes entirely frozen at 1210° C. Draw the equilibrium diagram.

7-6. Outline the changes that take place when a mixture of 40 per cent gold and 60 per cent silver is cooled from 1200° C. (Fig. 7-4).

7-7. Describe the changes that take place when a mixture of 65 per cent water and 35 per cent salt has its temperature reduced from 20° C. to −40° C. (Fig. 7-6).

7-8. Describe the changes that occur in a mixture of 75 per cent of element A and 25 per cent of element B (Fig. 7-7) when cooled from 600° C. to 0° C.

BIBLIOGRAPHY

Barrett, C. S., *Structure of Metals*, McGraw-Hill Book Co., Inc., New York, 1943.

Chalmers, B., *The Structure and Mechanical Properties of Metals*, John Wiley & Sons, Inc., New York, 1951.

Freudenthal, A. M., *The Inelastic Behavior of Engineering Materials and Structures*, John Wiley & Sons, Inc., New York, 1950.

Hollomon, J. H., and Jaffe, L. D., *Ferrous Metallurgical Design*, John Wiley & Sons, Inc., New York, 1947.

Houwink, R., *Elasticity, Plasticity and Structure of Metals*, Cambridge University Press, London, 1937.

Jeffries, Z., and Archer, R. F., *Science of Metals*, McGraw-Hill Book Co., Inc., New York, 1924.

Sachs, G., and Van Horn, K. L., *Practical Metallurgy*, American Society for Metals, Cleveland, 1940.

Seitz, F., *The Physics of Metals*, McGraw-Hill Book Co., Inc., New York, 1943.

Young, J. F., *Materials and Processes*, John Wiley & Sons, Inc., New York, 1944.

Metals Handbook, American Society for Metals, Cleveland, 1948.

Chapter 8

Ferrous Metals and Alloys

8-1. INTRODUCTION

In this chapter on Ferrous Metals, and in Chapters 9 and 10 on Nonferrous Metals and Nonmetallic Materials, a brief description is given of the manufacture, uses, and properties of specific materials. Emphasis is placed on the discussion of factors that influence the mechanical properties, thereby giving a basis for the correct selection of a material for use in a given application.

The basis for the selection of a material for a given purpose involves a number of considerations. Four main considerations are the properties, the method of fabrication or manufacture, the cost, and the availability of the material. In addition to the mechanical properties, electrical, acoustical, thermal, and optical properties are sometimes important considerations. The method of fabrication is influenced by the character of the part to be manufactured, and the material selected is often governed by the method of manufacture that can be used.

In estimating the cost of the material, the final cost rather than the initial cost must be considered. A change in design or shop operation may be helpful in eliminating extra charges such as those for particular tolerances, special composition, special heat-treatment, particular size or form, and special surface finish. Cost of metals and alloys is also increased when specifications include metallographic and magnaflux inspection, grain-size restrictions, annealing, stress-relieving, and straightening requirements.

8-2. COMPOSITION OF FERROUS ALLOYS

Common ferrous metals such as steel, cast iron, and wrought iron are primarily alloys of iron and carbon containing small amounts of sulphur, phosphorus, silicon, and manganese. Steel alloys are obtained by combining steel with nickel, chromium, molybdenum, vanadium, or certain other elements added to modify the physical and mechanical properties.

The composition of steel is essentially carbon and iron with a percentage of carbon by weight, usually varying from 0.10 to 2.0 per cent. Wrought iron may be considered as a low-carbon steel with small amounts of slag, usually less than three per cent. The carbon content of wrought iron is generally less than 0.10 per cent. The rolling operation employed in the manufacture of wrought iron results in long fibrous elements of slag. These slag fibers serve to distinguish wrought iron from steel. Commercial cast irons have high carbon contents varying from about 2.0 to 4.5 per cent. Ordinary cast iron is called "gray" cast iron and is produced by slow cooling. Slow cooling separates some of the carbon in the form of graphite, which gives gray cast iron a characteristic color at fracture. The carbon that does not separate in the form of graphite remains chemically combined with iron to form iron carbide or *cementite* (Fe_3C). Rapid cooling of molten cast iron does not permit the formation of graphite, and "white" cast iron is produced. White cast iron derives its name from the fact that a fractured surface of this material has a characteristic silvery white color. The composition of the ferrous metals is more completely explained by the use of an equilibrium diagram.

8-3. EQUILIBRIUM DIAGRAM FOR THE IRON-CARBON SYSTEM

The iron-carbon equilibrium diagram is shown in Fig. 8-1. In general, the crystals formed in combining iron and carbon are either solid solutions or eutectics or both. The solid solution is one of carbon in iron called austenite, and the eutectic is a saturated austenite and carbide of iron (Fe_3C) or cementite. Cementite is the hardest constituent in iron and steel. In order to understand the mechanism of crystallization of steel, consider a steel with 0.2 per cent carbon, representing structural steel, heated to 1600° C. and then slowly cooled. When the temperature has been reduced to a point A

(Fig. 8-1), to about 1520° C., small crystals of austenite will begin to form in the liquid. These crystals will have the composition designated by point *B*, which represents about 0.1 per cent carbon. As the liquid continues to cool, more crystals of austenite are formed with a resulting increase in the proportion of carbon. Then at about 1480° C. all the liquid becomes a solid solution of carbon in iron. The iron in this form is known as *gamma-iron* and has a face-centered cubic lattice. During the process of cooling, the steel is not homogeneous but soon becomes so through diffusion with the

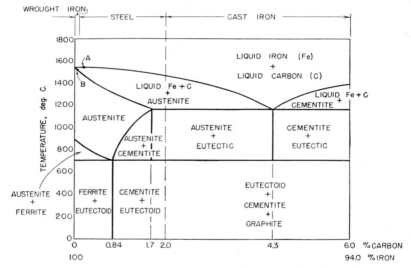

Fig. 8-1.   Equilibrium diagram for iron and steel.

liquid. As the temperature continues to drop below 1480° C. to about 850° C., no change takes place in the solid solution. At 850° C., however, an internal adjustment takes place; the steel, which is a dull red, begins to glow and liberate heat. At this stage the space lattice of the iron changes from the face-centered cubic form of gamma-iron to the body-centered cubic form called *alpha-iron* or *ferrite*. The solubility of carbon in the alpha-iron is limited to about 0.03 per cent. With decrease in temperature to 690° C., precipitation of ferrite or alpha-iron continues, accompanied by absorption of the displaced carbon in the austenite. At 690° C. the

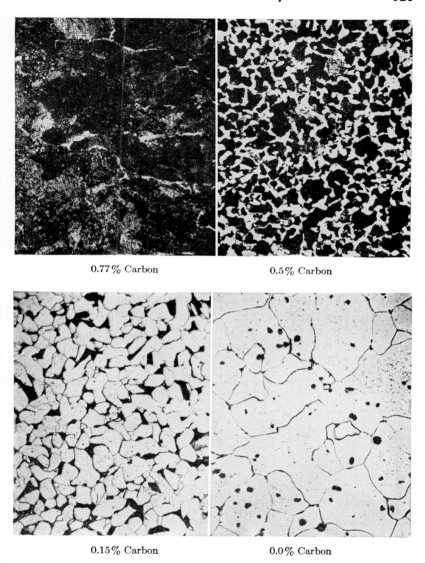

0.77% Carbon   0.5% Carbon

0.15% Carbon   0.0% Carbon

Fig. 8-2.   Influence of carbon on structure of ferrous metals (magnification 250 times).   (Courtesy J. M. Snook and R. W. Lindsay, Pennsylvania State College.)

carbon and part of the iron combine chemically to form iron carbide (Fe_3C) or cementite. The cementite combines mechanically with some of the ferrite to form grains of combined cementite and ferrite called *pearlite*, so called because of its pearl-like appearance. Pearlite is an iron-carbon eutectoid with 0.84 per cent carbon. The transformation on cooling for other iron-carbon solutions with other percentages of carbon can be evaluated using Fig. 8-1 in a manner similar to that used above for the 0.2 per cent carbon steel.

The structure of carbon steels is illustrated in Fig. 8-2. For low-carbon steels the grains of ferrite are indicated by the white areas, and crystals of pearlite by the dark regions. With a higher percentage of carbon, as shown in Fig. 8-2, there is a greater relative amount of pearlite or dark areas and fewer light areas of ferrite.

8-4. MANUFACTURE OF FERROUS METALS AND ALLOYS

The basic ingredient in the manufacture of ferrous metals and alloys is pig iron. Pig iron is produced in a blast furnace as illustrated diagrammatically in Fig. 8-3. Iron ores including hematite (Fe_2O_3), magnetite (Fe_3O_4), siderite ($FeCO_3$), and limonite ($Fe_2O_3 + n\ H_2O$) are used in the manufacture of pig iron. The principal iron ores used are oxides of iron or ores that may be transformed into oxides by heating. The process of making pig iron consists of the removal of oxygen and impurities from iron ore. The iron ore is reduced to

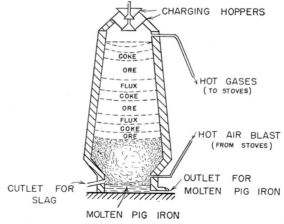

Fig. 8-3.   Schematic drawing of blast furnace.

pig iron by heating it with carbon, usually in the form of coke. The carbon combines with oxygen in the air to produce carbon monoxide (CO). The carbon monoxide combines with oxygen from the iron ore to produce carbon dioxide (CO_2). A flux, such as limestone, combines with the impurities in the ore to form a molten slag.

In operating a blast furnace to produce pig iron, the charge is first fed into the top of the furnace. The charge usually consists of about sixty per cent iron ore, including scrap iron, twenty-five per cent coke or some other high-carbon fuel, and about fifteen per cent flux in the form of limestone. The molten limestone gradually works toward the bottom of the furnace, combining with the impurities. Air, preheated to about 500° C., is forced under pressure through the charge from the bottom of the furnace. The oxygen in the air combines with the coke to form carbon monoxide, increasing the temperature at the bottom of the furnace to about 1600° C. As the ore works down to the bottom of the stack it comes in contact with the carbon monoxide gas, which reduces the iron oxides. That is, the carbon monoxide (CO) removes oxygen (O) from the iron ores to produce carbon dioxide (CO_2). The molten reduced iron ore, called pig iron, is removed through an outlet at the base of the blast furnace and is then cast into "pigs" weighing about 100 pounds.

Cast iron is produced by remelting pig iron with coke and heated air in a cupola or air furnace. This process further reduces the pig iron by removing both oxygen and impurities and yields a more uniform product.

Most of the pig iron from blast furnaces is used to make steel rather than cast iron. The refinement of pig iron to produce steel is usually accomplished by a Bessemer converter, an open-hearth furnace, or an electric furnace.[1] The open-hearth process is used more than any other. For the production of high-quality steel, however, the electric furnace is used. The Bessemer process has the limitation that it can be used only with special grades of pig iron. In all methods of steelmaking the principal object is to decrease the amount of impurities to within specified limits. This is done by removing excess carbon as carbon dioxide gas and by removing the oxides or other impurities in the form of a slag, which

---

[1] For a more detailed discussion of these methods of manufacture the reader is referred to books on materials as, for example, *Materials and Processes*, by J. F. Young, John Wiley & Sons, Inc., 1944.

floats on top of the molten steel. The molten iron is finally recarburized by adding a small amount of molten pig iron or some other material with a high carbon content.

8-5. SHAPING AND FABRICATION OF STEEL

As the steel comes from the Bessemer converter, open-hearth furnace, or electric furnace, it may be cast either directly to the desired shape or into ingots. The ingots, in turn, are given a preliminary rolling or forging into billets. The billets are then reduced to the final dimensions required by various procedures, including rolling, forging, and drawing.

Casting is used for the production of complex shapes such as frames for locomotives, cars, and other large equipment. Castings are made with sand, plaster, or permanent molds. When permanent molds are used they may be centrifugal or die castings. Pipe is cast by the centrifugal method, by rotating the mold during casting. Thus the impurities are found nearest the center of rotation, as they are in general lighter than the cast metal. Castings with a high degree of dimensional accuracy are obtained with die casting, since the metal is injected into the mold at a high pressure. Die casting is used primarily for casting of some of the nonferrous metals and alloys.

Rolling is used for the production of plates, sheets, rods, and common structural shapes as, for example, angles, channels, and I-beams. Most steel parts formed by rolling are *hot-rolled*. Where dimensions must be held to close tolerances, however, *cold-rolling* is used. Cold-rolling gives the steel a higher strength than does hot-rolling. Steel that is cold-rolled can be distinguished from hot-rolled steel by the smoother, shiny surface that is produced with cold-rolling. Shapes that cannot be rolled are formed by *forging*. Thick plates, sheets, and various machine parts are forged into the desired shapes. *Drawing* is used to produce steel wire and small rods. Steel parts are occasionally fabricated by extruding. This method of fabrication consists of applying sufficient pressure to a rod of material so that it is forced through an opening having the shape of the desired cross section. The assembly of steel parts is performed by the conventional methods of riveting, bolting, and welding.

Figure 8-4 illustrates the influence of various shaping operations on the stress-strain diagram in tension for low-carbon steel and shows

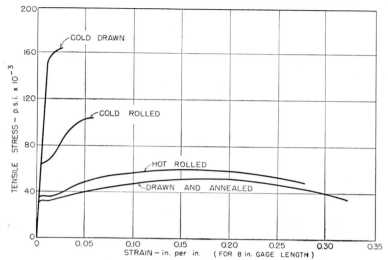

Fig. 8-4. Influence of fabrication upon the stress-strain relations for medium carbon steel. (After G. Murphy, *Properties of Engineering Materials*, 1947. Courtesy International Textbook Co.)

the increase in strength produced by cold-drawing and cold-rolling. This increase in strength, however, is accompanied by a decrease in ductility. For a more complete treatment of shaping and fabrication of metals see the *Metals Handbook*.[2]

8-6. HEAT-TREATMENT OF STEEL

Heat-treatment of steel is used to obtain certain specific properties. It is performed by processes of heating and cooling. When a metal is heated to a specific temperature and then rapidly cooled by sudden immersion in some cooling liquid such as oil, water, or brine, the metal is *hardened* and an increase in ultimate strength is produced. This sudden immersion leaves the metal very brittle or low in ductility. To increase ductility the steel is *tempered* by reheating to some temperature between 400° and 1000° F. (a temperature well below the initial temperature used in hardening). The steel is cooled at a controlled rate to obtain the desired ductility, hardness, and strength.

In the hardening of metals, cooling is done rapidly. If a slow

[2] Published by the American Society for Metals, 1948, pp. 33-85.

cooling is used after the metal is heated, hardness and strength are
reduced while the ductility is increased.   This process of heating
followed by slow cooling is called *annealing.*

Annealing may also be used to remove residual stresses or gases,
to alter mechanical or physical properties, or to produce a definite
grain structure.   Annealing is usually accomplished by heating steel
to about 1400° or 1600° F. and maintaining this temperature for a

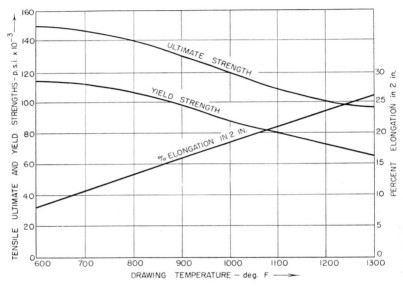

Fig. 8-5.   Influence of drawing temperature on 0.45% carbon water-
quenched steel.   (After G. Murphy, *Properties of Engineering Materials*,
1947.   Courtesy International Textbook Co.)

sufficient time to permit the change of grain size, to increase ductility,
to relieve internal strains produced by cold-working or rapid cooling,
or to eliminate any coarse crystalline structure produced by cooling
from excessive temperatures.   The slow cooling used leaves the steel
in a strain-free condition with a coarse grain size acquired during
the heating period.   The annealed steel has a reduced strength but
increased ductility compared to the unannealed steel.   Figure 8-5
shows the range of tensile properties that can be obtained by tempering in the case of a 0.45 per cent carbon steel.

Numerous technical terms in addition to those given are used to designate various heat-treatments employed in producing specific properties.   These are given in various publications including those of the American Society for Testing Materials.[3]

8-7. MECHANICAL PROPERTIES OF STEEL

Typical stress-strain diagrams in tension for medium carbon steels are shown in Fig. 8-4.   It has been previously noted how the method of fabrication influences the stress-strain curve and the mechanical properties by increasing the strength and decreasing the ductility.

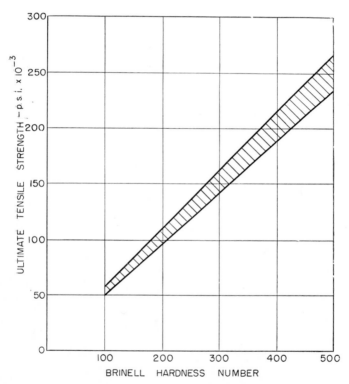

Fig. 8-6.   Relation between hardness and ultimate tensile strength for various carbon and alloy steels. (Courtesy *SAE Handbook.*)

[3] Standards of the American Society for Testing Materials, Philadelphia, Pennsylvania.

Table 8-1

Average Physical Properties of Common Ferrous Metals

The properties given may be greatly modified by changes in composition, cold-working, and heat-treatment.

Metal	Density (lb. per cu. in.)	Temp. coef. per deg. (°F × 10⁶)	Yield strength[a] (psi × 10⁻³)		Ult. strength[c] (psi × 10⁻³)		Mod. elasticity (psi × 10⁻⁶)		% Elong. (in 2 in.)
			Tension[b]	Shear	Tension	Shear[d]	Tension E	Shear E_s	
Gray cast iron (A.S.T.M. No. 20)	0.260	6.0			20		15	6	1
Malleable cast iron	0.268	6.2	30		50	40	24	10	10
Wrought iron, as rolled	0.278	6.7	30	18	50	40	27	10	30
Structural steel or SAE 1020, hot-rolled	0.283	6.5	35	21	60	45	29	12	30
Steel, SAE 1020, cold-rolled	0.283		60	36	80	60	29	12	18
Steel, SAE 1095, oil-quenched, drawn at 850° F	0.283		97	55	108		29	12	10
Nickel steel, SAE 2340, oil-quenched, drawn at 400° F			174	96	282		29	12	8
Stainless steel, 18-8 (18% Cr, 8% Ni) water-quenched			33	18	75		29	12	55
Steel casting, 0.35% C, 1.71% Mn, annealed			60	35	104		29	12	22
Cold-drawn steel rod (0.20% C)			60	36	80		29	12	18

[a] Except for cast iron, the yield strength and modulus of elasticity for compression may be assumed as for tension.

[b] Yield strength based on 0.2 per cent offset strain when a yield point does not exist.

[c] For practical purposes the yield strength in tension can be assumed for the ultimate compressive strength, since the ultimate

A similar effect is produced by heat treatment.   As shown in Fig. 8-5, an increase in strength is accompanied by a decrease in ductility when certain heat treatments are used.

Table 8-1 gives some of the mechanical properties of several types of ferrous metals.   For more complete information the reader is referred to publications of the American Society for Metals[2] and the Bureau of Standards.[4]

The American Society for Testing Materials[3] has prepared specifications for materials used for various particular purposes.   For example, a plain carbon steel of structural quality for use in the

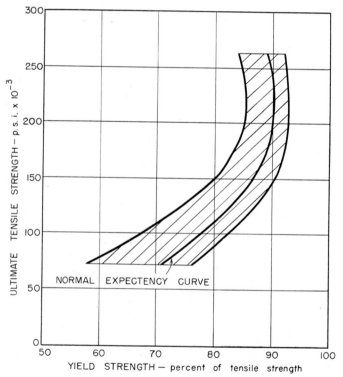

Fig. 8-7.   Relation between ultimate and yield tensile strength
for carbon and alloy steels.   (Courtesy *SAE Handbook*.)

[4] John S. Everhart *et al.*, "Mechanical Properties of Metals and Alloys," *Circular No. C-447*, National Bureau of Standards, 1943.

construction of bridges and building and for general structural purposes must have the following tensile properties to be acceptable:

Tensile Strength in psi, 60,000 to 72,000.

Yield Point, minimum, in psi, 0.5 tensile strength, but in no case less than 33,000 psi.

Elongation in 8 in. (minimum per cent), 1.5×10^6/tensile strength.

Elongation in 2 in. (minimum per cent), 22.

Another widely used specification for steel is that of the Society of Automotive Engineers.[5] Various plain carbon and alloy steels are classified by this society, and allowable ranges in the principal constituents are stated for each class of steel. For example, an S.A.E. 1020 steel is a carbon steel containing 0.20 per cent or 20 "points" of carbon. This particular steel corresponds to a structural grade of steel similar to that specified above. Various numbering systems used for alloys are given in the reference in Footnote 2.

Charts showing the relationships between the mechanical prop-

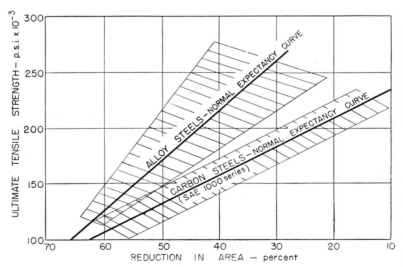

Fig. 8-8.   Relation between ultimate tensile strength and ductility for steels.   (Courtesy *SAE Handbook*.)

[5] "Standard Specifications for Steels," *Handbook* of the Society of Automotive Engineers, New York, 1942.

erties of steels have been prepared by the Society of Automotive Engineers.[5] Relationships between tensile strength and hardness, tensile strength and yield strength, and tensile strength and reduction in area are shown in Figs. 8-6, 8-7, and 8-8. Figure 8-6 shows that, regardless of composition, steels of the same hardness produced by tempering after hardening have approximately the same tensile strengths. Figure 8-7 shows the relation between the yield and ultimate tensile strengths and shows that for the higher ultimate strengths the ratio of yield to ultimate strength increases. Figure 8-8 shows that the reduction in area or ductility varies inversely with the strength. Figure 8-8 also shows that the reduction in area is higher for alloy steels than it is for plain carbon steels for a given strength. Graphs and tables of values giving properties of ferrous metals at various temperatures are given in the reference in Footnote 4.

8-8. FACTORS AFFECTING THE MECHANICAL PROPERTIES OF STEELS

The mechanical properties of steel and steel alloys are affected by method of manufacture, composition, mechanical work, and heat-treatment.

Effect of Composition. Carbon is one of the main elements in regulating the properties of both plain carbon and alloy steels. The most important influence of carbon is on the strength, hardness, and ductility. Figure 8-9 shows the influence of carbon content on the tensile properties of hot-worked carbon steels.[5] It shows that an increase in carbon content increases the yield strength, tensile strength, and hardness, but decreases the ductility as measured by the percentage elongation or reduction in area. Only steels with carbon content below 0.25 per cent have well-defined yield points. Figure 8-10 shows the influence of carbon content on the stress-strain curves. The carbon content has only a slight effect on the stiffness. The modulus of elasticity is practically the same for all grades of steel and averages about 29×10^6 psi. For wrought iron the modulus of elasticity is slightly lower and about 27×10^6 psi. The values of the modulus of elasticity for cast iron are still lower, with values from about 11×10^6 psi to 23×10^6 psi.

Alloying elements including manganese, chromium, nickel, silicon, molybdenum, tungsten, vanadium, and titanium are used to improve the properties of carbon steels. Chromium produces stainless iron and steel and increases the strength and hardness of steel. It is

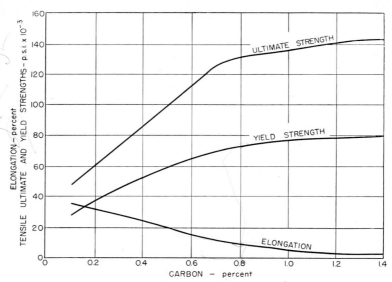

Fig. 8-9.   Average variation between tensile properties and carbon content for hot-worked carbon steels.   (After F. T. Sisco, *Alloys of Iron and Carbon*, 1937.   Courtesy McGraw-Hill Book Co., Inc.)

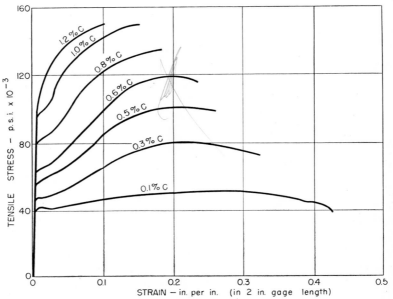

Fig. 8-10.   Average stress-strain diagrams for hot-rolled carbon steels.

effective in increasing corrosion-resistance at both ordinary and elevated temperatures. Chromium is usually used with other alloying elements such as nickel and vanadium. The influence of chromium on properties in tension is illustrated in Fig. 8-11. Steels with chromium content up to two per cent are used for ball bearings, crushing

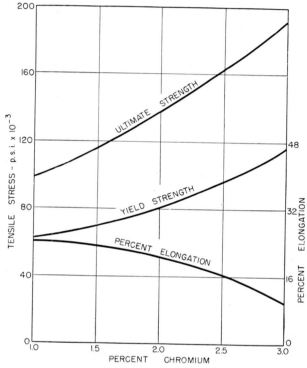

Fig. 8-11. Variation of properties of 0.3% normalized carbon steel with per cent chromium. (After H. J. French, *Alloy Structural Steels*. Courtesy Amer. Soc. for Metals.)

machinery, dies, rolls for rolling mills, tools of various types, and various machine parts. Combinations of nickel and chromium produce the nickel-chrome stainless-steel alloys. One particular chrome-nickel alloy, "18-8," is a high-strength stainless steel that has been found effective at both low and high temperatures where resistance to creep is desirable.

Next to carbon, molybdenum is the most effective element as a hardening agent in the manufacture of steel. Fig. 8-12 illustrates the influence of molybdenum on the tensile properties. Molybdenum, with or without tungsten, is used in high-speed tool steels since it is effective in maintaining hardness and cutting properties in steel for normal as well as high temperatures.

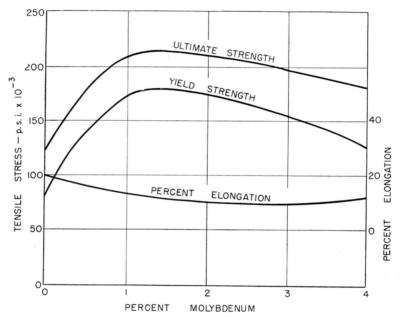

Fig. 8-12. Influence of molybdenum on properties of steel (oil-quenched and tempered—carbon 0.44 to 0.50%). (After J. L. Gregg, *Alloys of Iron and Molybdenum*, Alloys of Iron Monograph Series. Courtesy McGraw-Hill Book Co., Inc.)

Silicon in amounts up to about two per cent increases the yield strength of steel with little reduction in ductility. Silicon is also a deoxidizing agent when added to steel and, for this reason, reduces blow holes in castings. Silicon steels are used for applications requiring high strengths, such as bridges and springs.

Manganese is used in steel to eliminate the harmful elements of oxygen and sulphur by withdrawing them into the slag. Manganese in solid solution with iron also increases the strength and reduces

the ductility of steel as indicated in Fig. 8-13. Manganese steel
alloys have a high resistance to abrasion when properly tempered.
This abrasion resistance combined with high strength makes manganese steels suitable for mining, rock crushing, and railway equipment.
   Tungsten raises the critical temperature and is, therefore, of value

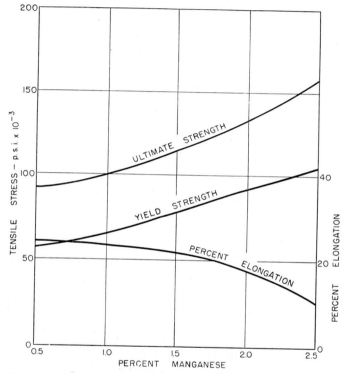

Fig. 8-13.   Influence of manganese on properties of steel (normalized steel with 0.4% C).   (After H. J. French, "Alloy Constructional
Steels."   Courtesy Amer. Soc. for Metals.)

in increasing the strength of alloy steels at high temperatures.   For
this reason it is used for high-speed cutting tools.   The high strength
at high temperatures in tungsten steel makes it useful in forging dies.
   Vanadium is used to increase both the yield and tensile strengths
of low- and medium-carbon steels.   It is extensively used for springs
and for high-speed tool steels.   Vanadium steels are quality steels

with a fine grain, and would be used more if they were less expensive.

Copper imparts corrosion-resistance qualities to steel in addition to increasing the strength. Titanium is a strong deoxidizing agent. In this respect it is stronger than silicon. Titanium also decreases grain size and thereby improves the yield strength and creep resist-

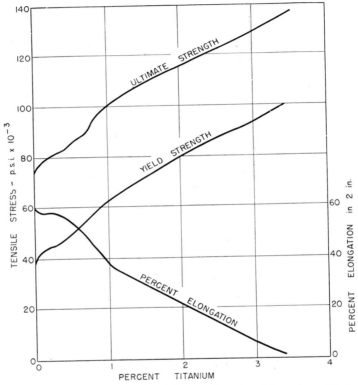

Fig. 8-14. Effect of titanium on properties of cast chromium-nickel steels. (Tests by J. A. Dunn. Courtesy Amer. Soc. for Metals.)

ance. Figure 8-14 shows the influence of titanium on the properties in tension.

The foregoing elements in alloy steels are beneficial. There are, however, certain elements in steel, including sulphur, phosphorus, oxygen, hydrogen, and nitrogen, that are considered harmful. Sulphur makes steel "hot short" or brittle at high temperatures. For this reason it causes difficulty during hot-rolling or other shaping processes. Most specifications for structural steel limit sulphur to an amount less than 0.05 per cent. Phosphorus makes steel "cold short" or brittle at low temperatures. It is undesirable, therefore, in parts operating at low temperatures. Phosphorus increases the sharpness of castings and is sometimes added to cast iron for this reason. Most structural steel specifications, however, limit phosphorus to less than 0.05 per cent. Oxygen is usually objectionable because it combines with iron to form iron oxide inclusions throughout the metal. These inclusions are undesirable because they are points of weakness and increase brittleness. Deoxidizers including aluminum, silicon, calcium, manganese, and titanium are used to

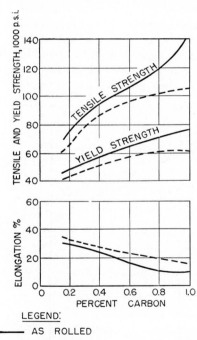

LEGEND:

——— AS ROLLED

— — — ANNEALED

Fig. 8-15. Influence of annealing on properties of carbon steels. (After G. T. Williams, "What Steel Shall I Use?" Courtesy Amer. Soc. for Metals.)

remove oxygen in steelmaking. Hydrogen increases hardenability or the ability of steels to acquire hardness. It is removed by heating the steel for a few hours. Nitrogen increases the hardness and brittleness of steel. This characteristic is used to advantage in the nitriding process by exposing steel to ammonia gas at about 600° C. to produce a wear-resisting surface having a high hardness. In other instances, however, too much nitrogen may be objectionable because of the brittleness that might result.

The influence of the alloying element on the strength may be considerable in some cases. Using heat-treated silicon-molybdenum steels, tensile strengths of about 290,000 psi are obtained. When plain carbon steels of about 0.8 per cent carbon are drawn into fine wires, tensile strengths of about 500,000 psi are obtained.

Effect of Heat-Treatment. The influence of heat-treatment in increasing or reducing hardness has already been noted. By heating to certain temperatures and controlling the rate of cooling, various properties can be produced in steel. In this way the strength can be increased or decreased with a corresponding decrease or in-

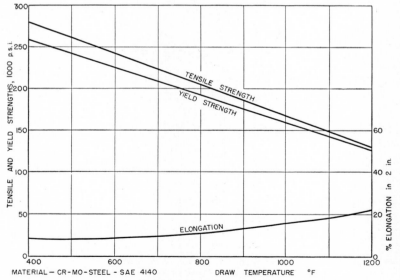

Fig. 8-16. Normal expectancy property-tempering temperature relations. (After G. T. Williams, "What Steel Shall I Use?" Courtesy Amer. Soc. for Metals.)

crease in the ductility. That is, if the heat-treatment produces an increase in strength or hardness, the ductility is reduced and vice versa. The influence of annealing is shown in Fig. 8-15. The importance of the tempering or drawing temperature in heat-treatment is illustrated for a SAE 4140 steel in Fig. 8-16. That is, the tempera-

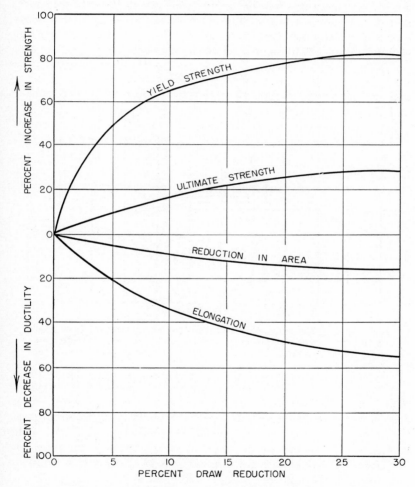

Fig. 8-17. Influence of moderate cold drawing on tensile properties of alloy steel bars. (After G. T. Williams, "What Steel Shall I Use?" Courtesy Amer. Soc. for Metals.)

ture selected in the tempering process will greatly affect the properties
in the resulting steel.

Effect of Forming Operations. Hot-working processes, including hot-rolling, result in a steel that is comparatively free from
residual strains and has a fine-grained structure. Furthermore, the
steel produced in this way has higher yield strength, tensile strength,
and ductility as a result of the hot-working. The improved properties of hot-worked steel are evident when a comparison is made
with properties of the same steel when it is cast.

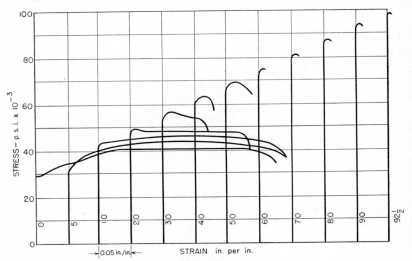

Fig. 8-18. Influence of cold rolling on stress-strain curve in tension for
ingot iron. (*Note:* Numbers on graphs denote per cent reduction by
cold rolling.) (From *Metals Handbook.* Courtesy Amer. Soc. for
Metals.)

Cold-working produces steels with higher yield and tensile strengths
than hot-worked steels. This increase in strength, however, is accompanied by a decrease in ductility. The effect of cold-rolling on
the mechanical properties of alloy steels is shown in Fig. 8-17. The
influence of cold-working on the shape of the stress-strain curve in
tension is illustrated for ingot iron in Fig. 8-18. For a more complete
discussion of the influence of heat-treatment and forming operations
on the properties of ferrous metals see references given in Footnote 6.

---

[6] *Engineering Metals and Their Alloys*, by Carl H. Samans, The Macmillan
Company, 1949.

NUMERICAL EXAMPLE. Determine the required cross-sectional area of a tension member 20 in. long subjected to 200,000 lb. if the minimum elongation is to be 0.5 in. and the stress is not to exceed 50,000 psi. Factors of safety of 4 based on the elongation and 3 based on the ultimate tensile strength were used in obtaining these values. Determine the minimum area considering the following materials:

(a) A hot-worked carbon steel with properties as given in Fig. 8-9;

(b) A chromium-molybdenum steel or SAE 4140 steel with properties as given in Fig. 8-16;

(c) An ingot iron with properties as given in Fig. 8-18.

For each of the three materials determine, respectively, the optimum value of carbon content, tempering temperature, and percentage reduction by cold-rolling.

SOLUTION. For an allowable elongation of 0.5 in. the minimum percentage elongation required is the allowable unit elongation times the factor of safety times 100, or $(0.5/20)(4)(100) = 10\%$. For an allowable stress of 50,000 psi and a factor of safety of 3, the minimum ultimate strength is $50,000 \times 3 = 150,000$ psi. That is, a material must be selected that has a minimum ultimate tensile strength of 150,000 psi and a minimum elongation of 10 per cent.

(a) For the hot-worked carbon steel, by Fig. 8-9, a 10 per cent elongation corresponds to a steel with a carbon content of about 0.8 per cent and an ultimate strength of about 130,000 psi. Since this stress is less than 150,000 psi, the elongation requirement governs and a steel of strength equal to 130,000 psi will be used. Then for an ultimate stress of 130,000 psi and a factor of safety of 3, the area required is

$$A = \frac{P}{S} = \frac{200,000}{(130,000/3)} = 4.6 \text{ sq. in.}$$

(b) For the chromium-molybdenum steel, by Fig. 8-16, a 10 per cent elongation corresponds to a draw-tempering temperature of about 750° F. and an ultimate tensile strength of about 220,000 psi. Since this stress is greater than 150,000 psi, the strength requirement governs. For a chromium-molybdenum steel with an ultimate tensile strength of 150,000 psi, the draw temperature, by Fig. 8-16, is about 1100° F. The required area for an ultimate strength of 150,000 psi is

$$A = \frac{P}{S} = \frac{200,000}{(150,000/3)} = 4 \text{ sq. in.}$$

(c) For the ingot iron, from Fig. 8-18, the amount of reduction by cold-rolling to be selected to give 10 per cent elongation is, by interpolation, about 25 per cent. For this percentage reduction, the approximate ultimate tensile strength is about 53,000 psi. Since this stress is less than 150,000 psi, the elongation requirement governs and the required area for a factor of safety of 3 is

$$A = \frac{P}{S} = \frac{200,000}{(53,000/3)} = 11.3 \text{ sq. in.}$$

A comparison of the foregoing areas shows that the chromium-molybdenum SAE 4140 steel with a draw-tempering temperature of 750° F. requires the minimum area.

8-9. MECHANICAL PROPERTIES OF CAST IRON

As in the case of steels, carbon has a very important effect on cast iron. Both the amount and form of the carbon present affect the properties. In gray cast iron some of the carbon is in the form of graphite, or free carbon, which produces a weak and soft material. On the other hand, in white cast iron some of the carbon is combined with iron to form cementite (Fe_3C) yielding a stronger and harder material, in some cases three or four times as strong as gray cast iron.

The annealing of white cast iron changes the combined carbon to a finely divided, free, amorphous form, and a material called *malleable cast iron* results. Malleable cast iron is more ductile and is stronger than white cast iron. A typical stress-strain diagram in tension for gray cast iron is shown in Fig. 8-19.

The ultimate tensile strengths of gray cast iron vary from 10,000 to 70,000 psi, while the compressive strength is considerably higher, varying from 50,000 to 200,000 psi. Compressive strengths of white and malleable cast irons are also higher than the tensile strengths. Cast irons have relatively high damping capacity or ability to absorb energy under vibrations, which is desirable in applications where vibrations occur. Defects such as blow-holes, surface cracks, impurities, and coarse-grain structure are important factors in reducing the strength of cast iron. As for steel, sulphur and phosphorus are impurities that reduce both the strength and the ductility. High silicon content increases hardness and acid-resistance. However, silicon in cast iron promotes the formation of graphite and results in a weaker, softer, and more machinable material. Nickel retards formation of cementite and graphite and thereby increases both the strength and ductility. The improved properties of nickel cast iron make it suitable for dies, crankshafts, gears, and similar parts. Chromium is used as an alloying element in cast iron. The influence of chromium is to increase the percentage of combined carbon, thus increasing the strength. Copper and molybdenum are also used to increase the tensile strength.

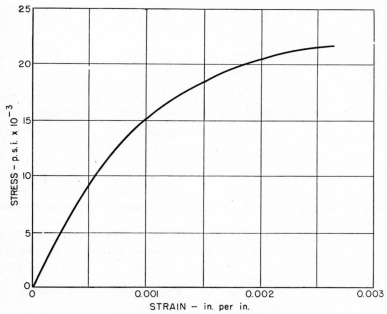

Fig. 8-19.   Average tensile stress-strain curve for gray cast iron.

In the foregoing discussion of ferrous metals and alloys, only a summary is given of what are considered the most important factors influencing the mechanical properties. Information is given in this chapter to show how composition, heat-treatment, and forming operations change the mechanical properties of ferrous metals and alloys. For a more detailed and thorough treatment of the subject the student is referred to the bibliography at the end of the chapter.

PROBLEMS AND QUESTIONS

Note: In the following problems use a value of

$$toughness = \tfrac{1}{2}(S_{yp} + S_u)(D_e);$$

where D_e = the elongation at fracture in in. per in., S_{yp} = the yield stress, and S_u = the ultimate stress.

8-1. Using the data in Fig. 8-10, determine elastic strengths, ultimate strengths, and ductility, and plot graphs showing the variation of these properties with carbon content.

8-2. Plot the variation between the modulus of resilience and carbon content using the data in Fig. 8-10 for hot-worked iron carbon alloys. Use a value of $E = 30 \times 10^6$ psi.

8-3. Show the relation between the toughness and carbon content using strength and ductility values given in Fig. 8-10.

8-4. For hot-rolled steels the influence of carbon content (up to 1 per cent) on the yield strength, ultimate strength, ductility (per cent elongation in 2 in.) may be expressed approximately by the following equations:

$$S_{yp} = 38,000 + 42,000\,C \tag{a}$$

$$S_u = 45,000 + 115,000\,C \tag{b}$$

$$D_e = 0.42 - 0.34\,C \tag{c}$$

where C is the per cent carbon content and D_e is the ductility in in. per in. Determine an equation giving the relation between the toughness and the carbon content.

8-5. Determine an equation giving the relation between the modulus of resilience and carbon content for hot-rolled steel if the modulus of elasticity is 30×10^6 psi and $S_{yp} = 38,000 + 42,000\,C$, where C = the per cent carbon and S_{yp} = the yield strength.

Ans. $u = (0.024 + 0.0532\,C + 0.0294\,C^2)(10^3)$

8-6. (a) A structural member of length L and cross-sectional area A is to be equally as strong with respect to a gradually applied static tensile load P lb. and an impact load of U in. lb. What should the carbon content be if the member is to be made of a hot-rolled steel with modulus of resilience as given in Prob. 8-5? Base the solution on the yield strength and assume equal values of yield strengths under static and impact loads. (b) If the length of the member in Prob. 8-6(a) is 6 ft., the static load P is 5000 lb., and the dynamic load U is 500 in. lb., determine the required area based on the yield strength. *Ans.* (b) 0.060 sq. in.

8-7. (a) Compare the toughness of the cold-rolled and hot-rolled steels shown in Fig. 8-4. (b) A tension member is to be subjected to a static load of 10,000 lb. or an impact load of 500 ft. lb. If the length of the member is to be 6 in. and there is a choice between the cold- or hot-rolled steel shown in Fig. 8-4, which steel would be selected? Base the design on ultimate strength for the static load and toughness for the dynamic load.

Ans. Select the cold-rolled steel.

8-8. Determine the variation between the toughness and the carbon content for hot-rolled steels shown in Fig. 8-9. Use a value of $E = 30 \times 10^6$ psi.

8-9. Plot the variation between the modulus of resilience and carbon content for hot-rolled steels shown in Fig. 8-9. Use a value of $E = 30 \times 10^6$ psi.

8-10. A tension member is subjected to either an impact load of 6000 ft. lb. or a static load of 50,000 lb. The member is 1 ft. long. Assuming the costs of both materials to be the same, which hot-rolled steel should be selected—one with 0.2 per cent carbon or 0.8 per cent carbon? Base the calculations on the properties given in Fig. 8-9.

Ans. Use the 0.8 per cent carbon steel.

8-11. Plot a graph showing the variation between toughness and percentage of chromium. Use Fig. 8-11.

8-12. Using the data in Fig. 8-11, plot the relation between the modulus of resilience and percentage of chromium.

8-13. Prepare a graph based on Fig. 8-13 showing (a) the variation in toughness with percentage of manganese, and (b) the variation in modulus of resilience with percentage of manganese.

8-14. A wire is to be subjected to either an impact tensile load of 3000 ft. lb. or a static load of 5000 lb. The wire is 10 ft. long. Using the graphs in Fig. 8-16, should the steel selected be one made with a tempering temperature of 1200° or 400°?

8-15. Plot a graph showing the variation between toughness and tempering temperature for the stainless steels with properties as given in Fig. 8-16.

8-16. Using Fig. 8-18 determine the relation between the mechanical properties and percentage reduction by cold-rolling. Plot graphs for yield strength, ultimate strength, ductility, modulus of resilience, and toughness.

8-17. Name the main iron ores used in the manufacture of pig iron.

8-18. Describe briefly the manufacture of pig iron.

8-19. What are the various m thods used for shaping and fabricating steel?

8-20. Define hardening, tempering, and annealing.

8-21. What are the effects of hardening, tempering, and annealing on the properties of steel?

8-22. What are the main effects of carbon, chromium, molybdenum, nitrogen, silicon, tungsten, vanadium, sulphur, manganese, copper, titanium, oxygen, and phosphorus on the properties of steel? Prepare a table showing the major effects.

8-23. How are the properties of steel changed by heat treatment?

8-24. What effect does cold-working have on the mechanical properties of steel?

8-25. Distinguish between gray, white, and malleable cast iron.

8-26. What factors influence the strength of cast iron?

8-27. Using the carbon-iron equilibrium diagram of Fig. 8-1, describe the action of a steel containing 1.6 per cent carbon as it is slowly cooled from 1650° C. to room temperature.

8-28. Answer Question 8-27 if the steel contains 0.84 per cent carbon.

8-29. For a tension member 20 in. in length subjected to 200,000 lb. the stress is not to exceed 50,000 psi and the minimum elongation is 0.6 in. If factors of safety of 3 were used for both ultimate strength and elongation, determine the minimum area required considering (a) a hot-worked carbon steel (Fig. 8-9), (b) a chromium-molybdenum SAE 4140 steel (Fig. 8-16), and (c) a manganese steel (Fig. 8-13).

8-30. Solve Prob. 8-29 if the minimum elongation is to be 0.3 in.

BIBLIOGRAPHY

Carpenter, H., and Robertson, J. M., *Metals*, Oxford University Press, London, 1939.

Gillet, H. W., *The Behavior of Engineering Metals*, John Wiley & Sons, Inc., New York, 1951.

Hollomon, J. H., and Jaffe, L. D., *Ferrous Metallurgical Design*, John Wiley & Sons, Inc., New York, 1947.

Sachs, G., and Van Horn, K. R., *Practical Metallurgy*, American Society for Metals, Cleveland, 1941.

Samans, Carl H., *Engineering Metals and Alloys*, The Macmillan Company, New York, 1949.

Sisco, F. T., *Modern Metallurgy for Engineers*, Pitman Publishing Corp., New York, 1948.

Williams, G. T., *What Steel Shall I Use?*, American Society for Metals, Cleveland, 1941.

Metals Handbook, American Society for Metals, Cleveland, 1948.

Chapter 9

Nonferrous Metals and Alloys

9-1. INTRODUCTION

Nonferrous metals and alloys include all those in which iron is not present in large quantities. Although the total production of nonferrous materials is small compared to the ferrous metals, this is not

Table 9-1

Relative Volume of Materials Used (1947 Census)

Material	Volume in cubic feet	Percentage of total	Weight per cu. ft.
1. *Ferrous metals*			
Steel mill products	268,500,000		
Iron and steel castings	48,760,000		
Total ferrous metals	317,260,000	9.32	470
2. *Nonferrous metals*			
Aluminum	9,760,000	0.28	168
Copper	2,140,000	0.06	555
Zinc	1,900,000	0.06	448
Lead	854,000	0.02	710
Magnesium	72,000	. . .	107
3. *Nonmetallic materials*			
Wood	2,950,000,000	86.50	45
Glass	92,377,270*	2.70	200
Rubber	31,152,500	0.91	100
Plastics	5,220,000	0.15	90

* An estimate based on dollar value.

an accurate reflection of their economic value. The relative production of nonferrous materials compared to ferrous materials is indicated in Table 9-1.

The characteristic properties of a nonferrous alloy must be sufficiently important to justify its selection, since nonferrous alloys are generally more expensive than ferrous metals of the same strength. The main properties of nonferrous alloys that often govern their selection are:

1. Resistance to corrosion
2. Low density
3. Good electrical and thermal conductivity
4. Ease of fabrication
5. Appearance

There are nonferrous metals or combinations of them that will resist most kinds of corrosive action. The density of nonferrous metals may be as low as one-fourth that of iron. The light-weight nonferrous metals such as magnesium and aluminum are used in parts where weight is an important factor, as in aircraft. Some of the nonferrous metals are heavier than iron and do not, therefore, have the foregoing advantage. The advantages of the light-weight nonferrous metals are shown by the comparative values of the strength-density ratios in Table 9-2.

Table 9-2

Modulus-density and Strength-density Ratios of Selected Materials

Material	Density, lb./cu. in.	Mod. of elasticity-density ratio, in. $\times 10^{-6}$	Tensile strength-density ratio, in. $\times 10^{-3}$
Wood	0.0156–0.0197	83–86	584–603
Magnesium alloys	0.065	100	523–662
Beryllium	0.007	409	. . .
Aluminum alloys	0.101	103–105	545–680
High-strength steel wire	0.283	98–101	919–1053
Structural steel	0.283	102–104	206–345
Carbon-steel tubing	0.282	98	195–267
Chromium-molybdenum steel tubing	0.282	105–107	337–633
Stainless steel tubing	0.285	91	614–653
Beryllium-copper alloys	0.295–0.298	51–64	198–664
Monel metal	0.318	79–82	220–283

The electrical and thermal conductivities of nonferrous metals vary widely and may be well above or well below the values for ferrous metals.   Copper has high conductivity and is therefore used in electrical conductors.   On the other hand, nickel alloys have low conductivity and are used for electrical resistance wire.

Nonferrous metals are frequently used for parts involving considerable forming.   A number of the nonferrous alloys are easily cast because of their low melting points and high fluidity when molten. Hot-forming can be applied for many nonferrous alloys, since many are malleable and ductile while hot.   Their fabrication properties vary widely so that a nonferrous metal or alloy can be selected for practically every forming process.

Finish or color is an important property for architectural fittings or household equipment.   Several of the nonferrous metals such as aluminum, nickel, and their alloys are used because of their smooth finish and bright silvery color.   Red-gold and yellow colors are found with copper and its alloys.

In general, the strengths of nonferrous metals are below those of the strong steels.   The strength-weight ratios of the strong alloys of aluminum and magnesium compare favorably, however, with the steels.   The heavier nonferrous metals and alloys are not used because of their strength alone, since steel is both stronger and less expensive.

The light-weight nonferrous alloys, in particular, have low moduli of elasticity.   To obtain a given stiffness, more material would be required than for steel.   Often, however, the lower density yields a construction of lower total weight.

The nonferrous metals are subject, in general, to changes in properties by cold-working.   They are less affected by heat-treatment, however, than are the ferrous metals.

There are many considerations other than the foregoing in the selection of a nonferrous alloy for a given application.   These include cost, mechanical properties, form of available materials, and method of fabrication desired.

9-2. COPPER AND ITS ALLOYS

Copper is found in the free state or in the form of oxides or sulphides. The most important copper ores are cuprite (Cu_2O), copper pyrite ($CuFeS_2$), and copper sulphide (Cu_2S).

The method used to extract copper from copper ores depends on the type of ore. For example, in the case of sulphide ores, the first step includes the mechanical treatment of concentrating, washing, and grinding. The preliminary mechanical treatment is followed by roasting, reducing, and refining. Roasting partially converts the sulphide to an oxide; reducing removes the oxygen and remaining sulphur from chemical combination with copper; and refining, usually by electrolysis, purifies the free copper. The foregoing process

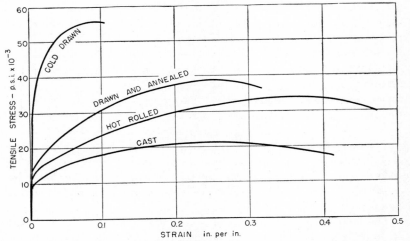

Fig. 9-1. Average tensile stress-strain curves for copper. (After G. Murphy, *Properties of Engineering Materials*, 1947. Courtesy International Textbook Co.)

of roasting, reducing, and refining is called the "dry process." Another process in the manufacture of copper is the "wet process." This process consists in dissolving the ore in appropriate reagents and treating with chemicals to precipitate the metallic copper.

Properties of Copper. Some average stress-strain curves for copper are shown in Fig. 9-1. Figure 9-1 also shows the effects of cold-working in increasing strength and reducing ductility, and of annealing in increasing ductility. The effect of cold-working and annealing on the mechanical properties of oxygen free copper is shown in Fig. 9-2. Mechanical properties of copper are given in Table 9-3.

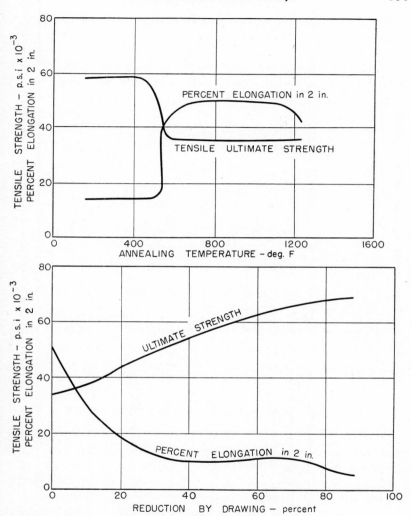

Fig. 9-2. Influence of annealing and cold-drawing on oxygen free copper. (Tests by S. Rolle and H. M. Schliecher. Courtesy Reinhold Publishing Co.)

Table 9-3

Average Physical Properties of Heavy Nonferrous Metals and Alloys

Form	Material	Density (lb. per cu. in.)	Temp. coef. per deg. (°F × 10⁶)	Strength in tension (psi × 10⁻³) Yield[a]	Ultimate[b]	Mod. of elas. in tension (psi × 10⁻⁶)	% Elong.
Cast	Brass, ounce metal (80-5-3-5).......	0.32		20.5	39.5	11.95	25
	Bronze, bearing bronze (80-10-10)..	0.33		18.5	32.0		9
	Bronze, gun metal (88-10-2)........	0.32		22.0	41.0	13.3	20
	Zinc-base die-casting alloy (SAE 921)	0.24	15.4	8.0	42.5		3.8
	Copper.................	0.32	9.3	8.0	30.0	13.0	
Wrought	Brass, Muntz metal (66) sheet:						
	hard..................	0.30	11.6	60	80	14	8
	soft...................	0.30	11.6	20	54	14	45
	Brass, leaded brass (221) rod:						
	hard..................	0.31	11.1	48	65	14	20
	soft...................	0.31	11.1	17	46	14	60
	Bronze, phosphor bronze (356) sheet:						
	hard..................	0.32	9.9	50	65	15	6
	soft...................	0.32	9.9	14	40	15	48
	Copper, pure copper (939) deoxidized:						
	hard..................	0.32	9.8	40	45	16	10
	soft...................	0.32	9.8	10	35	16	45
	Monel metal, hot-rolled............	0.32		50	90		40

[a] The yield strength in compression can be assumed equal to the yield strength in tension, and the yield strength in shear can be assumed equal to 60 per cent of the yield strength in tension.

[b] The ultimate strength in compression can be considered as slightly above the yield strength in compression, and the ultimate strength in compression can be assumed as 60 per cent of the ultimate strength in tension.

The outstanding properties of copper are high resistance to atmospheric corrosion and high electrical conductivity.

Uses of Copper.   Copper is used mainly in electrical equipment, transmission lines, and in the automotive industry.   It is also used in the form of sheeting and plating.   Copper in small percentages increases the corrosion resistance of many other metals.

Alloys of Copper.   Many alloys containing copper have been developed.   Copper is added to steel to make it corrosion-resistant, as mentioned in Chapter 8.   Various elements have been added to copper to produce alloys with a specific strength and hardness greater than that of copper.   Alloys of this kind are used where both high strength and high electrical conductivity are desired.   Beryllium, manganese, nickel, silicon, and titanium are alloyed with copper to increase its strength.   Other alloys containing copper are duralumin, brass, bronze, and Monel metal.   These alloys are discussed in remaining sections of this chapter.   Properties of some of the nonferrous alloys are given in Table 9-3.

9-3. ALUMINUM AND ITS ALLOYS

The discovery in 1886 of the electrolytic process for the commercial production of aluminum led to the development of one of the most important engineering materials.   The importance of aluminum alloys is due primarily to a combination of low density and high strength.

Aluminum ore of commercial value is bauxite, which is a hydrate of alumina containing about sixty per cent alumina (Al_2O_3).   In the most common method of processing aluminum, sodium hydroxide is added to bauxite that has been crushed and dried.   Sodium hydroxide and bauxite form sodium aluminate, from which pure aluminum hydrate is precipitated.   Calcination of the hydrate removes chemically combined water and pure alumina (Al_2O_3) is formed.   Electrolytic reduction is then used to obtain aluminum from the pure alumina.   The molten aluminum is cast into molds and then shaped by rolling, drawing, forging, or extruding.

Properties of Aluminum.   As a result of its high ductility, aluminum is widely used for tube containers, as in toothpaste tubes.   Aluminum can be alloyed with other metals to form alloys with desirable properties.   The resistance of aluminum to corrosion makes it useful in chemical equipment.   However, aluminum is attacked by hydrochloric acid and by strong alkalies.   The properties of

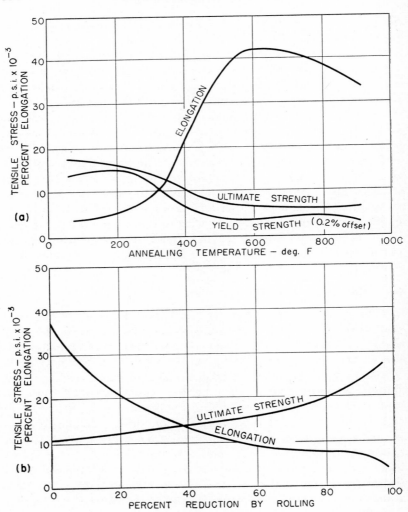

Fig. 9-3.   Influence of annealing and cold-rolling on aluminum sheet. (From "Mechanical Properties of Metals and Alloys," *Circ. C* 447, U. S. Bureau of Standards.)

aluminum can be changed by annealing and by cold-working, as shown in Fig. 9-3. The influence of elevated temperatures on the properties of wrought aluminum is shown in Fig. 9-4.

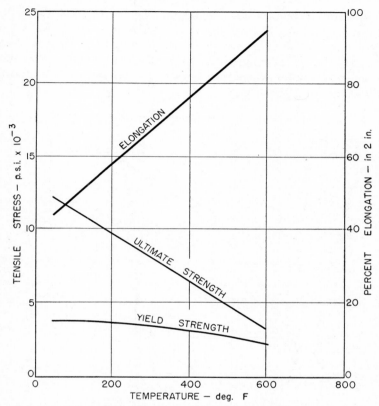

Fig. 9-4. Tensile properties of wrought aluminum at high temperatures (cold rolled.) (Tests by F. M. Howell and D. A. Paul. Courtesy Reinhold Publishing Co.)

Alloys of Aluminum. Aluminum does not have adequate strength for structural purposes. A number of metals are added to it, however, to form alloys that have the necessary strengths for many structural applications. The main properties of aluminum alloys are their light weight with comparatively high strength, high ductility, high electrical conductivity, and high resistance to atmospheric corrosion. Aluminum alloys have been used for aircraft, railroad cars, buses, truck bodies, dredge booms, bridge floors, electrical transmission lines, and transmission towers. Aluminum alloys are also widely used for domestic purposes, particularly kitchen utensils.

The most commonly used alloying elements in alloys of aluminum are copper, silicon, manganese, and magnesium. The influence of magnesium on the properties is shown in Fig. 9-5. Cold-working is effective in the changing of the properties of aluminum alloys and, for some aluminum alloys, heat-treatment can be used to change the mechanical properties.

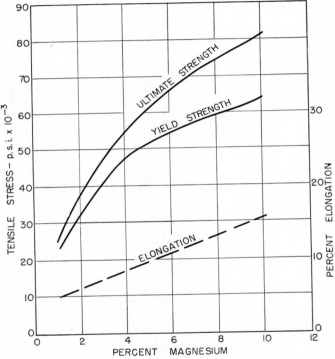

Fig. 9-5. Influence of magnesium on tensile properties of aluminum-magnesium alloy sheet (heat-treated and cold-rolled). (From *Metals Handbook*. Courtesy Amer. Soc. for Metals.)

Commercial aluminum alloys may be classified as cast alloys or wrought alloys. Properties of these alloys are greatly changed by heat-treatment or cold-working. Table 9-4 gives the nominal composition of structural aluminum alloys, and Table 9-5 lists the properties of some of the common aluminum alloys. Each wrought

Table 9-4
Nominal Compositions of Several Structural Aluminum Alloys

Alloy temper	ASTM designation		Nominal composition						Weight lb. per cu. in.
	Spec. No.	Alloy	Cu	Si	Mn	Mg	Zn	Cr	
Wrought									
3S	B79-44T	M1	..	..	1.2	..	..	..	0.099
14S	..	..	4.4	0.8	0.8	0.4	..	..	0.101
24S	..	..	4.5	..	0.6	1.5	..	..	0.100
52S	B109-44T	Mr1	..	..	..	2.5	..	0.25	0.097
61S	..	..	0.25	0.6	..	1.0	..	0.25	0.098
75S	..	..	1.6	..	0.2	2.5	5.6	0.3	0.101
Cast									
195	B26-44T	C1	4.5	0.8	..	..	..	..	0.101
214	B26-44T	C1	..	..	..	3.8	..	..	0.096
356	B26-44T	SG.1	..	7.0	..	0.3	..	..	0.097

From *Structural Aluminum Handbook*, The Aluminum Company of America.

Table 9-5

Average Physical Properties of Aluminum Alloys

Type	Alloy	Density (lb. per cu in.)	Temp. coef. per deg. (°F × 10⁶)	Yield strength[a] (psi × 10⁻³)		Ult. strength (psi × 10⁻³)		Mod. elas. (psi × 10⁻⁶)		Endurance limit[b] (psi × 10⁻³)
				Tension	Comp.	Tension	Shear	Tension and comp.	Shear	
Wrought	3S-O	0.099	12.9	6.0	6.0	16.0	11.0	10.0	3.8	.70
	3S-H	0.099		25.0	25.0	29.0	16.0	10.0	3.8	10.0
	14S-W	0.101		40.0	20.0	56.0	34.0	10.6	4.0	18.0
	14S-T	0.101	12.8	60.0	60.0	70.0	42.0	10.6	4.0	18.0
	Alc 14ST			58.0	58.0	65.0	41.0	10.5		
	24S-T		12.9	46.0	46.0	68.0	41.0	10.6	4.0	18.0
	Alc 24ST	0.100		43.0	43.0	64.0	40.0	10.1		
	52S-O	0.097	13.2	14.0	14.0	29.0	18.0	10.2	3.85	17.0
	52S-H	0.097		36.0	36.0	41.0	24.0	10.2	3.85	19.0
	61S-O	0.098	13.1	8.0	8.0	18.0	12.5	10.0	3.8	9.0
	61S-W	0.098		21.0	21.0	35.0	24.0	10.0	3.8	13.5
	61S-T	0.098	13.1	40.0	40.0	45.0	30.0	10.0	3.8	13.5
	75S-T	0.101	13.1	72.0	72.0	82.0	47.0	10.4	3.9	21.0
	Alc 75ST			67.0	67.0	76.0	46.0	9.6		
Cast	195-T4	0.101	12.7	16.0	16.0	32.0	24.0	10.3	3.85	6.0
	195-T6	0.101	12.7	24.0	25.0	36.0	30.0	10.3	3.85	6.5
	195-T62	0.101	12.7	30.0	38.0	40.0	31.0	10.3	3.85	7.0
	214	0.096	13.3	12.0	12.0	25.0	20.0	10.3	3.85	5.5
	356-T6	0.097	11.9	24.0	22.0	33.0	27.0	10.3	3.85	8.0
	356-T51	0.097	11.9	20.0	22.0	25.0	18.0	10.3	3.85	7.5

[a] The yield strength values given are based on 0.2 per cent offset strain.
[b] Rotating beam endurance limit values based on 500 million cycles.

360

alloy is designated by a number followed by the letter S. The number indicates the chemical composition of the alloy. Letters O, W, or T after the numbers of the alloy are used to designate various conditions. The letter O designates the soft condition, W the heat-treated condition, and T the final condition of heat treatment and aging. For example, 24S-T is a commonly used heat-treated alloy. For wrought alloys with properties controlled by cold-working, designations of O, 1/4H, 1/2H, 3/4H, and H after the S are used. The letter O indicates the fully annealed condition, while H is the fully hardened condition. Intermediate designations such as 1/2H indicate intermediate degrees of hardening. When a wrought alloy is strain-hardened after heat-treatment the designation RT is used. Cast alloys are designated by a number followed by the letter T and another number that indicates the specific heat-treatment as, for example, 356-T4. Some aluminum alloys such as 24S-T sheet used in aircraft are given a thin coat of aluminum to increase their resistance to corrosion. The sheet is then known as alclad 24S-T.

NUMERICAL EXAMPLE. A flat aluminum sheet is subjected to a tension load of 12,000 lb. The minimum elongation is to be 0.04 in. per in. and the allowable stress is 10,000 psi. Factors of safety of 2 based on per cent elongation and ultimate tensile strength were used. If the material has properties as given in Fig. 9-3, determine if a process of annealing or cold-rolling should be used and find the minimum required cross-sectional area of the member.

SOLUTION. Using an allowable elongation of 0.04 in. per in., the corresponding percentage elongation is $0.04 \times 2 \times 100 = 8\%$. For this elongation, from Fig. 9-3(a), the annealing temperature required is about 300° F. and the ultimate tensile strength for this temperature is about 14,000 psi. For this strength the allowable stress is $14,000/2 = 7000$ psi, which is less than the allowable stress of 10,000 psi and, hence, is the governing stress. For this stress the area required is $A = P/S_w = 12,000/7000 = 1.72$ sq. in. The material selected is then one that is to be annealed at 300° F. so that it has an elongation of about 8 per cent.

To determine whether cold-rolling should be used, consider Fig. 9-3(b). For an 8 per cent elongation the percentage reduction by rolling is about 70 per cent and the ultimate strength is about 17,500 psi. The allowable stress based on this strength is $17,500/2$

or 8750 psi, which is the governing allowable stress since it is less than 10,000 psi. For an allowable stress of 8750 psi the area required is $A = P/S_w = 12,000/8750 = 1.37$ sq. in. A comparison of the foregoing shows that the cold-rolled aluminum sheet with 70 per cent reduction requires a smaller area than would be required if the sheet were annealed.

9-4. MAGNESIUM AND ITS ALLOYS

Magnesium is the lightest of commercial metals, having a density about two-thirds that of aluminum. Because of its low strength, magnesium is rarely used as a structural material. Magnesium alloys, however, have adequate strength, and this increased strength makes it possible for magnesium to compete with aluminum in many

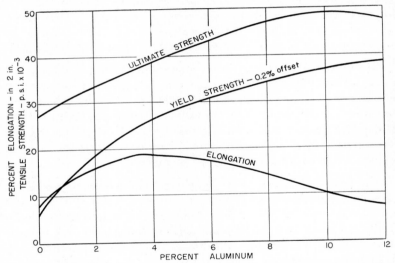

Fig. 9-6. Influence of aluminum on properties of magnesium-aluminum alloys (manganese 0.1 to 0.3%). (From *Metals Handbook*. Courtesy Amer. Soc. for Metals.)

applications. The strength-weight ratio of precipitation-hardened magnesium alloys is comparable to strong alloys of aluminum or to alloys of steel. An adequate modulus of elasticity combined with low density makes magnesium alloys suitable for parts where strength is governed by buckling. Magnesium alloys are also used where a

Table 9-6

Average Physical Properties of Magnesium Alloys

Type	Alloy	Density (lb. per cu. in.)	Temp. coef. per deg. (°F × 10⁶)	Yield strength[a] (psi × 10⁻³)		Ult. strength (psi × 10⁻³)		Mod. elas. (psi × 10⁻⁶)		Endurance limit[b] (psi × 10⁻³)
				Tension	Comp.	Tension	Shear	Tension and comp.	Shear	
Wrought	AM-C54S-O	0.065	14.5	22.0	16.0	40.0	21.0	6.5	2.4	
	AM-C54S-H	0.065	14.5	34.0	30.0	44.0	23.0	6.5	2.4	17.0
	AM-C57S	0.065	14.5	29.0	18.0	44.0	20.5	6.5	2.4	17.5
	AM-C58S	0.066	14.5	32.0	21.0	46.0	21.5	6.5	2.4	16.0
	AM-C58S-T5	0.066	14.5	34.0	26.0	48.0	22.0	6.5	2.4	11.0
	AM-65S	0.067	14.5	28.0	21.0	40.0	16.0	6.5	2.4	
Cast	AM-260-C	0.066	14.5	14.0	14.0	25.0	18.0	6.5	2.4	12.0
	AM-260-T6	0.066	14.5	22.0	22.0	40.0	22.0	6.5	2.4	12.0
	AM-265-C	0.036	14.5	11.0	11.0	27.0	18.0	6.5	2.4	11.0
	AM-265-T6	0.066	14.5	19.0	19.0	40.0	20.0	6.5	2.4	11.0

[a] The yield strength values given are based on 0.2 per cent offset strain.
[b] Rotating beam endurance limit values are based on 500 million cycles.

combination of strength and light form is necessary, such as in housings for aircraft members or for rapidly rotating or reciprocating parts.

Magnesium is obtained from magnesite ($MgCO_3$), dolomite ($MgCO_3 \cdot CaCO_3$), and from sea water. Magnesium is produced by converting the raw material to magnesium chloride ($MgCl_2$) or magnesium oxide (MgO). These compounds may be reduced to magnesium by heating with a specific reducing agent or by electrolysis.

Magnesium alloys can be fabricated by the same methods used for steel. That is, it can be hot- and cold-rolled, cast, welded, soldered, and riveted. Furthermore, magnesium alloys have good machining characteristics. Some of the properties of the more common magnesium alloys are given in Table 9-6.

Most of the commercial magnesium alloys contain aluminum and manganese. Zinc is also a common alloying element. Figure 9-6 shows the increase in strength of magnesium alloys produced by the addition of aluminum. The influence of other elements on the properties of magnesium alloys is described in the reference given in Footnote 1.

9-5. LEAD AND ITS ALLOYS

The most common lead ore is lead sulphide (PbS), called *galena*. Lead ores also occur in the form of carbonite and sulphite of lead. Lead is extracted from lead sulphide by first removing the sulphur. This is done by heating crushed ore and blowing air through it. The oxygen in the air combines with the lead to form an oxide. The oxide is reduced to lead in a blast furnace using coke as the reducing agent. The final step consists in refining of the lead by methods that vary depending upon the impurities present.

Lead has the highest density of the common metals, with a specific gravity of approximately 11. The short-time tensile yield strength of lead is about 1600 psi, and the ultimate strength is about 2400 psi. It creeps at room temperature and at stresses as low as 150 psi. When exposed to air, it forms a thin protective coating of lead oxide, which prevents further corrosion. The workability and resistance of lead to corrosion makes it useful for pipes. In sheet form it is used for lining tanks and for roofing. Because of its chem-

---

[1] John L. Everhart *et al.*, "Mechanical Properties of Metals and Alloys," Circular No. C 447, National Bureau of Standards, 1943.

ical and electrical characteristics it is used for storage batteries. Lead is also used in the manufacture of paint.

Lead alloyed with tin produces different grades of solder and pewter that are harder than lead. In general, tin increases the strength, hardness, and ductility of lead. Antimony increases the strength of lead but decreases its creep resistance. Antimony-lead alloys and alloys of lead and tin are employed as bearing metals. Lead is also alloyed with bismuth and cadmium. Calcium or copper in small percentages increase its fatigue and creep resistance.

9-6. TIN AND ITS ALLOYS

Tin is obtained from the tin oxide *cassiterite* (SnO_2). It usually occurs in alluvial deposits and is mined by pumps or dredging. Screening and sluicing are then used to concentrate the ore. Impurities such as iron are removed by roasting and treatment with hydrochloric acid. The tin oxide is reduced to tin by smelting in a blast furnace with coal and limestone. The tin obtained from the

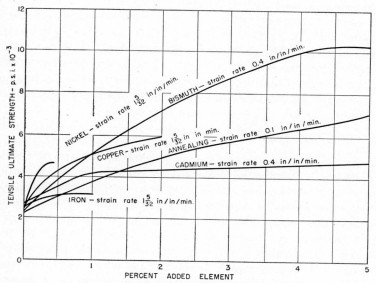

Fig. 9-7. Variation of tensile strength of tin alloys with per cent of alloying element. (From "Mechanical Properties of Metals and Alloys," *Circ. C* 447, U. S. Bureau of Standards.)

blast furnace is refined by electrolysis or by reheating. The reheating to just above 230° C. melts the tin, which can be drained off, leaving the impurities which have a higher melting point. After the refining process, the molten tin is cast into pigs.

The ultimate tensile strength of tin in the annealed condition is about 2200 psi, the yield strength is about 1300 psi, and the elongation in 2 in. is about 45 per cent. Cold-working has only a temporary effect on tin, since normal temperatures have an annealing effect. The high resistance of tin to corrosion makes it suitable for plating. Tin is also used for making solder.

Copper and lead are the most common metals used with tin to produce alloys. The influence of various elements on the strength of tin is shown in Fig. 9-7. The word bronze has been used for a number of alloys, but primarily designates copper-tin alloys. Figure 9-7 shows how copper increases the strength of tin. Copper-tin alloys may be strengthened by cold-working. Gun metal is one of the best known bronzes and contains about 10 per cent tin. Another bronze called Government bronze contains about 88 per cent copper, 10 per cent tin, and 2 per cent zinc. It is commonly used for valves and gears. Phosphor bronze is bronze with phosphorus added in amounts up to 4 per cent. Phosphorus is added to improve the corrosion resistance in applications such as turbine blades and gears. Phosphor bronze, with 20 per cent tin, makes a suitable material for bearings subjected to high pressures and low speeds. Tin alloys of antimony and copper are also suitable for bearings and are known as Babbitt metal.

9-7. ZINC AND ZINC ALLOYS

Zinc is used for many important alloys such as the various bronzes and brasses. The zinc sulphide *sphalerite* (ZnS) is the most important zinc ore. However, zinc may also occur in the form of carbonate or oxide. The method of manufacturing zinc is similar to the procedure used for other metals and consists of roasting, reducing, and refining. After grinding and heating the ore in a furnace, zinc sulphide is reduced to zinc oxide. Oxygen is removed from the zinc oxide by heating with carbon, usually in the form of coal. In this reducing process the carbon combines with oxygen and the oxygen is removed in the form of a gas, while the oxide is reduced to zinc. With the temperature used, the zinc is in the gaseous state and it is collected and condensed in cooling chambers. Additional impurities are removed from the zinc by reheating. Electrolysis is used as an alternate method in the manufacture of zinc.

There are a number of copper-zinc alloys known as brass, which vary in the relative amounts of copper and zinc. The trade names for some of these alloys are Red Brass, Cartridge Brass, Deep Draw-

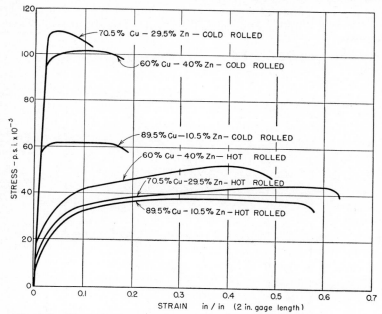

Fig. 9-8. Typical stress-strain diagrams in tension for copper-zinc alloys. (After G. Murphy, *Properties of Engineering Materials.* Courtesy International Textbook Co.)

ing Brass, Yellow Brass, and Muntz metal. Typical stress-strain diagrams for copper and copper-zinc alloys are shown in Fig. 9-8. This figure shows that the strength of the copper-zinc alloys increases with the increase in percentage of zinc. *Manganese bronze* is an alloy of copper and zinc with small amounts of tin, iron, and manganese. *Naval brass* is a zinc alloy similar to manganese bronze but it does not contain iron. For use in die-casting, a series of zinc alloys known as *Zamak* have been developed. In addition to zinc, these alloys contain aluminum, magnesium, iron, and copper. Zinc is used also for galvanizing, in batteries, and in the manufacture of paint. Properties of some of the foregoing alloys are given in Table 9-3.

9-8. NICKEL AND NICKEL ALLOYS

Nickel is used for the manufacture of several important nickel alloys. The most commonly used nickel ore is a sulphide (NiS) called nickel pyrite. As for other metals, nickel is extracted by the usual processes

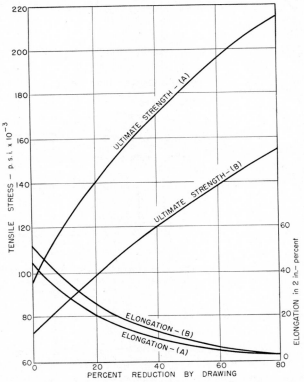

(A) Mn 15%, Fe 0.25%, Si 0.20%,   (B) Mn 0.15%, Fe 0.20%, Si 0.07%,
C 0.12%, Cu 0.10%, S 0.005%.   C 0.10%, Cu 0.05%, S 0.005%.

Fig. 9-9. Influence of cold drawing on properties of nickel and a nickel-manganese alloy. (From *Metals Handbook*. Courtesy Amer. Soc. for Metals.)

of roasting, reducing, and refining. The refining of nickel is usually accomplished by electrolysis.

Nickel is ductile so that it can be rolled into sheets or drawn into fine wire. The ultimate strength of nickel can be increased from 60,000 psi to over 100,000 psi by cold-rolling, as indicated in Fig. 9-9.

Nickel is most commonly used as an element in alloys or as a protective covering for other metals. It is also used for heating coils, condensers, pumps, and other equipment where a high degree of resistance to corrosion and heat is desirable.

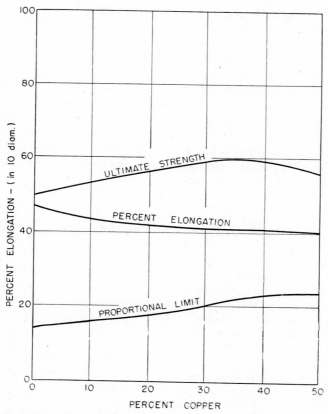

Fig. 9-10. Effect of copper on tensile properties of annealed wrought nickel-copper alloys. (From "Properties of Metals and Alloys," *Circ. C* 447, U. S. Bureau of Standards.)

High-strength structural steel can be obtained with nickel in amounts up to 3 per cent. Stainless steel and invar are other important alloys of steel and nickel. Copper alloyed with nickel increases the tensile strength, as shown in Fig. 9-10. An important copper-nickel alloy is *Monel metal*, containing about 30 per cent copper and small amounts of iron, manganese, silicon, and carbon. Monel metal has a high resistance to corrosion and retains its properties at elevated temperatures. It undergoes little change in properties at low temperatures and is, therefore, useful for liquid-air equipment. Nickel-copper alloys of about 40 per cent nickel have high electrical resistance and are, therefore, used for electrical control instruments. An alloy of nickel that has a high resistance to corrosion is *German silver* or *nickel silver*. Its average composition is about 20 per cent nickel, 30 per cent zinc, and 50 per cent copper.

There are many other alloys of nickel, including nickel-chromium, nickel-iron-molybdenum, and nickel-aluminum-cobalt. The high resistance of nickel to oxidation at high temperatures makes it a valuable element in alloys used for parts operating at elevated temperatures, such as jet-propulsion units and turbosuperchargers. Inconel "X" is a high-temperature nickel alloy composed of 75 per cent nickel, 14 per cent chromium, 6 per cent iron, 3 per cent titanium, and 0.6 per cent aluminum.

PROBLEMS AND QUESTIONS

9-1. Compare the relative costs of a tension member of 75S-T wrought aluminum alloy and structural steel if the members are of the same length. The aluminum alloy costs three times as much per pound as the steel. Base the calculations on the same factors of safety for each material and compare the costs for each of the following conditions if both members carry the same load: (a) failure by yielding, (b) failure by fracture.

Ans. (a) $C_a/C_s = 0.52$, (b) $C_a/C_s = 0.79$.

9-2. (a) Compare the weights of a tension member made of structural steel and of wrought aluminum alloy 24S-T. Base the comparison on the modulus of elastic resilience. (b) If the aluminum alloy costs three times as much per pound as the steel, which would be the more economical material to use in Prob. 9-2(a)?   *Ans.* (a) $W_a/W_s = 0.071$, (b) $C_a/C_s = 0.21$.

9-3. Compare the resilience of the hard wrought nonferrous metals in Table 9-3 with structural steel.

9-4. Compare the toughness of the hard wrought nonferrous metals in Table 9-3 with structural steel. *Given:* toughness = $\frac{1}{2}(S_{yp} + S_u)D_e$, where S_{yp} = the yield strength, S_u = the ultimate strength, and D_e = the elongation.   *Ans.* 0.39, 0.79, 0.24, and 0.29.

9-5. A structural tension member is 4 ft. long. The member may be subjected to a gradually applied tensile load of 100,000 lb. Which material would require the minimum weight, magnesium alloy (AM-C58S), or aluminum alloy (24S-T)? Base static load design on the ultimate strength.   *Ans.* W_m = 6.9 lb., W_a = 7.10 lb.

9-6. Prepare a table listing the main ores from which the nonferrous metals are obtained.

9-7. For the aluminum with properties as shown in Fig. 9-3, would an annealing temperature of 200° or 800° F. be selected if it is desired to obtain a material with maximum toughness?

9-8. For the wrought aluminum with tensile properties as given in Fig. 9-4, plot the variation in toughness with temperature.

9-9. A magnesium-aluminum alloy with tensile properties as shown in Fig. 9-5 is to be used for a tension member. By what percentage does an increase in magnesium from 2 to 10 per cent decrease the weight of the member if the design is based on (a) the yield strength, (b) the ultimate strength, and (c) the toughness?   *Ans.* (a) 50%, (b) 54%, (c) 80%.

9-10. Compare the toughness of the aluminum-magnesium alloys with 4 and 12 per cent aluminum having properties as shown in Fig. 9-6.

9-11. Compare the elastic strength, stiffness, and resilience of three tension members made of an aluminum alloy 75-ST, structural SAE 1020 steel, and a magnesium alloy AM-C58S. Solve if (a) the members have the same width, depth, and length, and (b) if the members have the same width, length, and weight.

9-12. Solve Prob. 9-11 if the members are simply supported beams with center-concentrated loads and the values of the elastic strength and modulus of elasticity in bending are assumed to be the same as in tension.

9-13. An aluminum sheet is to be used for a tension member to resist 20,000 lb. The minimum elongation is to be 0.06 in. per in. and the allowable stress is 12,000 psi. Determine, using Fig. 9-3, whether the material should be annealed or cold-rolled. Use a factor of safety of 2 based on both the percentage elongation and the ultimate strength. What is the required area for the material selected?

BIBLIOGRAPHY

Beck, A., *The Technology of Magnesium and Its Alloys*, F. A. Hughes & Co., Ltd., Swinton, England, 1940.

Bray, J. L., *Non-ferrous Production Metallurgy*, John Wiley & Sons, Inc., New York, 1941.

Gillet, H. W., *The Behavior of Engineering Materials*, John Wiley & Sons, Inc., New York, 1951.

Liddell, D. M., *Handbook of Non-ferrous Metallurgy*, McGraw-Hill Book Co., Inc., New York, 1945.

Newton, J., and Wilson, C. L., *Metallurgy of Copper*, John Wiley & Sons, Inc., New York, 1942.

Samans, C. H., *Engineering Metals and Their Alloys*, The Macmillan Co., New York, 1949.

Schulze, R. B., *Aluminum and Magnesium Design and Fabrication*, McGraw-Hill Book Co., Inc., New York, 1949.

White, A. E., *Engineering Materials*, McGraw-Hill Book Co., Inc., New York, 1939.

Metals Handbook, published by the American Society for Metals, Cleveland, 1948.

Designing with Magnesium. published by the American Magnesium Corp., 1947.

Alcoa Structural Handbook, published by The Aluminum Company of America, Pittsburgh, 1945.

Chapter 10

Nonmetallic Materials

10-1. INTRODUCTION

Nonmetallic materials, including wood, concrete, stone, clay products, cementing materials, and various types of plastics, represent a large percentage of the entire volume of engineering materials that are manufactured. The main reasons why they are used in such large quantities are the ease of manufacture, the low relative cost, and the abundance of these materials.

10-2. WOOD

The adaptability of wood to being shaped, its availability, and its desirable properties make it a commonly used material for structural purposes. Wood in the form of pulp is also used in the manufacture of paper and rayon.

Kinds of Wood. There are numerous kinds of commercial woods. They may be classified in two groups—hardwoods and softwoods. *Softwoods* usually come from trees with needlelike leaves (mostly cone-bearing), while *hardwoods* come from trees with broad leaves. The main softwoods are pine, cedar, fir, spruce, hemlock, and cypress. The principal hardwoods are oak, maple, walnut, hickory, ash, and poplar. Trees may also be classified according to the manner of growth as exogenous or endogenous. The exogenous tree's growth occurs by the formation of rings between the old wood and the bark, while in endogenous trees the new fibers grow intermingled with the old. Palm, bamboo, and yucca trees are examples of endogenous trees.

Structure of Wood.   The structure of wood may be described as fibers of cellulose cemented together with lignin.   The fibers are about 0.03 to 0.25 in. long and of diameter equal to about 1/100 their lengths.   Fibers take an active part in the life of trees for a few years after their formation.   They then gradually become inactive and form heartwood.   The active part of the trees is the sapwood. Woods are identified by their differences in structure.   In the exogenous trees new fibers are added between the bark and the old wood.   In the spring this growth is more rapid than in the summer and is distinguished by the larger size and thinner walls of the fibers. As might be expected, spring wood is softer and weaker than summer wood.

Manufacturing and Seasoning of Lumber.   The first step in the manufacture of lumber is logging.   Trees are usually cut in the fall or winter when there is a minimum amount of sap.   The logs are then transported to a saw mill by floating down streams or by truck.   At the saw mill the lumber is cut into standard sizes.   Finally the lumber is dried or seasoned, since when it comes from the mill it may contain about 35 per cent moisture.   Loss of moisture in lumber is accompanied by shrinkage.   This condition is undesirable if it occurs after the structure or product is constructed.   Removal of moisture in lumber by seasoning is accomplished by stacking boards in the open in such a way that air circulates freely, or it may be accomplished by placing the lumber in kilns or ovens and drying by artificial heat.   Excess moisture in lumber may also be removed by chemical means.   Chemicals may be applied on the outside of green lumber or the lumber may be immersed in a solution.   Tests show that there is no marked difference in properties of air-dried, kiln-dried, or chemically treated lumber.

Defects in Lumber.   Defects in lumber may be either defects in the original wood or defects produced by incorrect cutting and seasoning.   In general, defects are undesirable since they mar the appearance and decrease the mechanical properties of wood.   Knots, cross-grain, compression wood, shakes, rot, and pitch pockets are defects in the original wood.   *Checks* and *warping* are produced during seasoning, while *wane* is produced during cutting.   Knots are cross sections of limbs growing out from the main trunk of a tree; they produce discontinuity which decreases the strength, particularly in tension.   Cross-grain is grain not parallel to the axis of the specimen. It decreases the values of the mechanical properties. *Compression wood* is an abnormal growth, denser and weaker than normal wood. *Shakes* are cracks produced during growth. These cracks may be accentuated due to shrinkage while drying. *Rot* is decayed wood produced by bacterial action. *Pitch pockets* are deposits of resin between fibers. *Checks* are cracks produced during seasoning because of unequal drying rates in different directions. *Wane* is bark left on the edge of lumber as a result of cutting too near the outside of the tree. Changes in moisture content produce *warping,* the amount of warping depending upon the orientation of the board relative to the rings.

The wide variation in the quality of lumber has led to grading. Usually the grading rules are on the basis of number or size of defects, but they may also be based on the working stresses. In order of decrease in quality the usual grades are firsts, seconds, select, No. 1 common, No. 2 common, sound wormy, No. 3A common, and No. 3B common. Other grade designations and classifications are also used.

Size of Lumber. Standard sizes of rectangular sections or special shapes are available. These include flooring, shingles, shiplap,

Table 10-1

Relation of Strength of Wood to Specific Gravity

	Moisture content	
Property	Green	Air—dry (12% moisture)
Static bending:		
Fiber stress at prop. limit — psi	$10,200G^{1.25}$	$16,700G^{1.25}$
Modulus of rupture — psi	$17,600G^{1.25}$	$26,200G^{1.25}$
Modulus of elasticity — psi	$2.36 \times 10^6 G$	$2.8 \times 10^6 G$
Compression parallel to grain:		
Fiber stress at prop. limit — psi	$5,250G$	$8,750G$
Stress at ultimate — psi	$6,730G$	$12,200G$
Modulus of elasticity — psi	$2.91 \times 10^6 G$	$3.38 \times 10^6 G$
Compression perpendicular to grain:		
Fiber stress at prop. limit — psi	$3,000G^{2.25}$	$4,630G^{2.25}$

Note: G is the specific gravity.
Data by U. S. Forest Service, U. S. Dept. of Agriculture.

siding, and molding of various shapes. Lumber is cut to certain nominal sizes when green. For example, as a result of waste in cutting and because of shrinkage, a 2-in. by 4-in. size is actually about $1\frac{3}{4}$ in. by $3\frac{5}{8}$ in. Lumber is measured in board feet and prices are usually quoted in terms of 1000 board feet. One board foot of lumber is a piece 1 foot square by 1 inch thick.

Properties of Lumber. Although all species of wood have about the same percentage of cellulose and lignin, their mechanical properties differ considerably because of differences in structure. Furthermore, the structure of wood is such that it is nonisotropic and has, therefore, different properties in different directions. In

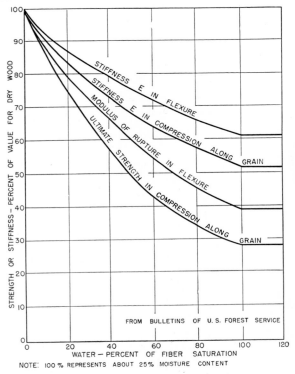

Fig. 10-1. Effect of moisture on strength and stiffness of softwoods.

general, the presence of defects decreases the strength values. The specific gravities of woods are related to the mechanical properties, as indicated by the test results obtained on different species of wood at the Forest Products Laboratory (Table 10-1). An increase in density increases the value of the mechanical properties. The moisture content also has a marked effect on the mechanical properties; an increase in moisture up to the saturation point decreases the strength, as indicated in Fig. 10-1. Typical stress-strain diagrams

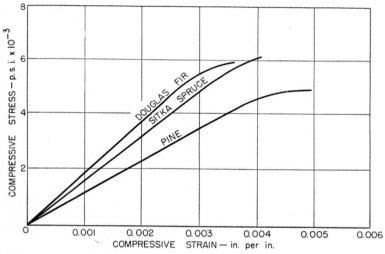

Fig. 10-2.   Typical stress-strain curves for wood in compression parallel to grain.

in compression for some of the common woods are shown in Fig. 10-2. The rate of loading and duration of load also influence the strength of wood. The uncertainties in the nature of the loading, moisture content, and defects in wood have led to the use of high factors of safety, often 10 to 20, based on the ultimate strengths.

The durability, appearance, and cost of lumber compare favorably with those of other materials. The ease with which lumber can be worked and fabricated by nailing and gluing makes it a valuable engineering material. Average properties of the most common woods are shown in Table 10-2.

Table 10-2

Average Physical Properties of Wood

Commercial name	Specific gravity[b]	Bending			Compression parallel to grain		Prop. limit in compression perp. to grain (psi × 10⁻³)	Ult. shear strength parallel to grain (psi × 10⁻³)
		Prop. limit (psi × 10⁻³)	Modulus of rupture (psi × 10⁻³)	Modulus of elasticity (psi × 10⁻⁶)	Prop. limit (psi × 10⁻³)	Ult. str. (psi × 10⁻³)		
Ash, commercial white	0.58	8.9	14.6	1.68	5.58	7.28	1.51	1.92
Cedar, eastern red	0.47	3.8	8.8	0.88		6.02	1.14	
Cypress, southern	0.46	7.2	10.6	1.44	4.74	6.36	0.90	1.00
Douglas fir, Rocky Mt.	0.43	6.3	9.6	1.40	4.66	6.06	0.82	1.07
Elm, American	0.50	7.6	11.8	1.34	4.03	5.52	0.85	1.51
Hemlock, eastern	0.40	6.1	8.9	1.20	4.02	5.41	0.80	1.06
Hickory, true	0.73	10.9	19.7	2.18		8.97	2.31	2.14
Maple, red	0.54	8.7	13.4	1.64	4.65	6.54	1.24	1.85
Oak, red	0.63	8.4	14.4	1.81	4.61	6.92	1.26	1.83
Oak, white	0.67	7.9	13.9	1.62	4.35	7.04	1.41	1.89
Pine, northern white	0.36	6.0	8.8	1.28	3.68	4.84	0.55	0.86
Pine, southern yellow:								
Longleaf	0.58	9.3	14.7	1.99	6.15	8.44	1.19	1.50
Shortleaf	0.51	7.7	12.8	1.76	5.09	7.07	1.00	1.31
Redwood (virgin)	0.40	6.9	10.0	1.34	4.56	6.15	0.86	0.94
Spruce, Sitka	0.40	6.7	10.2	1.57	4.78	5.61	0.71	1.15
Tamarack	0.53	8.0	11.6	1.64	4.78	7.16	0.99	1.28

Results of tests on small[a] clear specimens under air-dry condition with 12 per cent moisture content as reported in *Wood Handbook*, 1935. Forest Products Laboratory, U. S. Department of Agriculture, Washington, D. C.

[a] Test specimens 2 × 2 in. in cross section. Bending specimens 30 in. long; other specimens shorter depending upon kind of test.

[b] Based on weight when ovendry, and volume at 12 per cent moisture content.

Deterioration and Preservation of Lumber. Lumber deterioration is usually caused by decay, insects, marine borers, or fire. Decay is caused by various bacteria and fungi. Termites, beetles, and ants damage wood by digging tunnels through it. Decay of wood can be decreased by use of preservatives such as coal-tar creosote or zinc chloride. Two processes are used in applying the preservative. In the full-cell process the lumber is placed in an air-tight cylinder, a vacuum is applied to remove the air, and the preservative is then introduced at a pressure of 100 to 200 psi. In the empty-cell process the initial vacuum is not used.

Fire-resistance of wood may be increased by use of surface treatments or by impregnation. Special paints and various chemicals are used for these treatments.

Processing of Wood. Processing is used to increase the strength and uniformity of lumber. Processed woods are produced by impregnating the wood with a plastic or resin, or by compressing it to increase its density. Sometimes both methods are used.

Sheets of wood are glued together to form plywood sheets. Plywood is a more isotropic material than the original wood and provides a material with greater strength and less tendency to warp than ordinary lumber.

The importance of lumber is realized when its various uses are noted. It is used in many temporary and permanent structures, for manufacture of pulp and rayon, and for the manufacture of other materials.

Numerical Example. A simply supported beam with a center-concentrated load is of rectangular cross section. Consider two beams of the same length and width, one made of structural steel with $E = 30 \times 10^6$ psi and a yield strength of 80,000 psi, and another made of white pine with $E = 1.28 \times 10^6$ psi and a yield strength of 7000 psi. If steel weighs 0.284 lb. per cu. in. and white pine weighs 0.013 lb. per cu. in., and both beams weigh the same, compare (a) the depths of the beams, (b) the stiffness, and (c) the flexure strengths.

Solution. (a). If d_w and d_s are the depths of the wood and steel beams, then the weight of the wood beam is equal to the density times the volume, or

$$W_w = \gamma(bdL) = 0.013 \times b \times d_w \times L$$

and the weight of the steel beam is

$$W_s = \gamma(bdL) = 0.284 \times b \times d_s \times L$$

Since the weights of the two beams are equal, $W_w = W_s$, or

$$0.013 \, d_w L = 0.284 \, d_s L$$

or
$$\frac{d_w}{d_s} = 21.8$$

(b). The stiffness of the beams is defined by the deflections for equal load values. For a simply supported beam with a center load the deflection is $y = \dfrac{PL^3}{48EI}$. Then for the wood and steel beams, respectively,

$$y_w = \frac{PL^3}{48E_w I_w} \quad \text{and} \quad y_s = \frac{PL^3}{48E_s I_s}$$

or
$$\frac{y_w}{y_s} = \frac{E_s I_s}{E_w I_w} = \left(\frac{E_s}{E_w}\right)\left(\frac{bd_s^3/12}{bd_w^3/12}\right)$$
$$= \left(\frac{E_s}{E_w}\right)\left(\frac{d_s}{d_w}\right)^3 = \left(\frac{30 \times 10^6}{1.28 \times 10^6}\right)\left(\frac{1}{21.8}\right)^3 = 0.00226$$

That is, the wood beam will deflect only 0.00226 times as much as the steel beam of equal weight.

(c). The flexure strengths of the beams are defined by the loads that can be resisted in bending. Since

$$S = \frac{Mc}{I} = \frac{PL}{4}\left(\frac{d/2}{bd^3/12}\right) = \frac{3}{2}\left(\frac{PL}{bd^2}\right)$$

then the resisting load is $P = 2bd^2S/(3L)$. For the wood and steel beams the strengths are

$$P_w = \frac{2bd_w^2 S_w}{3L} \quad \text{and} \quad P_s = \frac{2bd_s^2 S_s}{3L}$$

Then the strength ratios become

$$\frac{P_w}{P_s} = \left(\frac{2bd_w^2 S_w}{3L}\right)\left(\frac{3L}{2bd_s^2 S_s}\right)$$
$$= \left(\frac{S_w}{S_s}\right)\left(\frac{d_w}{d_s}\right)^2 = \left(\frac{7000}{80,000}\right)(21.8)^2 = 41.6$$

That is, the strength of the wood beam is 41.6 times that of the steel beam of equal weight.

Although the wood beam is much stiffer and stronger than the steel beam of equal weight, it should be noted that the size of the wood beam is much greater than the steel and that other considerations may also govern in the selection of the material to be used.

10-3. STONE

For many years public and monumental works have been constructed of stone. Stone has been a desirable material for these structures because of its appearance together with its properties of strength and durability. Stone as a constructional material competes with many other materials and is used for bridges, dams, retaining walls, concrete aggregates, roofing materials, paving blocks, and crushed rock for roads. On this basis of use and shape, stone is classified as building stone, crushed stone, gravel, and sand.

The preparation of stone consists of quarrying and finishing. Quarrying is removing soil and inferior stone from the surface and cutting by the use of a channeling machine. The resulting blocks are removed by cranes. The shaping and finishing of the rough blocks is done by hand or by saws, lathes, grinders, and planers. Depending upon the use made of the stone, it may be roughly dressed or highly finished.

The kinds of stone may be classified on a chemical or physical basis. On the chemical basis, calcium carbonate ($CaCO_3$), silicates of alumina, and silica (SiO_2) are of engineering value. Granite and sandstone contain silica. Shale and slate are primarily silicates of alumina. The principal building stones of the calcium carbonate

Table 10-3

Approximate Values of Mechanical Properties of Stone

Kind of stone	Weight lb. per cu. ft.	Compressive strength (psi $\times 10^{-3}$)	Shearing strength (psi $\times 10^{-3}$)	Modulus of rupture (psi $\times 10^{-3}$)	Flexural modulus of elasticity (psi $\times 10^{-6}$)
Granite......	$160 \pm 10\%$	$20 \pm 50\%$	$2.8 \pm 35\%$	$2.5 \pm 60\%$	$8.0 \pm 30\%$
Limestone....	$155 \pm 10\%$	$15 \pm 80\%$	$2.0 \pm 50\%$	$2.5 \pm 80\%$	$10.0 \pm 50\%$
Marble.......	$165 \pm 5\%$	$18 \pm 30\%$	$3.0 \pm 60\%$	$2.0 \pm 50\%$	$9.0 \pm 50\%$
Sandstone....	$145 \pm 10\%$	$14 \pm 50\%$	$1.8 \pm 50\%$	$1.5 \pm 60\%$	$4.5 \pm 70\%$
Slate........	$175 \pm 3\%$	$14 \pm 50\%$	$2.5 \pm 40\%$	$8.0 \pm 20\%$	...

group are limestone and marble. On a physical basis, classification of stone as igneous, sedimentary, and metamorphic is based on the geological process involved in its formation. *Igneous rocks* (granite, basalt, and lava) are formed by cooling of molten material. *Sedimentary rocks* (sand and limestone) are formed by cementation of particles deposited in layers by wind or water. *Metamorphic rocks* (marble and slate) are formed when igneous or sedimentary rocks are subjected to pressure or heat.

Properties of Stone. Stone is greatly nonhomogeneous and the properties of two samples may vary considerably. Average values of some of the properties of building stone are shown in Table 10-3. Average stress-strain diagrams in compression for the common building stones are given in Fig. 10-3. Porosity of stone is a good index

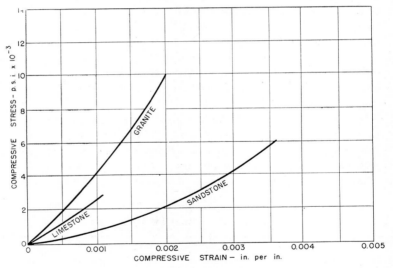

Fig. 10-3. Types of stress-strain diagrams in compression for building stones.

of its strength. As might be expected, the greater the porosity the less the strength, as indicated in Fig. 10-4. It is logical that the strength should decrease with increase in porosity, since greater porosity means less material per unit volume and a change in structure. The porosity values shown in Fig. 10-4 are measured by the percentage absorption by weight. The character and size of the pores on the surface of the stone influence the values obtained for the porosity so that an exact value of porosity is not obtained from measurements of absorption. The porosity values based on percentage absorption do, however, give a good index of the strength.

The nonhomogeneous nature of stone and its low impact resistance require that a high factor of safety be used in design. Values of factor of safety of 20 are commonly used.

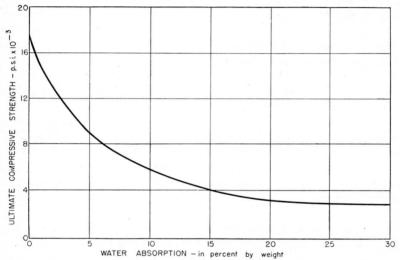

Fig. 10-4. Influence of porosity upon the strength of dry stone. (Data by J. H. Griffith, from *Bull. 131*, Iowa Eng. Exp. Sta., 1937.)

The durability of stone is dependent upon several factors. The presence of discontinuities such as bedding planes and cracks tends to weaken the stone and provide openings for disintegration. Chemical composition also influences the durability. For example, limestone can be decomposed by acids, while silicates are more resistant to chemical action. The texture of stone also influences the durability, and a fine texture gives greater strength and durability than a coarse structure.

Uses of Stone. Sandstone is used for general building purposes, while slate is widely used for blackboards and roofing material. Limestone is used for buildings, bridges, and stone masonry in general. It is also employed in the manufacture of ferrous metals and cement, and as an aggregate in making concrete.

Marble is limestone which has been subjected to pressure and heat. It yields a denser and harder material than the original limestone and is used for decorative stone work, floors, steps, and monuments. Granite has relatively poor resistance to fire and water.

10-4. CLAY PRODUCTS

Primitive peoples dried or burnt clay into molded shapes of various kinds. At the present time, clay products are used as building and paving blocks, for roofing, wall tile, lining of furnaces, and in the form of drainage conduits.

The materials most commonly found in natural clays are the hydrated silicates of alumina, commonly in the form $Al_2O_3 \cdot 2SiO_2 \cdot 2H_2O$, or kaolinite. Impurities such as lime, potash, magnesia, and soda are usually present in clay.

Clay is found in the form of *residual, glacial, sedimentary*, or *loess* clay. Clay is also obtained from shale or slate. Residual clays occur in deposits at the site of rocks from which they were formed. Glacial clays are those which have been transported and deposited in banks by the action of glaciers. Clays deposited by sedimentation and transported by water are sedimentary clays, while loess clays are those deposited by winds.

Manufacture of Brick and Terra Cotta. In the manufacture of brick and terra cotta, the raw materials (consisting of clays, shale, or other materials) are first washed and ground. They are then mixed with water and allowed to stand. The mixture is then placed in a *pug mill*, which consists of a horizontal cylindrical container with a shaft to which a group of blades are attached. The rotation of the shaft makes it possible for the blades to produce a uniform plastic mass of the clay. When the pug mill has served its purpose the clay is transferred to molds if special shapes are desired. In the *stiff mud process* used for brick, hollow tile building blocks, and similar shapes, the plastic clay is extruded through dies. The brick is then dried and is subsequently fired in kilns to produce partial vitrification. The rate of cooling used influences the properties. Too rapid cooling will produce warping and brittleness. Paving brick of maximum quality is obtained by a cooling or annealing period of about a week. Shapes such as sewer pipe and paving brick require a hard impervious surface; a coating is added that vitrifies the surface. This is accomplished by including with the clay materials such as magnesia, lime, and ferric oxide that will fuse with the clay during the burning process.

Defects. Incorrect mixing, shaping, burning, and undesirable chemical composition are the causes of defects in clay products. Air bubbles during burning produce air pockets or blisters. Friction at the edges during the extrusion process may retard the movement of the clay so that unbalanced masses produce laminations. Incorrect drying before burning will produce cracks and checks, and overburning will produce warping. Underburned or soft-burned brick is weak and soft.

Types of Clay Products. Clay products include building, paving, and fire brick, terra cotta, hollow building blocks, roofing, wall and floor tile, sewer and drain tile, and porcelain shapes of various kinds, such as insulators for transmission lines.

In addition to the use of clay in making these products, kaolins obtained from clay are used as a filler in rubber products and in the manufacture of linoleum, textiles, and composition roofings. They are also used as fillers to give body to paper. Clay is used in kalsomine and as a filler in paint to reduce the cost. It is also added to plaster and is used as a binder in the manufacture of abrasives. The most common use of clay is in the manufacture of various household products including dishes, vases, and stoneware.

Properties of Clay Products. Some of the properties of clay products are given in Table 10-4. In engineering, the properties of

Table 10-4

Average Properties of Brick and Building Blocks

Material	Compressive strength (psi)	Modulus of rupture (psi)	Shearing strength (psi)	Modulus of elasticity (psi $\times 10^{-6}$)
Terra cotta......	$3500 \pm 15\%$	$750 \pm 30\%$	....	....
Hollow blocks...	2000	500	....	....
Brick..........	$3500 \pm 70\%$	$750 \pm 60\%$	$1200 \pm 20\%$	$2 \pm 25\%$
Paving brick....	$1000 \pm 10\%$	$2000 \pm 25\%$	$1600 \pm 25\%$	$6 \pm 30\%$
Fire brick.......	$4500 \pm 30\%$	$1000 \pm 70\%$	$700 \pm 30\%$	....

clay products that are of main interest are strength and durability.
Chemical composition and degree of burning determine the porosity
of clay products, and the porosity in turn is directly related to the
strength (Fig. 10-5). Vitrified clay products, since they have the

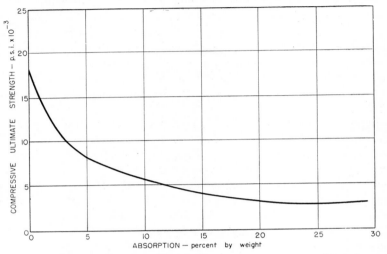

Fig. 10-5. Influence of porosity on the compressive strength of dry
brick. (Data by J. H. Griffith, from *Bull. 131*, Iowa Eng. Exp. Sta.,
1937.)

least absorption, have the highest strength. Porosity reduces not
only strength but also durability. This decrease in durability results
because high absorption permits water to destroy the product by
alternate freezing and thawing. Porosity also permits the action of
destructive chemicals.

10-5. CEMENTING MATERIALS

Cementing materials of engineering interest are of three types—
compounds of calcium, bituminous materials, and glues. This article will consider only the calcium compounds. Calcium cements are
of two classes. One is *gypsum*, which is obtained from calcium
sulphate ($CaSO_4 + 2H_2O$), while the other is *lime* which is obtained
from calcium carbonate ($CaCO_3$). Gypsum cements include plaster
of Paris, wall plaster, and hard-finish plaster. Calcium carbonate

cements include lime, natural cement, portland cement, and high-early-strength cement.

Calcium cements have the property of hardening and developing adhesive properties when combined with water. They are used in layers to bind together brick or stones in the forming of masonry. With rock and similar materials they are used to make concrete, and in thin layers they are used as a decorative coating.

Gypsum. Gypsum is obtained by removing the water of crys-

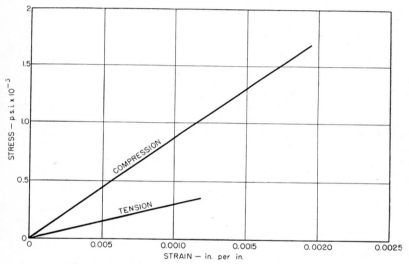

Fig. 10-6. Stress-strain diagrams for plaster of Paris.

tallization from gypsum rock ($CaSO_4 + 2H_2O$). The rock is first ground, then heated or calcined, and finally reground. With incomplete calcining at lower temperatures, dehydration is not complete and plaster of Paris ($2CaSO_4 + H_2O$) is obtained. Complete dehydration produces flooring plaster ($CaSO_4$). When alum, borax, or other similar materials are added to flooring plaster, hard-finish plaster is obtained. The setting time for gypsum plasters varies from about five minutes for plaster of Paris to several hours for hard-finish plaster. The time of setting may be decreased by the addition of various ingredients.

The tensile strength of gypsum products is low, and to increase the cohesive strength, wood and hair fibers are added.   The strength of plaster increases with time after setting and approximately one-half the maximum strength is reached in about 24 hours.   Plaster of Paris has linear stress-strain diagrams to fracture for both tension and compression (Fig. 10-6).   The ratio of the water to the plaster influences the strength of plaster of Paris, as shown in Fig. 10-7.

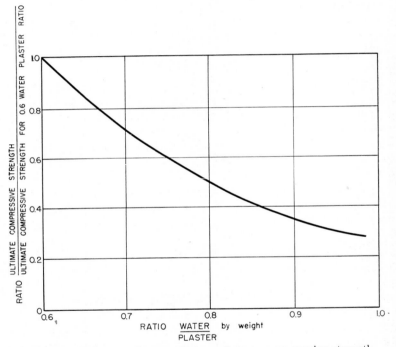

Fig. 10-7.   Influence of water-plaster ratio upon compressive strength of plaster of Paris.

In Fig. 10-7 a minimum value of water-plaster ratio equal to 0.6 is shown, since below this value the material is not plastic enough to form plaster of Paris.

Plaster of Paris is useful in making casts and architectural adorn-ments, as it expands on hardening and leaves a clear impression of the mold used.   It is used for molds in the ceramic industry and also for casting metals.

Wall plaster with sand is used for covering walls. Wall plaster mixed with sawdust and cinders is cast into blocks for construction of floors, walls, roofing, or fireproofing. Finely ground gypsum is used as a filler for toothpaste, plastics, cloth, paint, and paper.

Lime. Lime is produced from calcite or limestone ($CaCO_3$) or from magnesium limestone ($CaCO_3$ and $MgCO_3$) by removing carbon dioxide using heat. At about 900° F., calcium carbonate will become CaO and CO_2. The calcined material CaO is known as *quicklime*. In order to use quicklime it must be mixed with water. A minimum amount of water is used to convert quicklime to $Ca(OH)_2$. This product is known as *slaked lime* or *hydrated lime* and is the form of lime sold commercially.

When water is added to quicklime or slaked lime in amounts greater than is needed for hydration, the excess water will eventually evaporate and the mass will set. The hardening and setting as evidenced by increase in strength will continue for several months. Too much mixing water will decrease the strength of lime, since excess water leaves voids when the paste is eventually dried out. Sand, when added to lime to produce lime mortar, decreases the strength but also decreases the shrinkage of the hardened paste.

Lime is used as a plastering material and for mortar in brick and masonry constructions. For plastering, lime has an advantage over gypsum in that it can be mixed with about four parts of sand. In some cases, however, it has the disadvantage that it sets slower than gypsum. Hydrated lime when mixed with sand is used in the manufacture of building brick. Lime is also used in the manufacture of iron and steel, in making paper, and in other chemical processes. Some soil deficiencies are remedied by the use of lime.

Cements. Cements are composed primarily of oxides of silicon, calcium, and aluminum; namely, silica (SiO_2), lime (CaO), and alumina (Al_2O_3). There are also small amounts of Fe_2O_3, SO_3, and MgO present in cements. The properties of cement will depend upon the relative proportions of silica, lime, and alumina present. Portland cement, for example, has about 60 per cent lime, 20 per cent silica, and 20 per cent alumina plus impurities.

The cements include *hydraulic lime, Puzzolan cement, slag cement,* and *natural cement.* Hydraulic lime is produced by heating limestone that contains sufficient silica to yield a cement that will harden under water. Puzzolan cement is made from volcanic ash, sand,

and slaked lime mixed together and ground. Slag cement is finely
ground blast-furnace slag and hydrated lime. Slag cement is used
in bulk constructions where strength is not too important. Natural
cements are made by heating limestone that contains alumina and
silica.

Portland Cement. The materials used in the manufacture of portland cement are combinations of clay-bearing (argillaceous) and
lime-bearing (calcareous) materials. In some localities these materials are found blended in the correct proportions. Usually, however,
shale and limestone from different localities must be mixed together.
In the manufacture of portland cement the raw materials are first
crushed and finely ground. Next they are mixed in their correct
proportions and ground again. They are then fed into a rotating
kiln where burning takes place. After removal from the kiln the
cement is finely ground and then usually placed in sacks or bags
containing 94 lb. or about one cubic foot of cement. Another less
frequently employed method of manufacture of portland cement
uses the materials in a moist state and is called the *wet process.*

The chemical reactions that take place in the kiln are complicated. The lime silica and alumina are changed into three principal compounds—tri-calcium silicate ($3CaO \cdot SiO_2$), di-calcium silicate
($2CaO \cdot S_2O_2$), tri-calcium aluminate ($3CaO \cdot Al_2O_3$), and other compounds in small amounts.

When water is added to portland cement it gradually begins to
set and stiffen. The specification for portland cement requires that
it does not set within one hour, but that it be fully set within ten
hours. The strength of portland cement mortars increases with time
after mixing. The rate of hardening or the rate of the chemical
action that occurs depends upon the size and chemical composition
of the cement constituents, the temperature, and the amount of
available moisture for combination with the cement.

The influence of the relative amount of water to cement is shown
in Fig. 10-8, which gives the relation between the water-cement
ratio and the compressive strength for well-cured concrete specimens.
The tensile strength of portland cement mortars made of water,
cement, and sand is relatively low—about 10 per cent of the compressive strength. For this reason it is common practice to assume that
mortars will not resist tensile stresses.

There are various types of portland cements. The American Society for Testing Materials has issued specifications that cover five types. *Type 1* is ordinary portland cement used for general concrete construction. *Type 2* is designed for use where concrete must have high resistance to disintegration. *Type 3* is the high-early-strength cement used where strength is required within a few

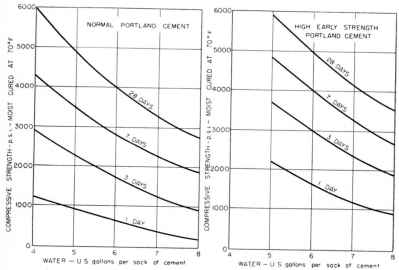

Fig. 10-8. Influence of water-cement ratio on compressive strength of concrete. (From "Design and Control of Concrete Mixtures." Courtesy Portland Cement Assoc.)

hours after placement. *Type 4* is for use where a low heat of hydration is desired, as in massive constructions such as the Hoover Dam. *Type 5* is specified for use where a high resistance to disintegration under the action of sulphates is desired. This type of cement is specified, for example, in construction of canals, culverts, and other hydraulic structures in regions where deterioration by chemicals is possible.

The Standards of the American Society for Testing Materials specify the minimum tensile and compressive strengths of cement mortars and their fineness as shown in Table 10-5.

Table 10-5

Physical Requirements for Five Types of Cement

Property	Ordinary portland cement	Portland cement for general construction	High-early-strength cement	Cement with low heat of hydration	"Sulphate-resisting" cement
Fineness, specific surface, sq. cm. per gram					
Average value, min.	1600	1700	...	1800	1800
Min. value, any one sample	1500	1600	...	1700	1700
Tensile strength, psi, min. (1:3 mortar)					
1 day in moist air	...	...	275	...	...
1 day in moist air, 27 days in water	350	325	...	300	300
Compressive strength, psi, min. (1:2.75 mortar)					
1 day in moist air	...	...	1250	...	...
1 day in moist air, 27 days in water	3000	3000	...	2000	2200

10-6. CONCRETE

The development of portland and special cements has made concrete one of the important construction materials. It is used in large quantities for dams, retaining walls, bridges, floors, pavements, sidewalks, and in the construction of buildings.

Concrete is a mixture of sand and rock or similar materials called *aggregate*, held together by a cementing material. The cementing material is usually a plastic made of cement and water. The most common aggregates are gravel and crushed stone. Sometimes slag, shale, cinders, crushed brick, or other materials may be used. The American Society for Testing Materials has established limits of grading in terms of size of particles for both the fine aggregate (sand) and the coarse aggregate (rock or gravel). The maximum permissible diameter of aggregate is governed by the type of construction.

To bind the aggregate, a standard portland cement is commonly used, although in some cases a high-early-strength, a low-heat, or a sulphate-resisting cement is more suitable. The binder is a cement paste made from cement and water. The main requirement regarding the water used is that it does not contain chemicals that will interfere with the hydration of the cement.

Small quantities of materials such as calcium chloride, hydrated lime, or soap are sometimes added to concrete mixtures to increase the workability. These materials are called *admixtures*.

The proportions of ingredients to select in making concrete are those which yield the desired strength and workability at the minimum cost. Depending upon the exposure of concrete to water and weathering, water-cement ratios vary from about six to eight gallons of water per sack of cement. Concrete is shaped by casting into molds and must, therefore, be workable. Workability is usually measured by the slump test. The slump test consists in placing freshly mixed concrete in a mold in the form of a truncated cone, 8 in. in diameter at the bottom, 4 in. in diameter at the top, and 12 in. high. After the mold is filled with concrete it is withdrawn and the slump is measured by the vertical distance from the tip of the mass to the original position of the top. The correct slump value depends upon the placement conditions.

The main difficulty in designing the most suitable concrete mixture lies in determining the optimum amount of cement-water paste to use with a given amount of aggregate so as to produce a workable, strong, and durable concrete at the minimum cost. In obtaining the best mix, the different sizes of particles in the aggregate have an important influence in the design of the mixture. The great number of possible gradings makes the problem a difficult one.

There are various methods that have been used in the design of concrete mixtures.[1] At the present time the *trial batch method*, based on the water-cement ratio, is usually considered the best. In this method a water-cement ratio is selected, based on available data, to provide the required strength or durability. A trial batch is then prepared by mixing the water-cement paste in the selected proportions and adding aggregate until the required workability is obtained. More than one combination of fine and coarse aggregate may give the desired workability. The one selected will be based on the relative cost of the aggregates.

To produce a concrete of maximum strength and durability with minimum cost, the aggregates and cement paste are so mixed that the spaces between the aggregate particles are completely filled with the paste. In addition, a practical consideration is that the paste must be of such consistency that the mixture is plastic and remains homogeneous during handling and placing.

Factors Affecting the Compressive Strength of Concrete.
(a) *Water-Cement Ratio.* The relation of strength to water-cement ratio shows that the proportion of water to cement mainly determines the strength for given materials and conditions of curing. Thus, the consistency and mix can be varied without noticeable change in strength. Figure 10-8 shows the influence of the water-cement ratio on the strength.

(b) *Size of Aggregate.* Test data show that the size of the aggregate is not an important factor in the water-cement ratio vs. strength relation, provided other variables are considered and the true water-cement ratio of the concrete in place is considered (*i.e.*, both the combined and uncombined water).

(c) *Grading of Aggregate.* The grading of the aggregate is not too important. Test data show the small effect of grading on the water-cement ratio vs. strength relation. The real significance of grading of the aggregate is in relation to the workability and economy of concrete mixtures.

(d) *Type of Aggregate.* It has often been noted that aggregates

---

[1] E. E. Bauer, *Plain Concrete*, McGraw-Hill Book Co., Inc., 1949.

of different types affect the water-cement ratio vs. strength relation very little.

(e) *Curing.* Concrete sets and hardens because of the chemical actions that take place between the compounds of cement and the mixing water. Hardening of the concrete is a result of the hydration of the cement, which continues as long as water is present and the temperature is favorable. Curing consists in supplying moisture

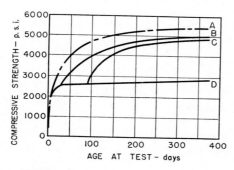

LEGEND:

CURVE A – MOIST CURED ENTIRE TIME
CURVE B – MOIST CURED AFTER 25 DAYS IN AIR
CURVE C – MOIST CURED AFTER 3 MO. IN AIR
CURVE D – IN AIR ENTIRE TIME

Fig. 10-9. Influence of curing condition on the compressive strength of concrete. (From "Design and Control of Concrete Mixtures." Courtesy Portland Cement Assoc.)

and maintaining favorable temperatures. Figure 10-9 shows the effect of curing conditions on the strength. Evidently important differences in strength result from additional moist curing.

(f) *Age.* Test data are shown diagrammatically in Fig. 10-10, giving the variation in strength with age for various water-cement ratios. The size of aggregate and the consistency were varied in these tests without appreciably affecting the relation.

(g) *Character of the Cement.* The characteristics of the cement are comparable in importance to the effect of curing. Figure 10-11 represents compressive strength tests of thirty-two brands of cement studied by Committee C-1 of the American Society for Testing Ma-

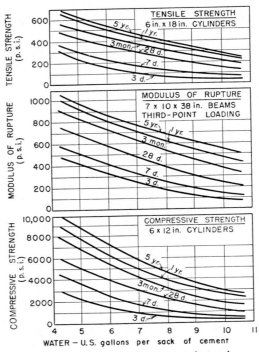

Fig. 10-10.   Influence of age on strength of concrete in tension, compression, and bending. (By permission from *Basic Principles of Concrete Making*, by F. R. MacMillan, Copyright McGraw-Hill Book Co., Inc.)

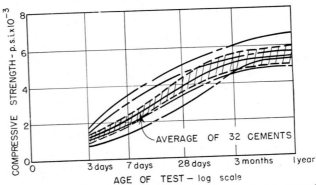

Fig. 10-11.   Age-strength relation for various portland cement concretes. (By permission from *Basic Principles of Concrete Making*, by F. R. MacMillan, Copyright McGraw-Hill Book Co., Inc.)

terials.   The mix used was 1 : 2.4 : 3.6 by weight, the water-cement
ratio was 6.2 gallons per sack, with curing performed in a moist room.
The proportions of cement, sand, and gravel in concrete are designated, for example, as a 1 : $2\frac{1}{4}$: 4 mix.   This means that 1 cu. ft. of
cement, $2\frac{1}{4}$ cu. ft. of sand, and 4 cu. ft. of gravel are used in these
proportions to produce this mix.   The water-cement ratio is sometimes expressed in terms of the ratio by volume of water to the
"loose" or uncompacted cement.   Figure 10-11 shows two of the
highest, two of the lowest, and the average of the thirty-two brands

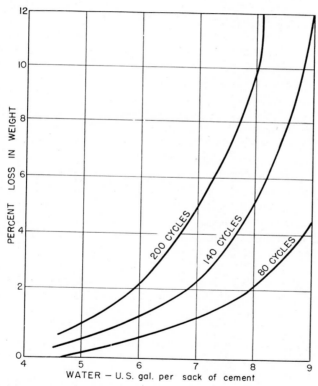

Fig. 10-12.   Effect of water cement ratio on durability.   (*Note:*
Curves show influence of freezing and thawing tests for 2-in.
mortar cubes, by indicating loss in weight for given number of
cycles of freezing and thawing.)   (From "Design and Control
of Concrete Mixtures."   Courtesy Portland Cement Assoc.)

studied. The shaded area represents a belt 10 per cent above and 10 per cent below the average curve.

Water-Tightness. Tests show that, as for the case of strength, the amount of leakage varies with the water-cement ratio and the degree of curing. Mixes containing admixtures are found to be less water-tight. The effect of the characteristics of the cement on the water-tightness is, in general, negligible.

Durability. Porosity is an important factor in its effect on durability. There is no direct test at present for the durability of concrete. The most destructive effect, however, is the freezing of absorbed moisture. Figure 10-12 shows the result of tests on the relation between water-cement ratio and number of cycles required to disintegrate completely the specimens in a freezing and thawing test. For the lower water ratios the disintegration of the stone was an important factor, so that if the curve could be made to represent only the resistance of the paste, the two curves in Fig. 10-12 would be more closely related. The diagram represents tests on 3 × 8-in. cores from 1 : 2 : 3½ concrete, frozen at −15 to −25 deg. F., and thawed at 70 deg. F.

Transverse and Tensile Strengths. Results of bending and tensile tests of concrete at various ages, in terms of water-cement ratio, show the same characteristics as noted for the compressive strength.

Determination of the Amounts of Materials for a Given Mix. The following example shows how the quantities of the materials are determined to produce a given amount of concrete. It is assumed in these calculations that all the voids are filled and that the cement, sand, and gravel contain no water.

NUMERICAL EXAMPLE. Determine the quantities of water, cement, sand, and gravel for a $1 : 2\frac{1}{4} : 4$ mix with a water-cement ratio of 1.1 to produce 4.4 cu. yds. of concrete. *Given:*

Weight of cement per cu. ft. (1 sack) . . . . = 94 lb.
Weight of sand per cu. ft. . . . . = 105 lb.
Weight of gravel per cu. ft. . . . . = 100 lb.
Specific gravity of cement . . . . = 3.1
Specific gravity of aggregate (sand and gravel) = 2.65
Weight of 1 cu. ft. of water . . . . = 62.5 lb.

SOLUTION.

1 cu. ft. of "loose" cement $= \dfrac{1 \times 94}{3.1 \times 62.5} = 0.49$ cu. ft. of cement in the concrete.

$2\frac{1}{4}$ cu. ft. of "loose" sand $= \dfrac{2.25 \times 105}{2.65 \times 62.5} = 1.43$ cu. ft. of sand in the concrete.

4 cu. ft. of "loose" gravel $= \dfrac{4 \times 100}{2.65 \times 62.5} = 2.42$ cu. ft. of gravel in the concrete.

The amount of water for 1 cu. ft. of cement is $1.1 \times 1 = 1.10$ cu. ft. of water in the concrete. Therefore the total volume of concrete using 1 cu. ft. of "loose" cement is 5.44 cu. ft.

The amounts of materials to be used to produce 4.4 cu. yds. of concrete can now be determined by proportion.

$$\text{Weight of cement} = \frac{4.4 \times 27}{5.44} \times 1 \times 94 = 2050 \text{ lb.}$$

$$\text{Weight of sand} = \frac{4.4 \times 27}{5.44} \times 2.25 \times 105 = 5150 \text{ lb.}$$

$$\text{Weight of gravel} = \frac{4.4 \times 27}{5.44} \times 4.0 \times 100 = 8720 \text{ lb.}$$

$$\text{Volume of water} = \frac{4.4 \times 27}{5.44} \times 1.1 = 24 \text{ cu. ft.}$$

After the concrete mix has been determined, concrete is either hand- or machine-mixed, the choice depending on the quantity required and the relative cost. Machine shaking gives a well-mixed concrete of uniform consistency.

The process of hardening in concrete is a chemical change produced by the combination of water with the cement particles. Curing supplies this chemical action and consists in maintaining proper temperature and moisture conditions. The control of these conditions is important, particularly during the early stages of the hardening. Poor curing reduces strength, watertightness, and resistance to abrasion.

The strength of concrete is dependent mainly upon the characteristics of the cement, the water-cement ratio, and the extent to which the water has combined with the cement (which is governed by the type and duration of curing). As previously noted, other factors that affect the strength are age, density of the material, consistency of the mixture, qualities of the water and aggregate, conditions of mixing and placing, and presence of impurities. Stress-strain curves for concrete in compression are shown in Fig. 10-13.

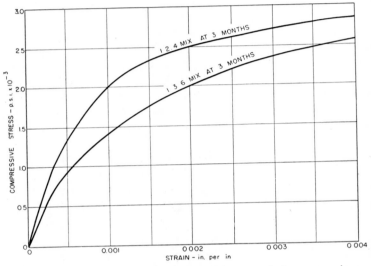

Fig. 10-13. Typical stress-strain curves for concrete in compression.

The data in Table 10-6 show that, for concretes with compressive strengths of from 2000 to 5000 psi, the modulus of rupture varies from 1/5 to 1/7 the compressive strength, and the tensile strength from about 1/10 to 1/12 the compressive strength, and from about 1/2 to 3/5 the modulus of rupture. Tests show that the average *strength in shear* is about 1/6 the compressive strength.

The *modulus of elasticity* of concrete is a variable quantity. Some tests show that the modulus of elasticity is a function of the compressive strength. In general, values vary from 2.5×10^6 psi to 5.5×10^6 psi.

The importance of the properties of watertightness and durability has been noted. Concrete shrinks and expands because of loss or absorption of moisture. The major portion of the volume change is due to the cement paste and depends upon the relative quantities

Table 10-6

Comparison of Compressive, Flexural, and Tensile Strengths of Concrete

Strength of plain concrete			Ratio—per cent		
Compressive (S_c)	Modulus of rupture (S_b)	Tensile (S_t)	S_b/S_c	S_t/S_c	S_t/S_b
1000	230	110	23	11	48
2000	375	200	19	10	53
3000	485	275	16	9	57
4000	580	340	15	9	59
5000	675	400	14	8	59
6000	765	460	13	8	60
7000	855	520	12	7	61
8000	930	580	12	7	62
9000	1010	630	11	7	63

Data by Portland Cement Association.

of cement and water. Volume changes taking place after hardening are provided for in design of structures by spacing of joints and arrangement of reinforcing bars. The fire-resistant properties of concrete are high. Concrete serves as a protection for steelwork in case of fire because it is noncombustible and has a temperature coefficient practically the same as that of steel. Concrete also serves as an effective preventive of corrosion in the steel of reinforced concrete members.

10-7. PLASTICS

Plastics are materials containing an organic substance, and although they are solid in their finished state at ordinary temperatures, at some stage in their manufacture they can be formed into various shapes by flow. The shaping is done by heat or pressure or both heat and pressure. In addition to the relatively rigid materials, the plastics industry also includes adhesives, rubber, and rubber-like materials.

The important properties of plastics that make them useful as an engineering material are (1) high dielectric strength, that is, good electrical insulating properties; (2) light weight; (3) resistance to certain chemicals (for some plastics); (4) good heat-insulating properties; and (5) colorability (for some plastics).

Table 10-7

Physical Properties of Plastics

Type and form	Filler	Specific volume (cu. in. per lb.)	Coef. of exp. per deg. (°C × 10⁻⁵)	Ultimate strength (psi × 10⁻³)			Mod. of elas. in tension (psi × 10⁻⁶)	Per cent elongation
				Tension	Comp.	Bending		
Phenol-formaldehyde (molded)............	Wood flour and cotton	20.9-19.1	3.0-4.5	6.5-8.5	22.7-36	8.5-12	8-12	0.4-0.8
	Macerated fabric and cord	20.4-19.4	1-3	3.3-9.0	15-30	8.5-15	9-13	0.37-0.57
Urea formaldehyde......	Cellulose	18.8-18.2	2.7	6-13	25-35	10-16	15	0.5-1.0
Melamine-formaldehyde (molded)............	Alpha cellulose	18.8-18.2	4.0	7.0-13.0	25-43	10-16	13.0	0.6-0.9
Vinyl chloride acetate resins (rigid)........		20.7-19.1	6.9-18.5	7.2-9.0	9.9-11.3	12.6-14.5	3.5-4.1	...
Allyl resins (cast)......		20.9-19.8	5-10	5-6	21-23	6-13	3.0	...
Methyl methacrylate resin (cast)..........		23.4-23.2	9	6-10	11-19	12-17	3.5-5	2.7
Polystyrene............		26.3-26.0	6-8	5-9.0	11.5-16	8-16	4-6	1.0-3.6
Polyethylene..........		30.1	16-18	1.3	...	...	0.19	300
Cellulose compounds:								
Ethyl cellulose........		25.5-23.6	10-20	2-8	3-35	4-12	0.5-4.0	5-25
Cellulose acetate (molding)..........		21.8-20.6	8-16	3-8	14-36	4-13	1.0-3.5	4-45
Cellulose acetate butyrate..........		24.0-22.2	11-17	1.9-6.8	7.5-22	1.5-9.3	0.7-2.0	38-75
Cellulose nitrate......		20.5-19.8	8-12	7-8	22-35	9-11	1.9-2.2	40-45

This data taken from the 1950 edition of the *Modern Plastics Encyclopedia*, copyright by Plastics Catalogue Corporation.

Plastics may be considered in three general classes: (a) thermo-plastics, which require cooling to harden them after softening by heat, and can also be resoftened and rehardened by repeated heating and cooling; (b) Thermo-setting plastics, which are hardened by chemical changes produced by heat, remain hardened without cooling, and do not soften appreciably when reheated; (c) Reaction-setting plastics, which are hardened by a chemical reaction taking place between the plastic and an external agent.

Plastics are made from coal, limestone, salt, petroleum, air, water, sulphur, and cellulose obtained from cotton and wood. Table 10-7 gives the properties of some of the more important plastics.

Methods used in fabricating other engineering materials are used also for plastics. Casting in molds is a simple fabricating process commonly employed for making novelties and other products. Thermo-setting compounds are generally molded by compression-molding, where pressure is applied to the material. The most inexpensive method of molding is cold-molding, since rapid manufacture is possible. In this process the products are baked in an oven after molding. Extruding is a process commonly used for both types of plastics to produce tubes, rods, and other cylindrical shapes. Boards or sheets of resin-impregnated paper, wood veneers, and fabrics are produced by laminating. Plastics of high strength are produced by using canvas, asbestos, fiber-glass, or rayon as a base. Blowing of thermoplastics is done in a manner similar to that used for glass. Various parts are also machined from rods, sheets, and tube stock. Riveting and cementing can be applied to laminated plastics. By the use of hot plates, thermoplastics can also be welded.

An important constituent in plastics is the resin or binder that cements the various other constituents together. The binder may be a phenolic, cellulose derivative, urea, shellac, or some other material. Another ingredient in plastics is the filler, which provides the plastics with properties not possessed by the binder. The filler may also be used to lower the cost of the plastic. Another ingredient in plastics is a plasticizer, which is usually an oily liquid. Plasticizers are added to improve impact resistance, flexibility, or flow qualities. Catalysts are also added to accelerate chemical reactions. To prevent sticking to molds, lubricants such as graphite are added. Color is imparted by adding dyes and pigments.

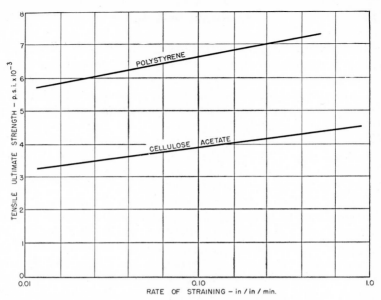

Fig. 10-14. Influence of strain rate on tensile strengths of plastics. (Data by Carswell and Nason, from "Symposium on Plastics," 1944, *Proc. A.S.T.M.*)

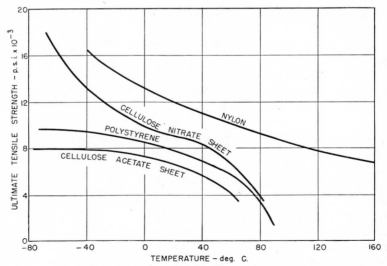

Fig. 10-15. Effect of temperature on tensile strength of thermoplastics. (Data by Carswell and Nason, from "Symposium on Plastics," 1944, *Proc. A.S.T.M.*)

Mechanical Properties of Plastics.   Rate of load application and the temperature influence the mechanical properties of plastics to a much greater extent than they do of metals.   The mechanical properties are also greatly influenced by humidity; and plastics, in general, creep at room temperatures and low stresses.

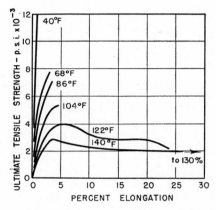

Fig. 10-16.   Effect of temperature on stress-strain curves of polymethylmethacrylate.   (Data by Carswell and Nason, from "Symposium on Plastics," 1944, *Proc. A.S.T.M.*)

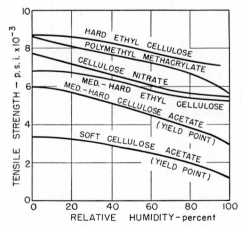

Fig. 10-17.   Influence of relative humidity on the tensile strength of several thermoplastics.   (Data by Carswell and Nason, from "Symposium on Plastics," 1944, *Proc. A.S.T.M.*)

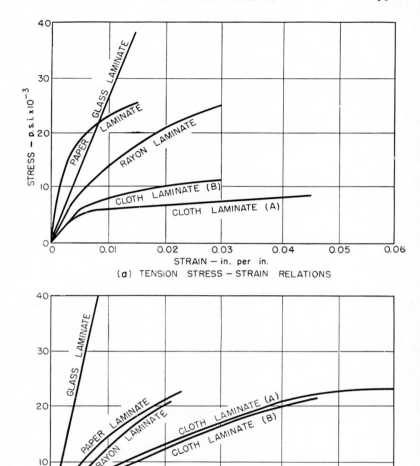

(a) TENSION STRESS — STRAIN RELATIONS

(b) COMPRESSION STRESS — STRAIN RELATIONS

Fig. 10-18.　Stress-strain curves for laminated plastics.

The influence of speed of testing on the tensile strength is shown in Fig. 10-14 for two plastics. The effect of temperature on the tensile strength for various plastics is shown in Fig. 10-15. Figure 10-16 shows how an increase in temperature decreases the strength and increases the ductility for one type of plastic. Increase in humidity decreases the tensile strength of plastics, as shown in Fig. 10-17. The influence of exposure to ultraviolet light is appreciable in decreasing the strength and ductility of some plastics as, for example, cellulose nitrate.

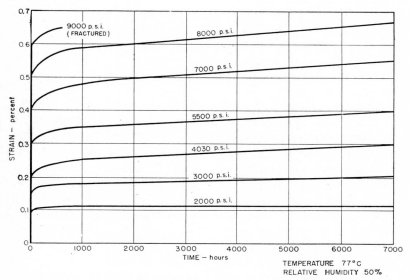

Fig. 10-19. Creep-time relations for a paper laminated plastic. (Data by Findley. Courtesy A.S.T.M.)

Stress-strain curves in tension and compression for several plastics are shown in Fig. 10-18, indicating various degrees of strength and ductility. Creep-time relations in tension for a laminated plastic are given in Fig. 10-19, showing the similarity in creep behavior of plastics and metals.

Table 10-7 shows that most plastics have lower strength and stiffness than the commonly used metals. The lower density of plastics, however, often yields a larger strength-weight ratio than for metals. The ease with which plastics can be shaped by molding, casting, laminating, and extruding has made them useful in the making of many products. It should be noted, however, that they cannot be used in parts requiring great strength.

10-8. MISCELLANEOUS MATERIALS

Rubber. Numerous products are manufactured from rubber, the most important being automobile tires. Natural rubber is made from latex, a milky juice found in the bark of a number of tropical trees and other plants. At the present time most commercial rubber comes from trees that are grown on plantations. Latex is collected from trees in the same manner as maple sap and turpentine. The rubber is separated from the latex by evaporation or by coagulation. Formic acid is the ingredient usually added to produce coagulation. After separation, the crude rubber is washed and rolled into thin sheets. It is then drained, dried, and smoked, leaving it in a condition ready for shipment.

Crude rubber has undesirable qualities including low strength. Vulcanization of the rubber by addition of sulphur at about 160° F. improves its properties. The exact action of vulcanization is not known, but it appears that sulphur first dissolves the rubber and then combines with it chemically.

The degree of vulcanization modifies the properties of rubber. If no sulphur has been added, the rubber has the undesirable properties of low strength, tendency to become tacky with time, and of being affected by temperature changes and by certain reagents. When sulphur is added, rubber becomes much stronger and can be stretched to eight to ten times its original length before breaking. Typical stress-strain curves for rubber are shown in Fig. 10-20.

Rubber containing a high percentage of sulphur is hard. Soft rubber, with a lower percentage of sulphur, has unusual stress-strain diagrams with reverse curves, as indicated in Fig. 10-20. At the higher stresses, soft rubber tends to stiffen with increasing load. Hard rubber may have ultimate strengths as high as 10,000 psi. Fillers such as carbon black, zinc oxide, and clay vary the properties of rubber. In amounts up to 30 per cent these fillers increase the strength of rubber.

Soft rubber has excellent energy-absorbing capacity, since large deformations can be produced before fracture. This property makes it very desirable for shock absorbers and buffers. Under cycles

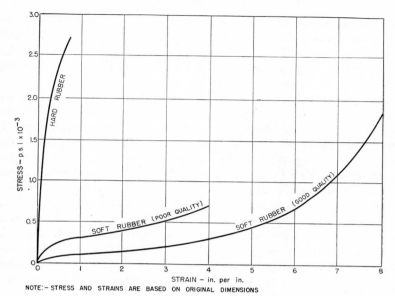

Fig. 10-20.   Typical stress-strain curves for rubber in tension.

of stress, the energy lost per cycle, or hysteresis, is large.   The loss
in energy appears as heat, which tends to deteriorate the rubber if
the hysteresis losses are high.   Rubber has low electrical conductivity
and is therefore used as an insulating material, either as cable covering or as instrument panels.

Synthetic Rubber.   Various synthetic rubbers have been developed in recent years.   These include *Neoprene,* produced from coal,
limestone, and hydrochloric acid; *Buna S,* which is a copolymer of
butadiene and styrene; *Buna N,* a copolymer of butadiene and
acrylonitrile; *Butyl,* made from petroleum; and *thiokols,* which are
polysulphides.

Glass.   There are many different types of glass, including safety
glass, optical glass, glass tile, glass building blocks, and glass used
for chemical ware and household purposes.

The simplest type of glass is made of silica (SiO_2), obtained from
sand.   In the manufacture, soda in the form of sodium carbonate,
sodium nitrate, or sodium sulfate is used to lower the melting point
of the silica, while lime in the form of limestone or slaked lime is
used to retain the low melting point and at the same time to increase

the strength. A proportioned mixture consisting of sand, soda and lime compounds, and broken or scrap glass is fed into an open-hearth furnace and heated to about 1500° C. The ingredients melt at this temperature to produce glass. The glass from the furnace may be shaped by blowing, drawing, rolling, molding, or pressing.

The optical properties of glass make it valuable. It is used for lenses in telescopes, microscopes, and cameras because of its refractive index. It also transmits light rays of short wavelengths and is therefore useful for photographic and therapeutic purposes. The comparative chemical stability of glass in its resistance to acids makes it useful for chemical laboratory equipment and for various manufacturing purposes.

The ultimate tensile strength of glass is about 10,000 psi for $\frac{1}{2}$ in. diameter rods, while for fibers of 0.00005 in. diameter, very great strengths up to 3,500,000 psi have been reported. The modulus of elasticity of soda-lime glass varies from 8.2×10^6 to 12.0×10^6 psi. Compressive strengths up to 140,000 psi have been obtained for glass rods. The creep resistance of glass is poor, since it is found to creep at low stresses and room temperatures.

Bituminous Materials. Bituminous materials are used mainly for road surfacings. They are complex hydrocarbons derived from vegetable material. For engineering purposes they may be classified as natural asphalts, petroleum asphalts, and tars. The natural asphalts are found in deposits resulting from the weathering of petroleum. In the distillation of petroleum, petroleum asphalts are produced in the form of residues. Tar is a by-product in the manufacture of gas from oil and water.

The important properties of bituminous materials used for paving purposes are the consistency, melting point, flash point, and fire point. The laboratory test for consistency is the distance that a standard needle will penetrate a sample of the material under a fixed force during a specified time. The flash point is the temperature at which a standard sample will flash under momentary application of a flame. The fire point is the temperature at which the material will ignite under momentary application of a flame.

In the foregoing, a brief description was given of the main non-metallic materials and the factors that influence their properties. A number of such materials could not be included in this short treatment. Protective coatings such as platings, paints, and varnishes, and materials such as yarn, rope, and various types of adhesives were not considered.

PROBLEMS AND QUESTIONS

10-1. Compare the elastic strength-weight ratios of green and air-dried wood for (a) static bending, (b) static compression parallel to grain, and (c) static compression perpendicular to grain. Use empirical relations for the strength in terms of the specific gravity as given in Table 10-1.

10-2. How does the modulus of elastic resilience in compression parallel to the grain vary with the specific gravity for (a) green wood, (b) air-dried wood? Use relations given in Table 10-1. *Ans.* (a) $4.75G$, (b) $11.3G$.

10-3. Compare the elastic strength-weight ratios in compression for spruce and Alcoa 24S-T. Consider strength of spruce parallel to grain.

10-4. A 4×4-in. Sitka spruce post 20 in. long supports a compressive load of 20,000 lb. parallel to the grain. Compare the factors of safety for green and air-dried conditions. Base calculations on the elastic strength. Use data given in Tables 10-1 and 10-2. *Ans.* $N_g = 1.68, N_d = 2.8$.

10-5. There is a choice between spruce and structural steel for a compression member of length L. If the compressive elastic strength is 35,000 psi for structural steel and 5000 psi for spruce, determine the most economical material. Use a factor of safety of 2.5 for the steel and 5 for the spruce. Assume that the cost of structural steel is six cents per pound and sixty dollars per 1000 board feet for the spruce. *Ans.* $C_{sp}/C_{st} = 0.41$.

10-6. What are the factors that influence the strength properties of wood?

10-7. A stone has 10 per cent voids by volume and weighs 165 lb. per cu. ft. in the dry condition. Determine (a) the solid specific gravity of the material, and (b) the approximate compressive strength. Use Fig. 10-4. *Ans.* (a) 2.93, (b) 10,400 psi.

10-8. A specimen of stone weighs 1500 grams when dry and 1700 grams when saturated. When immersed in water the dry specimen displaces 600 cc. of water. Determine (a) the percentage water absorption by weight, and (b) the solid specific gravity of the material. *Ans.* (a) 13.3%, (b) 2.5.

10-9. Based on the compression stress-strain curve for marble as shown in Fig. 10-3, determine (a) the modulus of elasticity and (b) the toughness.

10-10. Compare the toughness values of limestone and pine using data given in Figs. 10-2 and 10-3.

10-11. A block of limestone 8 in. by 8 in. by 24 in. weighs 130 lb. and contains 3 per cent moisture by weight. Determine an approximate value of the allowable compressive load that can be applied to the 8×8-in. face if a factor of safety of 7 is selected. The solid specific gravity of the material is 2.60. Use Fig. 10-4. *Ans.* 105,000 lb. (approx.)

10-12. What is the approximate ultimate compressive load that a building brick can resist? It has a cross-sectional area of 10 sq. in. The dry weight is 5.25 lb. and the actual weight is 5.60 lb. Figure 10-5 gives the approximate value of the compressive strength. *Ans.* 71,000 lb.

10-13. Compare the strengths of the building block with 1% and 20% absorptions by weight (Fig. 10-5).

10-14. Name the various uses of clay.

10-15. What are the main factors influencing the strength of brick?

10-16. Prepare a table listing the uses of lime and gypsum cements.

10-17. What are the factors that influence the properties of lime cements?

10-18. What weights of cement and water are required to produce a cubic foot of cement paste? The water-cement ratio is 0.70 by loose volume. The specific gravity of cement is 3.1 and the weight of cement (loose) is 94 lb. per cu. ft. *Ans.* 79 lb. cement and 37 lb. water.

10-19. Find the volume of a mortar containing one bag of cement, 180 lb. of dry sand of specific gravity = 2.65, and 8.9 gallons of water.
Ans. 2.77 cu. ft.

10-20. Based on Fig. 10-8, what is the expected 28-day compressive strength of a concrete made with six gallons of water per sack of cement?

10-21. What are the factors that influence the strength of sand-cement mortars?

10-22. Name the main processes used in the manufacture of portland cement.

10-23. List the constituents of portland cement and their effects.

10-24. What is the significance of each of the following properties of cement: specific gravity, soundness, time of setting?

10-25. Name the properties desired in concrete.

10-26. State the requirements for making a concrete with maximum strength and durability.

10-27. What are the main factors that influence the compressive strength, watertightness, and durability of concrete?

10-28. Determine the weights of cement, sand, gravel, and water required to produce 50 cu. ft. of concrete so that the mix is 1:2:4 and the water-cement ratio is 0.8. *Given:*

Weight of sand per cu. ft. (loose).. = 105 lb.
Weight of gravel per cu. ft. (loose). = 100 lb.
Weight of cement per cu. ft. (loose) = 94 lb.
Weight of water per cu. ft .... = 62.5 lb.
Specific gravity of cement........ = 3.1
Specific gravity of aggregate...... = 2.65

Ans. 945 lb. cement, 2120 lb. sand, 4030 lb. gravel, 503 lb. water.

10-29. How many cubic feet of freshly mixed concrete will be produced from 94 lb. of portland cement with a specific gravity = 3.10, 400 lb. of aggregate with a specific gravity = 2.65, and 50 lb. of water?

Ans. 3.70 cu. ft.

10-30. Which of the following materials would be the most economical for a compression member:

(a) A structural steel with a compressive yield strength of 40,000 psi at a cost of 6 cents per lb. and a density of 0.284 lb. per cu. in.

(b) An aluminum alloy (24S-T) with a compressive yield strength of 46,000 psi, at a cost of 18 cents per lb. and a density of 0.101 lb. per cu. in.

(c) White oak with a compressive yield strength of 4300 psi, at a cost of $50 per 1000 board feet, and a density of 0.0243 lb. per cu. in.

10-31. Compare the compressive strength-weight ratios of aluminum alloy 75S-T, white oak, and structural SAE 1020 steel based on (a) the elastic strength, (b) the ultimate strength, and (c) the stiffness. Assume that the properties for tension and compression of the aluminum alloy 75S-T and the structural steel are the same. Use tables given in the text.

10-32. Calculate the strength-weight ratios for each of the woods in Table 10-2 for (a) the elastic bending strength, (b) the elastic compressive strength parallel to the grain, and (c) the ultimate compressive strength parallel to the grain.

10-33. Consider two simply supported beams with a center concentrated load. The beams are of rectangular cross section with the same length and width. One is made of steel with $E = 30 \times 10^6$ psi and a yield strength of 90,000 psi. The other is made of white oak with $E = 1.62 \times 10^6$ psi and has a yield strength of 8000 psi. If the steel weighs 0.284 lb. per cu. in. and the oak weighs 0.020 lb. per cu. in. and the two beams are to weigh the same, compare (a) the depth of the two beams, (b) the stiffness, and (c) the flexure strength.

10-34. Solve Prob. 10-33 if the stress is simple compression and the yield strengths of the steel and oak are 85,000 and 4200 psi respectively. Assume the modulus of elasticity in compression to be the same as in bending.

BIBLIOGRAPHY

Wood

Desch, H. E., *Timber—Its Structure and Properties*, The Macmillan Company, New York, 1948.

Garratt, G. A., *The Mechanical Properties of Wood*, John Wiley & Sons, Inc., New York, 1931.

Markwardt, L. S., "Wood as an Engineering Material," *Proc. A.S.T.M.*, 1943, Vol. 43.

Wangard, F. F., *The Mechanical Properties of Wood*, John Wiley & Sons, Inc., New York, 1950.

Wood Handbook, Forest Products Laboratory, U. S. Dept. of Agriculture, 1935.

Stone and Clay Products

Eckel, E. C., *Building Stones and Clays*, John Wiley & Sons, Inc., New York, 1912.

Huntington, W. C., *Building Construction*, John Wiley & Sons, 1941.

Ries, Heinrich, *Building Stones and Clay Products*, John Wiley & Sons, 1912.

Cementing Materials and Concrete

Bauer, E. E., *Plain Concrete*, McGraw-Hill Book Co., Inc., New York, 1949.

Eckel, E. C., *Cements, Limes and Plasters*, John Wiley & Sons, Inc., New York, 1928.

McMillan, F. R., *Basic Principles of Concrete Making*, McGraw-Hill Book Co., Inc., New York, 1929.

Design and Control of Concrete Mixtures, Portland Cement Association, Chicago, 1945.

Plastics

Delmonte, J., *Plastics in Engineering*, Penton Publishing Co., Cleveland, 1942.

Mark, H., and Proskauer, E. S., *The Science of Plastics*, Interscience Publishers, Inc., New York, 1948.

Miscellaneous Materials

Abraham, H., *Asphalts and Allied Substances*, D. Van Nostrand Company, Inc., New York, 1937.

Davis, C. C., and Blake, J. T., *The Chemistry and Technology of Rubber*, Reinhold Publishing Corp., New York, 1937.

Furman, L., *Window Glass*, Little, London.

Memmler, K., *Science of Rubber*, Reinhold Publishing Corp., New York. 1934.

PART THREE

Materials Testing Machines

and Strain Gages

Materials Testing Machines

11-1. INTRODUCTION

In Parts I and II the mechanical properties of materials were defined and the factors influencing these properties for specific materials were discussed. In Part III, the equipment used to ascertain these properties is described briefly. Chapter 11 gives a description of materials testing machines used for the determination of both static and dynamic properties of materials. The various types of strain gages used for measuring strains are discussed briefly in Chapter 12.

Testing machines can be classified into two types: (1) those used to determine the mechanical properties of materials, and (2) those used to determine the behavior of built-up structural or machine members. Machines used to determine mechanical properties may be classified as to the type of stress, speed of loading, and temperature of the material tested, as shown in Table 11-1. There are certain miscellaneous tests of properties, however, such as hardness tests, that cannot be classified in this way, as indicated in Table 11-1(b). For all tests, certain specific means of load application and measurement are used. The principles of these methods will be discussed before each particular type of machine is considered.

11-2. METHODS OF APPLICATION OF LOADS

In testing machines, loads are applied to a test specimen by one or a combination of the following methods:

Weights. Weights of known magnitude can be used directly as a means of applying a tension, compression, or bending load to a speci-

Table 11-1(a)

Materials Testing Machines for Determination of Mechanical Properties

(Classified by types of load, stress, and temperature)

Type of loading	Temperature	Kind of stress

Static	Low, Normal, or Elevated	*Simple Stresses*
		
		 1. Tension
		 2. Compression
		 3. Bending
		 4. Shear
		 5. Torsion
		
		 Combined Stresses
		
		 1. Biaxial Stresses
		   (a) Tension-Tension
		   (b) Tension-Compression
		   (c) Compression-Compression
		 2. Triaxial Stresses

Dynamic Fatigue	Low, Normal, or Elevated	*Simple Stresses* (as for static loads) *Combined Stresses* Biaxial Stresses
Dynamic Impact	Low, Normal, or Elevated	*Simple Stresses* 1. Tension 2. Bending 3. Torsion

men. Although this method is limited in application, it was used in some of the early materials testing machines. The main disadvantage of applying loads directly is that, for most materials, the size of the specimen cross section is too small and, therefore, properties of the material corresponding to the actual size of the member cannot be obtained.

Weights and Levers. A horizontal lever with arms of different lengths, as in a steelyard, is sometimes used for applying loads [Fig. 11-1(a)]. A lever system of load application is particularly useful in cases where a constant load is to be applied for a long period of time, as, for example, in creep tests. If a greater magnification of load is desired, a compound system of levers can be used.

Table 11-1(b)

Special Materials Testing Machines

---

1. Machines for hardness measurement including measurement of resistance to:
   (1) Scratching
   (2) Indentation
   (3) Rebound
   (4) Abrasion and wear
   (5) Machinability

---

2. Equipment for determination of material structure:
   (1) Microstructure
   (2) Macrostructure

---

3. Machines for determination of uniformity, including:
   (1) Detection of flaws by X-ray, Magnaflux, etc.
   (2) Determination of moisture content
   (3) Determination of porosity

---

4. Machines for tests of structural and machine members used to determine:
   (1) Strength
   (2) Resonant frequencies
   (3) Durability—physical and chemical

---

5. Equipment for determination of miscellaneous properties, as:
   (1) Thermal conductivity and coefficient of expansion
   (2) Electrical and magnetic properties
   (3) Acoustical properties
   (4) Optical properties

Mechanical Gear Systems. Most mechanical systems for application of tensile or compressive loads consist of a motor-driven horizontal shaft with a screw-and-gear mechanism for transferring a rotary motion to a translatory motion of the machine head. In some torsion testing machines the specimen is rotated directly by a motor with a speed reducer.

Hydraulic Systems. A hydraulic system is often employed to move the head of a testing machine in place of a screw-and-gear mechanism. The hydraulic system depends upon the movement of a piston in a cylinder by means of oil pressure [Fig. 11-1(b)]. The pressure is usually applied by a motor-driven pump, and valves are used to regulate the rate of application of the load.

In addition to the foregoing methods, other special means of load application are used, such as in the repeated application of dynamic

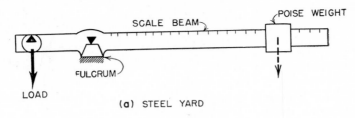

(a) STEEL YARD

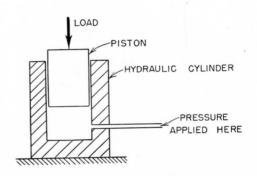

(b) HYDRAULIC SYSTEM FOR LOAD APPLICATION

Fig. 11-1.   Methods of application of loads.

loads by the inertia force of rotating eccentric weights.   Repeated loads are also applied by an electromagnetic force or by the displacement of a point on a specimen using a mechanically driven eccentric.

11-3. METHODS OF LOAD MEASUREMENT

When loads are applied to a specimen by a lever system, which is either a fixed, variable, or a compound system, the load is determined from the known weight applied and the length of the lever arms. Instead of the load having to be calculated, the variable-length arm, to which the balancing weight is applied, can be made self-indicating by means of a scale.

In hydraulic machines the pressure is usually measured by means of manometers or Bourdon tubes.   A manometer consists of a glass tube of U shape, usually placed vertically.   In this tube a liquid rises to such a level in one arm that it balances the applied pressure acting on the liquid in the other arm. The change in level of the liquid is read on a graduated scale and the pressure can then be determined. In materials testing, the manometer is limited in application because it can be used only for relatively low pressures, even when a high-density liquid such as mercury is used.

The Bourdon tube is generally used for measuring liquid pressures. It consists essentially of a closed curved tube which tends to straighten out as the pressure is increased in the tube (Fig. 11-2). In most

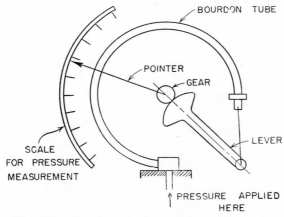

Fig. 11-2. Bourdon tube for measurement of loads.

Bourdon gages the end movement of the tube as it straightens is magnified mechanically. This motion is transferred into the rotation of a pointer over a scale. The mechanical device used to rotate the pointer consists of a lever, one end of which is attached to the tube, the other end having a ratchet that moves the gear to which the pointer is attached.

Dynamometers are often employed for measuring loads, and there are several types available for materials testing. One kind of dynamometer consists of a closely wound helical spring. The load to be measured is obtained by calibration from the deflection of the spring. Other types of dynamometers measure the load by determining the elastic deflection of a beam, frame, or ring. The Morehouse proving ring, used for calibration of testing machines, is an example of the ring-type dynamometer.

A mechanical means, using a dial gage, is a common method of measuring deflections in dynamometers. The deformations can also be measured by using micrometer microscopes or electric strain gages.

STATIC TESTING MACHINES

11-4. SIMPLE STRESS MACHINES

Static testing machines described in this article include those machines used for the determination of the mechanical properties of materials when subjected to simple static stresses such as tension, compression, bending, shear, and torsion. Static testing machines are of two main types: Universal testing machines used for tension, compression, bending, and transverse shear tests; and special machines, as, for example, those that can be used only for torsion, compression, or flexure tests.

Universal Testing Machines. The essential parts of a mechanical testing machine are (1) a means of applying the load to a specimen, and (2) a means for balancing and measuring the applied load. The two parts may be entirely separate or together, depending upon the design of the machine. In addition to the loading and load-measuring mechanisms, various accessory parts make up the Universal testing machine. These accessory parts include devices for gripping or supporting the test piece, the power unit, recorders, speed indicators, and shock absorbers.

The early types of testing machines consisted of a single lever used both for applying and measuring the load. With such machines there was no means to compensate for the deformation of the specimen. For this reason the next step in the development was in providing a method of loading mechanically or hydraulically, independent of the load-measuring mechanism. The development of Universal testing, from the early tests of Galileo to the present time, is completely described by Gibbons.[1] Most Universal machines now used are of the "screw-gear" or "hydraulic" type.

In Universal screw-gear testing machines the load is applied mechanically by a screw-and-gear mechanism. The load in the

---

[1] C. H. Gibbons, *Materials Testing Machines*, Instruments Publishing Co., Pittsburgh, 1935, 89 pp.

hydraulic Universal machine is applied by a hydraulic jack. The power in both types of machines may be supplied by hand or by a motor operating a gear train or pump.

Screw-Gear Machines. A screw-gear machine is shown in Fig. 11-3. The application of the load to the tension or compression specimen is made by the downward movement of a movable cross-head (E). The cross-head motion is provided by two or more vertical screws (F),

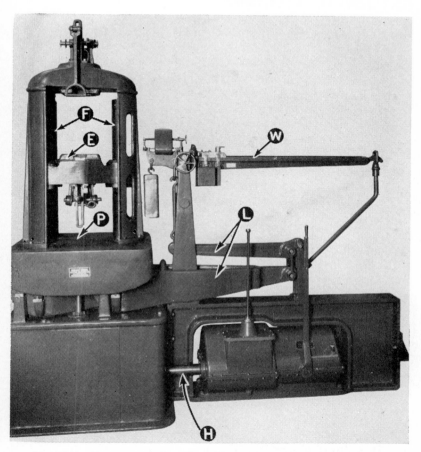

Fig. 11-3. Screw-gear universal machine with weighing beam. (Courtesy Riehle Testing Machine Division, American Machine & Metals, Inc.)

which have gears attached to their lower ends. The gears attached to the vertical screws, in turn, mesh with a central gear. The rotation of the central gear is made possible by beveled gears that transfer the rotation of a horizontal shaft (H), driven by a motor, to the rotation of the central vertical shaft. Between the beveled gears and motor, a system of gears is provided that can be shifted to give various speeds of loading and to reverse the direction of movement of the cross-head.

Fig. 11-4. Screw-gear universal machine with pendulum weighing device. (Courtesy Tinius Olsen Testing Machine Co.)

The load applied to the specimen is measured by a multiple lever system (L), as shown in Fig. 11-3. This lever system operates by transferring the load on the bed-plate or platen (P) of the machine through a system of levers with knife edges to one end of a scale or weighing beam (W), the load on the scale beam thereby being reduced. The other end of the scale beam has a poise weight attached, which can be moved horizontally until the beam is balanced. The beam has a scale attached indicating directly the load acting on the

Fig. 11-5.   Universal hydraulic testing machine.   (Courtesy Riehle Testing Machine Division, American Machine and Metals, Inc.)

specimen. Details regarding operation and variations in design of screw-gear machines are given in manufacturers' catalogs.[2,3,4]

Testing machines in which the weighing beam and poise are replaced by a swinging pendulum and a pointer that moves over a dial also are available.[3] In these machines the load is indicated

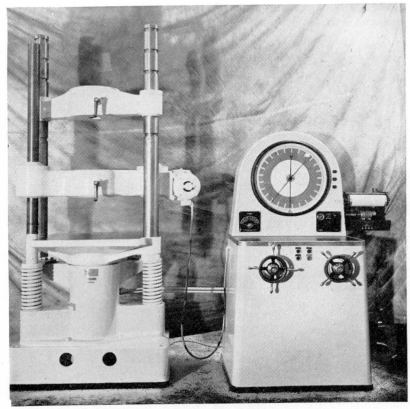

Fig. 11-6.   Hydraulic Tate-Emery universal testing machine.   (Courtesy Baldwin-Lima-Hamilton Corp.)

[2] Catalog on Materials Testing Machines, The Baldwin-Lima-Hamilton Corporation, Philadelphia, Pa.

[3] Catalogs on Materials Testing Machines, Riehle Testing Machine Division, American Machine and Metals, Inc., East Moline, Illinois.

[4] Catalogs on Materials Testing Machines, Tinius Olsen Testing Machine Co., Philadelphia, Pa.

directly without balancing of the scale beam being required, as indicated in Fig. 11-4.

Hydraulic Machines. Figures 11-5 and 11-6 show two types of hydraulic machines. In Type A, Fig. 11-5, first built by Amsler of Schaffhausen, Switzerland, the load is applied by a hydraulic cylinder. The main piston is carefully fitted and lapped. The load is meas-

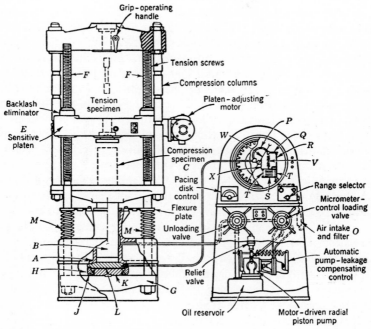

Fig. 11-7.   Hydraulic testing machine, Type-B, Tate-Emery universal testing machine.

ured by a pendulum device.   Details on the construction and operation of Amsler hydraulic machines can be found in the catalogs of the Riehle and Olsen Companies,[3,4]

In the Type B hydraulic machine (Fig. 11-6), the load is applied by a hydraulic press that is separate from the weighing system.   The Southwark-Emery and some Olsen machines are of this type.[2,4] A motor-driven pump is used to transmit oil into a cylinder (A), Fig. 11-7, thereby producing a pressure against the ram (B).   This pressure transmits a compressive force on the compression specimen (C) to the cross-head (E) and then through the specimen height adjusting screws (F) to the lower cross-head (G). The force on the lower cross-head (G) is transmitted to the hydraulic support or weighing capsule (H), which forms the head of the cylinder (A). The hydraulic support (H) is made up of a shallow cylinder (J), a short block (K), and a thin diaphragm (L). The shallow cavity in (J) is filled with oil and is connected by a pipe to the load-measuring mechanism at the right. Filling plugs for forcing oil into the capsule are used to provide a means of replacing oil lost by leakage. Springs (M) are used to produce an initial load on the hydraulic support to avoid slack motion under small loads. The oil pressure applied in cylinder (J) by the movement of the diaphragm (L) was measured directly by a Bourdon gage in the earlier Baldwin-Southwark machines. In later machines a load-weighing method, known as the "Tate-Emery" or "null" method, is used (Fig. 11-6). By this procedure, oil pressure from the hydraulic support (H) is transmitted to the Bourdon tube (P). As the tube tends to "straighten out," a baffle (Q), which is attached to the tube, moves away from the nozzle valve (R). By means of a small pump, filtered air under pressure is admitted through an orifice (O) to the pipe leading to the nozzle valve (R). A branch pipe admits air under pressure to the thin corrugated metal bellows (S). As the load on the specimen (C) increases, the baffle (Q) moves a small distance away from the valve (R) and the pressure in the air pipes and bellows decreases. This decrease in pressure pulls the springs (T) down and stretches the double weighing spring (V), thus tending to close the space between the baffle (Q) and valve (R). In a very short interval of time equilibrium is established and the stretch of the weighing spring (V) measures the force acting on the Bourdon tube (P). The force measured is proportional to the force acting on the specimen. The elongation of the spring (V) is measured by the rack-pinion (X) and pointer-scale device (W). An autographic record of the load can be obtained by the rack-pinion arrangement (X) using a drum and pen or pencil. The drum can be rotated automatically by the strain measuring apparatus, thereby recording on the drum the complete stress-strain diagram.

Machines are usually equipped with two or more weighing springs for accurately recording different ranges of load. In the modern hydraulic machines, various rates of loading can be obtained by the use of an appropriate pump speed or setting of the valve that controls the flow of oil from the pump to the loading cylinder.

For most purposes the hydraulic-type machine has advantages over the screw-type because of its simplicity of operation and ease of load control and measurement. The screw-gear machine, however, has freedom from leakage of oil and positive control of the rate of motion of the cross-head. The advantages of the balance-beam type of load-weighing mechanism are the high accuracy, when carefully balanced, and constancy of calibration. However, the advantages of the self-indicating type of load-weighing device are the elimination of the need to balance the beam and freedom from the personal variation in balancing the beam.

The testing machines described in the foregoing are used, with various modifications, for testing specimens in tension, compression, and bending. The mechanical properties obtained include the yield strength, ultimate strength for tension and compression (or modulus of rupture in bending), stiffness, and ductility. Bending tests are sometimes made on special small, manually operated testing machines, such as bending machines used for the "arbitration test" of cast iron. For tension tests, a gripping device with spherical seats should be provided so that the stress is as uniformly distributed as possible. Similarly, for compression tests, a bearing block with spherical seats makes it possible to apply a uniform stress.

It is important that testing machines be calibrated periodically, since the indicated load readings may not continue to be the true values. The Standards of the American Society for Testing Materials give in detail the various methods of calibration of testing machines. References in Footnote 5 also deal with the sensitivity and accuracy of testing machines and the methods of calibration. Errors in load measurement in testing machines are ordinarily required to be less than one per cent, but 0.5 per cent or less is desirable. In the Universal testing machines described above, the loading of the specimen is at either a constant (approximately) or variable strain

---

5 R. G. Batson and J. H. Hyde, "Testing of Materials of Construction," *Mechanical Testing*, Vol. 1, Chapman and Hall, Ltd., London (Dutton, N. Y.), 1922, 413 pp. See also H. E. Davis, G. E. Troxell, and C. T. Wiskocil, *The Testing and Inspection of Engineering Materials*, McGraw-Hill Book Co., Inc., New York, 1941, 372 pp.

rate.   Machines have been developed that test a specimen in tension at constant rates of load or strain.

A number of auxiliary devices for gripping, supporting, and holding the specimen have been devised for performing tension, compression, and bending tests on materials.   For a complete discussion of these devices see references in Footnote 5.

Torsion Testing Machines.   Torsion tests are most suitable for the determination of shear strength.   It is not convenient to adapt the Universal testing machine for torsion testing, so that special machines for this purpose have been developed.   Both screw-power and hydraulic torsion machines are available.   The load in

Fig. 11-8.   Screw-power pendulum-type torsion testing machine.   (Courtesy Riehle Testing Machine Division, American Machine and Metals, Inc.)

these machines is measured by a pendulum indicator or beam scale. A screw-type, 10,000 in. lb. capacity Riehle torsion machine is shown in Fig. 11-8.   Power is applied by hand through the crank (K), or a motor drive can be supplied to apply the torque.   The specimen (S) is placed between centering jaws and is gripped between the chucks (C) so that it is twisted as the crank is turned.   As the specimen is twisted, the heavy pendulum (P) swings out. An arm (T), attached to the pendulum, moves an indicator along a scale (E) a distance (d). The scale (E) can be graduated to read directly the amount of twisting moment. This direct reading of torque is possible because the twisting moment is the weight of the lever times the distance a, where a is the horizontal movement of the center of gravity of the lever weight. Since the distance d is proportional to a, the scale (E)

Fig. 11-9. Screw-power torsion testing machine. (Courtesy Riehle Testing Machine Division, American Machine and Metals, Inc.)

can be used to give the twisting moment values directly. A twistometer, which reads the angle of twist for each load increment, is attached to the specimen during a test. Most torsion test specimens are circular in cross section; they may be either solid or hollow. Figure 11-9 shows a recent model of the screw-power torsion machine with a dial pendulum weighing device.

Torsion machines in which the load is measured by a compound lever system and a weighing scale are also available. In another type, a lever or arm attached to the chuck actuates a hydraulic capsule.

Special Static Testing Machines. In addition to the torsion testing machines, other special machines for static tests include those used for cold-bend tests to determine ductility,[5] machines for special purposes such as wire or spring testing, machines for flexure tests (usually hand-operated), and machines for compression tests as used in highway laboratories.

11-5. COMBINED STRESS MACHINES

Many machine and structural parts are subjected to a combined state of stress, or to stresses in more than one direction. Information on material behavior under combined states of stress must be obtained, since the values of the mechanical properties for simple stresses cannot be used. A number of special combined-stress testing machines, which subject a specimen to combined stresses, have been built.

Some of the first experiments on combined stresses were made on solid round cylindrical specimens subjected to torsion combined with bending, or torsion combined with axial loading. A non-uniform

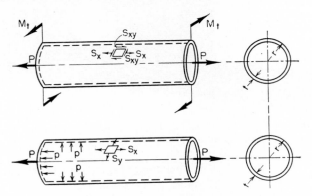

Fig. 11-10.   Specimens for combined biaxial-stress tests.

stress distribution is produced in such specimens and, in order to eliminate this objection, experiments were later made on thin-walled cylindrical tubes subjected to torsion and axial tension, internal pressure and axial tension, or internal pressure and axial compression (Fig. 11-10).

For a thin-walled tube subjected to torsion and axial tensile loading, principal stresses of opposite sign are produced, with values as determined in Chapter 3. For the thin-walled tube subjected to axial tensile loading and internal pressure (Fig. 11-10), principal stresses of the same sign are produced, with values as determined in Chapter 3.

In a combined stress test the usual method of loading is to apply both loads simultaneously at a constant ratio so that the ratio of the principal stresses remains essentially constant throughout the test. Another method of loading is to fix one of the loads and to increase the other until rupture occurs. In either method, readings are

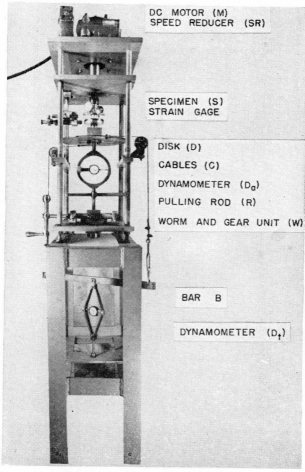

DC MOTOR (M)
SPEED REDUCER (SR)

SPECIMEN (S)
STRAIN GAGE

DISK (D)

CABLES (C)

DYNAMOMETER (D_a)

PULLING ROD (R)

WORM AND GEAR UNIT (W)

BAR B

DYNAMOMETER (D_t)

Fig. 11-11.   Combined stress tension-torsion testing machine.
(Courtesy Pennsylvania State College.)

taken of the strains that accompany loading so that stress-strain diagrams can be plotted and the biaxial mechanical properties such as yield strength, ultimate strength, and ductility can be determined. Experiments on static biaxial stresses have been made by many investigators. Some of the more important experimental work is reviewed in Footnote 6.

A machine for testing thin-walled tubes subjected to combined tension and torsion is shown in Fig. 11-11. In this machine the specimen shown at the top of Fig. 11-11 is subjected to a torque by means of tangential loads applied to the horizontal disk. The torsional forces can be applied by dead weights or by a worm-and-gear drive. A worm-and-gear drive applies the axial tensile load, and dynamometers with dials are provided for measuring both the ten-

Fig. 11-12. Machine for testing tubular specimens under combined internal pressure and axial load. (Courtesy Westinghouse Research Laboratories.)

⁶ J. Marin, *Mechanical Properties of Materials and Design*, McGraw-Hill Book Co., Inc., 1942, 273 pp.

sile and torque loads. Spherical seats and universal joints are used
to insure axial tensile stresses free from bending. The deformations
are measured by means of a twistometer to measure the angle of twist
and by a micrometer microscope to measure the axial strain (Fig.
11-11).

Combined Tension-Tension Machines. Most experiments
on biaxial stresses have been made on thin-walled tubular specimens
subjected to internal pressure and axial tensile loads. Figure 11-12
shows equipment used for applying internal pressure and axial tension
to a tubular specimen. By means of special grips, the tubular
specimen (S) is subjected to an axial tensile load by a standard
30-ton Amsler testing machine (A). The axial load is measured
by the gage (G). The internal pressure is produced by the high-
pressure Amsler pump (P) with a pendulum manometer for load
measurement (M), as shown on the right of Fig. 11-12. The measuring pendulum on the high-pressure pump can be adjusted to a
length such that, at full-scale deflection on both the axial testing
machine and the high-pressure pump, a given ratio between the

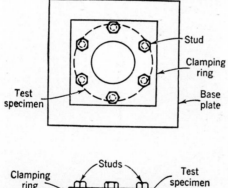

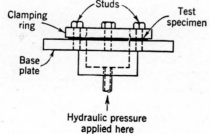

Fig. 11-13(a). "Bulge" test of a circular plate.

principal stresses can be produced. To maintain this ratio during
the operation of the test it is necessary to keep the indicating pointers
of the machine deflected through the same angle.

Tests on tubes subjected to internal pressures and axial loads
have been made using screw-power or various types of hydraulic

Fig. 11-13(b). "Bulge" test apparatus.
(Courtesy David Taylor Model Basin.)

machines for the application of the axial tensile load.   In these tests
the internal pressure has sometimes been applied by means of different types of pumps with pressure gages for load measurement in
place of the pendulum manometer referred to above.

"Bulge tests" have been made in order to study the plastic behavior of metals subjected to biaxial tensile stresses.   In these tests
a flat circular or elliptical plate, clamped at the edge, is subjected to
a liquid pressure on one side, thereby deforming the plate in the
form of a bulge (Fig. 11-13).   The deflections of various points on
the specimen are measured with dials, and a grid is marked initially
on the specimen to provide reference points for strain measurements.
A specimen that is initially circular gives a region of equal biaxial

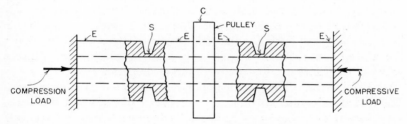

Fig. 11-14.   Specimen for combined compression-torsion testing.

tensile stresses in the plastic range.   An elliptical plate produces a
stress ratio different from 1, the value depending upon the relative
values of the major and minor axes of the ellipse.   The bulge test
is valuable for plastic flow investigations, including studies of forming operations.   It is not adequate, however, for defining elastic
failure.   Equal biaxial tensile stresses can be produced also by subjecting a hemispherical or spherical shell to internal fluid pressure.

Although the foregoing tests are the most common, other combined-
stress tests have been made as follows.

Tension-Compression Tests with the Compression Stress Maximum.
In order to investigate biaxial stresses in which the compressive
principal stress is greater than the tensile principal stress, Bridgman
used a specimen as shown in Fig. 11-14.   The thin-walled central
part of the specimen or test sections are separated from the thicker
ends by two deep and narrow notches.   The two ends of the specimen (E) are prevented from rotating, and the center (C) is twisted

between the ends by means of keyways. A longitudinal compressive load is applied at the same time as the torque by a small hydraulic ram in such a way that longitudinal deformations are free to occur. A central pin provides stability, and the central part of the specimen is attached to a pulley around which a flexible wire cable is wound. The cable from the pulley is wound over a drum actuated by a motor with variable gears to give a wide range of speeds. Measurements of angle of twist for various torque values are taken for different values of the compressive loads.

Tension-compression tests have also been made by subjecting a tubular specimen to internal pressure and axial compression, using equipment similar to that used for the internal pressure-axial tension tests. Care must be taken to design the specimen properly so that failure by buckling does not occur under axial compression.

Compression-Compression Tests. Biaxial compressive stresses can be applied by subjecting cylindrical specimens to a radial pressure. The radial pressure can be applied by inserting the specimen into a cylinder that is then subjected to internal pressure.

Triaxial Tests. Thick-walled cylinders subjected to internal pressure and axial loading are under a triaxial state of stress and offer some information on behavior of materials subjected to triaxial stresses. The presence of a non-uniform distribution of stress throughout the cylinder walls, however, introduces error in the evaluation of the results obtained by such tests. Cylindrical specimens subjected to a radial compressive pressure by a hydraulic pump, and axial compression by a universal testing machine, have yielded valuable information on the triaxial compression properties of brittle materials. Strengths of materials under equal triaxial compressive stresses have been thoroughly studied by Bridgman,[7] who has developed special equipment to apply the extremely high pressures required for such tests. Pressures up to 100,000 kg. per cm.^{2} have been produced using this equipment.

11-6. CREEP TESTING MACHINES

Testing machines of different types have been developed for the measurement of creep under various types of static and dynamic

---

[7] P. W. Bridgman, "Recent Work in the Field of High Pressures," *American Scientist*, 1943, No. 1, Vol. 31.

stresses.[8]　Most creep testing is done on specimens subjected to simple tension in machines similar to those shown in Fig. 11-15. Each tension-creep testing unit consists of a device for applying a fixed load to a specimen by means of a simple lever.　In addition, provision must be made for adequate attachment of the specimen,

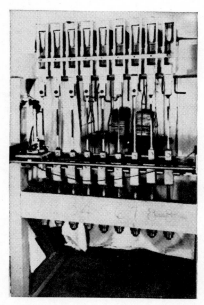

Fig. 11-15.　Tension-creep testing machine.
(Courtesy Pennsylvania State College.)

a thermocouple or other type of heating unit, and a micrometer microscope for measurement of creep strains.　A series of specimens, each subjected to different stresses, is tested simultaneously and creep-strain readings are usually recorded for a period of 1000 hours.

Automatic creep-tension machines in which creep-time curves are recorded automatically have been developed by Manjoine.[9]　For short-time creep-rupture tests, an automatic machine was developed

---

[8] Erich Siebel, *Handbuch der Werkstoffprüfung*, Vol. I, "Pruf und Messeinrichtungen," Julius Springer, Berlin, 1940.　Lithoprinted by Edwards Bros., Ann Arbor, Mich., 1944, 658 pp.

[9] M. J. Manjoine, "New Machines for Creep and Creep-Rupture Tests," *Trans. A.S.M.E.*, Feb., 1945, p. 111.

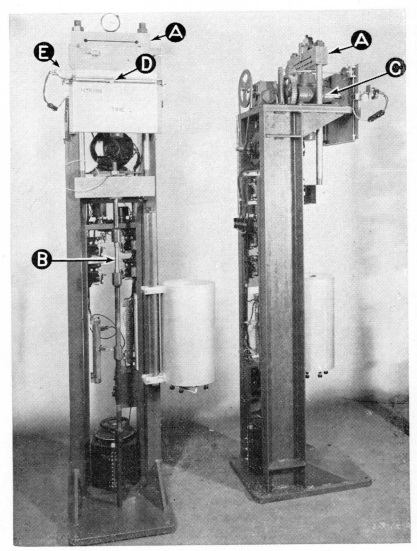

Fig. 11-16. Automatic screw-lever machine for creep-rupture tests. (Courtesy Westinghouse Research Laboratories.)

(a) Bending-creep machine.

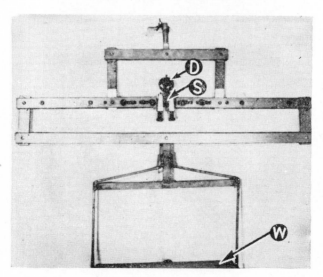

(b) Single bending-creep unit.

Fig. 11-17.　Bending-creep equipment.　(Courtesy Pennsylvania State College.)

by Manjoine.[9] This machine, a screw-driven type, is shown **in** Fig. 11-16. It consists of a stiff spring (A) in series with the test specimen (B), loaded by a screw-driven jack (C). By keeping **a**

(a) Torsion-creep machine.

(b) Single torsion-creep unit.

Fig. 11-18.   Torsion-creep equipment.   (Courtesy Pennsylvania State College.)

constant deflection of the spring (A), the load can be kept constant. The deflection of the spring is measured by a dial gage with an electrical contact that controls the motor. The motor, in turn, drives the jack to keep the load constant. The deformation of the test specimen is measured from the relative motion of the upper head of the machine and the stationary frame. This motion is magnified through a gear train and drives the pen on the recorder (D) vertically. A clock (E) drives the pen horizontally so that a continuous creep-time curve is plotted automatically.

Although most creep testing is done with specimens subjected to simple tension, some investigations have been made to determine creep for bending, torsion, and combined stresses. Figure 11-17 shows an eight-unit creep-bending apparatus, which subjects a specimen to pure bending stresses by applying a load W to a specimen S. Creep deflections are measured by a Federal or Ames dial (D) for a selected gage length. Figure 11-18 shows a six-unit torsion-creep machine used for tests at room temperature. Torsion is applied to a specimen (S) by weights (W) applied to a wheel (H). The

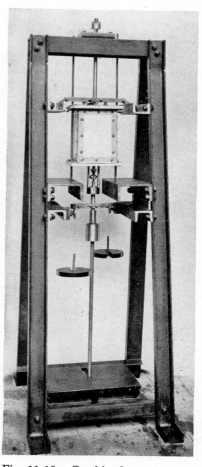

Fig. 11-19. Combined stress-creep testing machine. (Courtesy National Physical Laboratory, England.)

angles of twist at various time intervals are measured by the twistometer (T).

Combined stress-creep tests on steel tubes subjected to axial loading and torsion have been made (Fig. 11-19). Creep tests on tubes subjected to combined internal pressure and torsion, and tests of tubular specimens closed at the ends and subjected to internal pressures, have also been conducted.

In all the foregoing creep tests the stresses are kept fixed and the creep deformation is measured with time. However, there are applications in which the creep takes place with a diminishing stress value. The bolted joint is an example of such a stress-relaxation condition. Machines have been built to determine creep under varying stress conditions.

Table 11-2

Classification of Fatigue Testing Machines

Type	Kinds of stress

Constant Load (Dead Weights)	(a) *Simple Stresses*
	    1. Pure bending
	    2. Bending and Shear
	    3. Tension-Compression
	    4. Torsion
	
	 (b) *Combined Stresses* (Biaxial)
	    1. Tension-Tension
	    2. Tension-Compression

Constant Load (Inertia Forces)	(a) *Simple Stresses*
	    1. Pure bending
	    2. Tension-Compression
	    3. Torsion
	
	 (b) *Combined Stresses* (Biaxial)
	    1. Tension-Compression
	      (Torsion and Bending)

Constant Deflection	(a) *Simple Stresses*
	    1. Bending
	    2. Tension-Compression
	    3. Torsion
	
	 (b) *Combined Stresses* (Biaxial)
	    1. Tension-Tension

DYNAMIC TESTING MACHINES

In many machines and structures the stresses produced are not always static, as considered heretofore, but they are repeated and vary in magnitude, or they are impact loads having a high kinetic energy.

11-7. FATIGUE TESTING MACHINES

There are numerous kinds of machines for fatigue tests of materials and of structural and machine members. Only a few of the main types, as outlined in Table 11-2, can be discussed in this chapter.

Flexure Fatigue Machines. At the present time the R. R. Moore high-speed fatigue testing machine (Fig. 11-20) is the most commonly used. This machine subjects a round specimen to pure bending moments free from transverse shear forces. By rotating the

Fig. 11-20. R. R. Moore reversed bending-fatigue machine. (Courtesy Baldwin-Lima-Hamilton Corp.)

specimen one revolution, the stresses at a given point are completely reversed from a tensile stress value to an equal compressive value. This stress variation is accomplished by applying a fixed bending moment to the specimen by means of weights (W), as shown in Fig. 11-21. The specimen (S) is held at its ends in special holders and loaded by the weights (W) through two bearings (B_1) placed at equal distances from the center of the specimen. Two other bearings (B_2), at equal distances from the center of the specimen, provide support for the reactive forces. With such a loading arrangement the vertical

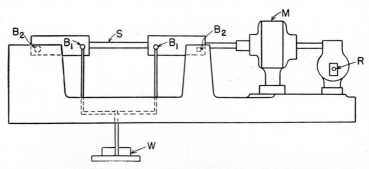

Fig. 11-21.   Diagram of R. R. Moore reversed bending-fatigue machine.

transverse shear force on the specimen is zero, or a pure bending stress free from shear stresses is produced. Cycles of stress variation are provided by the rotation of the specimen by a motor (M), and a record of the number of cycles to rupture is given by the revolution counter (R). A disengaging device is provided for stopping the motor when the specimen fails.

The main advantages of the rotating-beam testing machine are its simple design, low cost, accuracy with which the bending moment can be measured, and the high speed of operation. (Speeds of 12,000 r.p.m. can be provided.) The disadvantages are the limitations on range of stress, shape of specimen cross section, and cost of machining the specimens.

The R. R. Moore machine represents the constant-load type of machine in which the load remains constant during the test. There is another type of fatigue machine, the constant-deflection or constant-amplitude type, in which the specimen is subjected to a constant deflection during the test. Figure 11-22 shows the fixed-cantilever,

constant-amplitude fatigue machine. In this machine the end of
the cantilever specimen (A) is repeatedly bent back and forth by
the variable eccentric (B). The stress on the specimen is computed
by the beam formula ($S = Mc/I$), where the moment M is obtained
by calibration. In calibrating, dead weights are applied in order to
produce a given deflection, which is measured by a dial gage (C).
An eccentric is used to produce this same deflection in the fatigue
test. The number of cycles of stress is recorded on a counter, and a
toggle switch is provided to stop the machine when a specimen fractures. The main advantage of the constant-deflection type machine
is that fatigue tests on flat specimens such as thin sheet metal can
be made. The constant-amplitude type of machine has been found
useful in the testing of laminated plastics, and it has been accepted

Fig. 11-22. Fixed-cantilever constant-amplitude-type fatigue-testing
machine. (Courtesy Krouse Testing Machine Co.)

as a tentative method for repeated flexural stress tests of plastics. The main disadvantage is that for some materials and stress values the constant-deflection method of applying stress may not be sufficiently accurate unless periodic checks are made on the calibration during the test.

Another type of repeated bending or flexure fatigue machine applies the load by inertia forces. Figure 11-23(a) shows the essential features of an inertia machine designed by the Sonntag Scientific Corporation. A specimen (A) is held by the holder (O) and attached to a frame (C). A platen (F), attached to the specimen, moves up and down to produce repeated bending stresses in the specimen. The motion of the platen is produced by the mechanical oscillator (D), which is driven by the synchronous electric motor (I) through a flex-

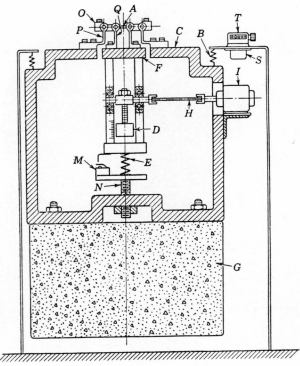

Fig. 11-23(a). Cross-section view of Sonntag inertia-type flexure-fatigue testing machine. (Courtesy Baldwin-Lima-Hamilton Corp.)

ible drive shaft (H). A compensating spring (E) makes it possible to read directly on the scale adjacent to the revolving eccentric (D) the force applied to the specimen, irrespective of the type of specimen or the deflection in the specimen. In running a test, the desired preload on the specimen is applied by a crank and measured by a dial indicator. The superimposed alternating force required is provided for by the proper setting of the eccentric (D). The cycles of stress are recorded by a counter (T-S) and a microswitch (M) stops the machine when the specimen ruptures.

Fig. 11-23(b).   Sonntag inertia-type fatigue testing machine.   (Courtesy Baldwin-Lima-Hamilton Corp.)

The main advantage of this type of machine is that, as with the R. R. Moore machine, the value of the load is accurately known. Although the cost of the inertia-type machine may be considered high in comparison to other types, it can be used for other kinds of fatigue tests, including axial tension and compression, and torsion. The fixture for torsional fatigue stresses for the inertia-type machine

Fig. 11-24.   Fixture for torsional fatigue stresses.   (Courtesy Baldwin-Lima-Hamilton Corp.)

is shown in Fig. 11-24. Many adaptations and modifications of the foregoing bending-fatigue machines have been developed.

Axial Stress Fatigue Machines. For fatigue tests in which the stresses are beyond the elastic range, a machine that produces axial tension or compression on the specimen permits a more accurate calculation of the stress than flexure machines, since the flexure formula does not apply beyond the elastic range.

A constant-deformation, spring-type axial fatigue machine developed by Jasper is shown in Fig. 11-25. Cycles of load are applied by a crank-and-connecting-rod mechanism (K). The magnitude of the load is measured by means of the deformation in the spring (G) to which the specimen (S) is directly attached. The crank mechanism can be adjusted to give any desired ratio of maximum to minimum stress. Single-, two-, and five-unit axial stress spring-type fatigue machines are manufactured by the Krouse Testing Machine Company.

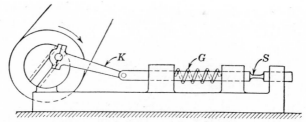

Fig. 11-25. Constant-deformation spring-type axial-fatigue machine.

A commonly used type of axial fatigue stress machine (Fig. 11-26) is the alternating-current magnet type developed by Haigh. This machine consists of an armature (A) moving rapidly back and forth between two electromagnets (M) energized by a two-phase alternating current, one phase being connected to each magnet (M). The specimen (S) is subjected to an alternating stress by means of the back-and-forth motion of the armature head. Flat springs (G) are used to compensate for the force required to accelerate the armature and other vibrating parts, the adjustment being made by four clamps (C) as shown. By applying suitable initial loads to the flat springs (G), different ranges of stress can be produced in the specimen.

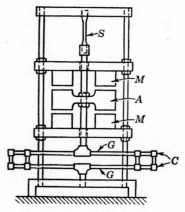

Fig. 11-26. A.C. magnet-type Haigh fatigue machine.

As previously stated, the inertia-type fatigue machine shown in Fig. 11-23 can be employed for axial fatigue tests by using special fixtures. The adaptability and

high speeds possible with this type of machine are making it a
widely used one.

Torsion Fatigue Machines. A constant-deflection type repeated-
torsion machine, as developed by Moore, is shown in Fig. 11-27.
Torsion in the specimen (S) is produced through a chuck (A) by a
variable-throw cam (C). The cam (C) consists of a double eccentric,
whose throw is adjusted by turning the outer eccentric around the
inner and clamping in any desired position. The torque is transmitted through the jaw (J) to a calibrated specimen (D). The

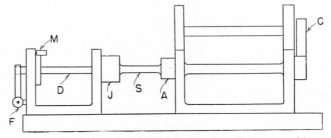

Fig. 11-27.   Constant-deflection-type torsion-fatigue machine.

angle of twist of the specimen (D) is proportional to the twisting
moment and is measured by the dial gages (M). The desired range
of twisting moment is applied to the specimen by hand-turning the
machine and adjusting the throw of the cam (C). The initial twisting moment on the bar (D) is applied by screws (F) acting on a
radial arm attached to the left-hand end of the bar (D).

Inertia-type torsion fatigue machines similar to those shown in
Fig. 11-23 have been developed. The repeated torsion is applied
by the special fixture illustrated in Fig. 11-24. Repeated-torsion
machines have the same disadvantage as flexure fatigue machines
for tests beyond the elastic range unless a hollow circular specimen
with thin walls is used.

Combined-Stress Fatigue Machines. Repeated combined-stress machines available are mainly of two types—repeated torsion-bending,
or repeated tension-tension.

Figure 11-28(a) shows the repeated torsion-bending type machine,
as developed by the National Physical Laboratory, England. In
this machine a specimen (S), as shown in Fig. 11-28(b), of circular
cross section, is subjected simultaneously to the torsional and bending

stresses by applying repeated flexure and torque moments.   The
specimen (S) is clamped in a chuck (C) at one end and in a bracket
(K) at the other end, which is attached to the base plate (B).   The

Fig. 11-28(a).   Combined torsion-bending fatigue machine.   (Courtesy
National Physical Laboratory, England.)

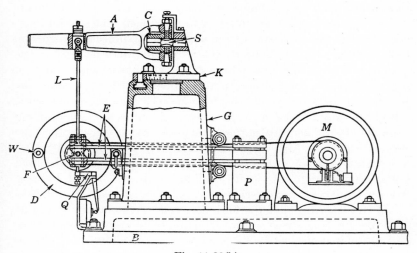

Fig. 11-28(b).

bracket (K) can be rotated to any desired position. An arm (A), pivoted about a vertical axis passing through the center of the specimen, is attached to the chuck (C). A disk (D), carrying the out-of-balance weights (W), is mounted on a spindle (F) and clamped to the ends of springs (E). The other ends of the springs are rigidly clamped to a bracket (P) attached to the base plate. The disk (D) is driven by a synchronous motor (M), which has a belt drive. The clamps at the left end of the springs (E), carrying the spindle (F), are connected by links (L) to the center of percussion of the arm (A). The general principle of operation of the machine is the application of an alternating force to the arm (A) by means of the out-of-balance forces developed at the spindle (F) of the disk by the rotation of the motor. The speed of the disk is adjusted to the resonant frequency of the moving parts on the outer ends of the springs (E) by varying the ratio of pulley diameters. This is an important feature of the machine, as all inertia forces, except those produced by the out-of-balance weights, are eliminated. In the position shown in Fig. 11-28(b), cycles of reversed bending are produced on the specimen. By rotating the bracket (K) and chuck (C), bending and twisting moments proportional to the cosine and sine of the angle of rotation are produced, and any desired ratio of the bending to the torsional stresses can be obtained. Combined bending and torsion is produced inasmuch as the axes of member A and specimen S no longer coincide.

Although the torsion-bending fatigue test yields valuable information, particularly for shafting and crankshafts subjected to torsion and bending, the non-uniform stress distribution throughout the specimen cross section is a source of error in the interpretation of test results. By modifying the torsion fixture in Fig. 11-23, the inertia-type machine can be used for combined torsion-bending tests.

Repeated stress tests on tubular specimens subjected to fluctuating internal pressure and fluctuating axial stress have been made on the machine shown in Fig. 11-29. By tests of this kind, various ratios of repeated biaxial tensile stresses can be considered. The essential features consist of a motor (T) driving a gear (G), which, in turn, drives a gear to which an eccentric is attached. This eccentric gives an up-and-down motion to the lever (KY), which thereby applies a fluctuating axial stress to the tubular specimen (S). The internal oil pressure is applied to the specimen by a Bosch pump (I). Leakage of oil from the specimen is replaced by an accumulator (A), which

Fig. 11-29. Combined tension-tension fatigue-testing machine. (Courtesy Pennsylvania State College.)

maintains a constant value of the maximum pressure. Two pressure gages (H) and (L), equipped with special check valves (G), are used to record the maximum and minimum values of the fluctuating internal pressure. A dynamometer is placed initially at (N) to determine the maximum and minimum values of the axial load. The stress cycles to failure are recorded on a counter (U), and electrical controls (M) are used to stop the motor when the specimen fractures. The low rate of application of the stress cycles necessary (200 per minute) is a major disadvantage. However, various ratios of the maximum biaxial stresses and ranges of stress can be investigated with this machine.

There are a number of fatigue testing machines not covered in the above discussion. For a more complete treatment of fatigue machines see reference given in Footnote 10. Special dynamic machines, not mentioned under fatigue or impact machines, are used to determine damping constants of materials. Several types of machines and tests have been used to determine the damping capacity. A summary of these tests is given by Von Heydekampf.[11]

11-8. IMPACT TESTING MACHINES

There are two main types of impact testing—tests using plain specimens and those using notched specimens. A classification of impact testing machines is given in Table 11-3.

Table 11-3

Classification of Impact Machines

Method of load application	Kind of stress	Machine
Swinging Pendulum	Tension	Modified Charpy or Izod
	Shear	McAdam
	Bending	Charpy or Izod or combination
Rotating Flywheel	Tension	Mann
	Torsion	Carpenter
	Bending	Guillery
Dropped Weight (Single and repeated blows)	Tension	Olsen
	Compression	Olsen
	Bending	Hatt-Turner

Pendulum-Type Impact Machines. The most commonly used impact testing machine is the pendulum type shown in Figs. 11-30(a) and 11-30(b). In this machine the specimen (S) is broken with a

---

[10] *Manual on Fatigue Testing*, published by the American Society for Testing Materials, 1949.

[11] G. S. Von Heydekampf, "Damping Capacity of Materials," *Proc. A.S.T.M.*, 1931, Part II, Vol. 31, pp. 157-171.

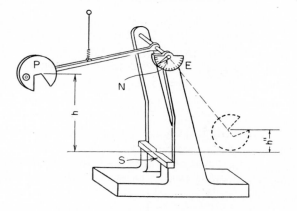

IMPACT   TESTING   MACHINE

Fig. 11-30(a).

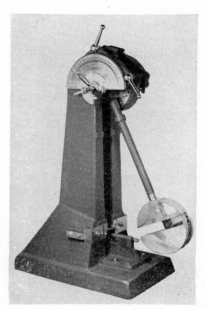

Fig. 11-30(b).   Pendulum-type impact testing machine.   (Courtesy Riehle Testing Machines, Division of American Machines and Metals, Inc.)

single blow by the pendulum (P) falling a height h. The energy absorbed in the fracture of the specimen is determined by noting the initial position of the pendulum and the highest position (h'') that the pendulum reaches after breaking the specimen. If (W) is the weight of the pendulum, the energy used to fracture the specimen is equal to

$$E_p = Wh - Wh''$$

where h = the vertical fall of the center of gravity of the pendulum and h'' = its vertical rise.

The readings of the pointer (N) measure h and h''. Energy values given by the above equation may be used to measure the relative toughness of various materials subjected to impact loads.

The machine shown in Fig. 11-30 can be used for axial tension-impact tests on plain specimens. Fixtures are also provided for bending tests of notched specimens when using Charpy or Izod type specimens. The Charpy specimen is supported at the ends and struck at the middle, while the Izod type is supported as a cantilever beam and struck at the free end. Test procedures for Charpy impact tests are standardized by the American Society for Testing Materials.

The Oxford Impact Machine is another pendulum-type design in which the specimen is a beam with a constant moment over part of its length (Fig. 11-31). A yoke (Y) applies the impact blow to two points $1\frac{1}{2}$ in. apart on the specimen. The designers claim that more consistent and reliable results can be obtained since "stray losses" are eliminated by having only normal stresses free from transverse shear. Another pendulum-type impact machine used for measuring shear impact toughness is manufactured by the Tinius Olsen Testing Machine Company.

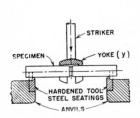

Fig. 11-31. Oxford impact machine.

Rotating-Flywheel Type Impact Machines. There are several flywheel-type impact machines that use a rotating flywheel as a source of energy for rupturing the specimen. The Guillery machine, of this type, is designed to break standard Charpy specimens at a velocity of blow equal to 29 ft. per sec. The striking member in this machine is held within the rim of the wheel until the desired rotational speed is reached. The energy used in breaking the specimen is measured by a manometer reading the output pressure of a small turbine coupled to the flywheel. The energy used for rupturing the specimen is obtained by measuring the pressure before and after breaking the specimen.

The Watertown or Mann flywheel machine, illustrated in Fig. 11-32, can be used for tension specimens and for speeds up to 1000 ft. per sec. In this machine a tup (T) attaches a specimen (S) to a pendulum (P). With the horns (H) retracted, the flywheel (W) is

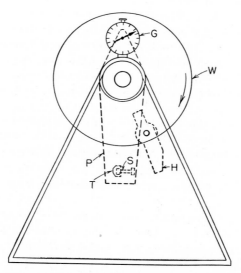

Fig. 11-32.   Mann or Watertown flywheel-type tension impact machine.

brought up to a selected speed by a motor geared to the supporting shaft. At the desired velocity, measured by means of a tachometer, the external mechanism is tripped, releasing the horns (H), which strike the tup (T), thereby rupturing the specimen (S). The angular movement produced in the pendulum is recorded on a dial gage (G). The dial gage reading can then be used to calculate the energy required for rupture. The Carpenter machine is a flywheel-type impact machine used for torsion tests.

Dropped-Weight Type Impact Machines. Impact tests are also made by dropping weights on specimens. The Hatt-Turner machine is used with either single or repeated blows applied to a specimen subjected to impact bending. It is a machine that has been found particularly useful for tests on wood and is specified for use in impact tests of wood by the American Society for Testing Materials. Single-blow impact machines for tension and compression are manufactured by the Tinius Olsen Testing Machine Company.

The energy necessary to produce rupture of a specimen is determined in the foregoing impact machines. Equipment has been developed to obtain more complete information on properties under impact loads by providing a means to determine the stress-strain diagram. Clark and Datwyler[12] obtained stress-strain diagrams for impact tension by winding fine constantin wire around a steel bar. The electrical resistance of the wire changes as the force is applied to the bar. A recording oscillograph apparatus for correlating force with time, and a means of converting force-time data to force-elongation diagrams, were developed to determine the stress-strain relations under impact.

A high-speed tension machine for tests at elevated temperatures was developed by Manjoine and Nadai.[13] The machine is of the flywheel type and the stress-strain data are obtained electrically.

SPECIAL TESTING MACHINES

There are many special testing machines not covered in the preceding articles. Of these, machines for tests of structural and machine parts and hardness testing machines will be discussed briefly in the following.

11-9. MACHINES FOR TESTS OF STRUCTURAL AND MACHINE MEMBERS

Many new machines have been developed and standard testing machines have been adapted for determining the strength of machines and structures. The large number of such special machines makes it impossible to discuss them adequately in this chapter, and only a few can be included.

---

[12] D. S. Clark and G. Datwyler, "Stress-Strain Relations under Tension Impact Loading," *Proc. A.S.T.M.*, 1938, Vol. 38, Part II, p. 98.

[13] M. Manjoine and A. Nadai, "High-Speed Tension Tests at Elevated Temperatures," *Proc. A.S.T.M.*, 1940, Vol. 40, Part I. See also *Trans. A.S.M.E.*, Parts II and III, 1941, Vol. 63, p. A-77.

Universal static testing machines of low and high capacities and special structural testing machines have been used to test large rein-forced-concrete and steel columns, reinforced-concrete arches, frames, bridge rollers, slabs, and many other structural members.   Fatigue

Fig. 11-33.   Fatigue testing machine for structural members.   (Cour-tesy Aluminum Company of America.)

tests on large beams, box girders, riveted and welded joints, and columns have been made by Templin.[14]   The machine shown in Fig. 11-33 is used for fatigue testing of column specimens (S).   The repeated load is applied through a lever (L) that is moved up and down by an eccentric drive and a motor (M).   Machines similar to the one shown in Fig. 11-33 have been used for testing welded and riveted joints in fluctuating tension.

The aircraft industry has developed numerous special machines

Fig. 11-34.   Electromagnetic vibrator test of a crankshaft component.   (Courtesy Chrysler Corp.)

[14] R. L. Templin, "Fatigue Machines for Testing Structural Units," *Proc. A.S.T.M.*, Vol. 39, 1939.

for both static and dynamic tests of airframe and propeller parts. Some of these include machines for testing wings, fuselages, propeller blades, propeller hubs, crankshafts, and engine mounts.

Electromagnetic vibrators are now frequently employed to produce resonant vibrations in structural and machine members. Figure 11-34 shows an electromagnetic vibrator (Y) used to determine the fatigue strength of a crankshaft component (C). Large vibratory loads can be produced by applying alternating current to the magnet at resonant frequencies of the part tested. The machine shown in Fig. 11-34 can be used for small parts such as compressor valves or larger items such as aircraft crankshafts.

11-10. HARDNESS TESTING MACHINES

Hardness of materials has several arbitrary definitions. It may be the resistance to permanent indentation, scratching, abrasion, cut-

Fig. 11-35.   Brinell   hardness-testing machine. (Courtesy Riehle Testing Machine Division, American Machine and Metals, Inc.)

ting, or drilling. In stress analysis and materials testing, tests to determine resistance to permanent indentation are those most commonly considered. Only a brief description of the most commonly used hardness testing machines will be given. References in Footnote 15 give a thorough discussion of hardness testing machines.

The *Brinell machine,* as shown in Figs. 11-35 and 11-36, consists of

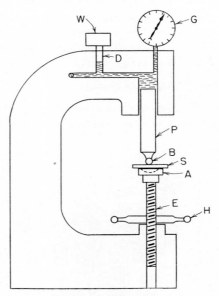

Fig. 11-36.   Brinell hardness-testing machine.

an anvil (A) for supporting the specimen (S), an elevating screw (E), and a handwheel (H) for raising the specimen to the desired height (Fig. 11-36).   A load of fixed amount is applied to the specimen through the ball (B) by a plunger (P).   The plunger is moved down by an oil pressure produced by a hand pump.   When the desired load is applied, the balance weight (W) is lifted by the action of the small piston (O), which insures that an overload is not applied to the ball.   The Bourdon gage (G) is used only to give a rough

---

[15] H. O'Neill, *The Hardness of Metals and Its Measurement,* Sherwood Press, Cleveland, 1934, 292 pp., and V. E. Lysaght, *Indentation Hardness Testing,* Reinhold Publishing Corp., New York, 1949.

indication of the load. The diameter of the indentation on the specimen is measured by a micrometer microscope, and the Brinell hardness value is determined as explained in Chapter 1.

The *Rockwell testing machine* shown in Fig. 11-37 differs from the Brinell machine in that the indenters and load values are smaller. The indenter or penetrator is either a steel ball or a conical-shaped diamond. The load is applied to the specimen through a system

Fig. 11-37. Rockwell hardness-testing machine. (Courtesy Wilson Mechanical Instrument Co.)

Fig. 11-38. Scleroscope. (Courtesy Shore Instrument and Manufacturing Co.)

of weights and levers, and the residual depth of penetration of the indenter is measured by a dial indicator. The hardness number is inversely proportional to the depth of penetration. The Rockwell machine is applicable to testing of materials having hardness values beyond the range of the Brinell machine. It is faster than the Brinell machine since it gives direct readings and is subject to less human error.

The *Vickers hardness machine*[15] is similar to the Brinell machine except that the penetrator is a square-based pyramid, and a lever system is used to apply the load.

A machine used to measure surface hardness is the *Scleroscope* shown in Fig. 11-38. In this machine the height of bounce of a diamond-pointed steel weight (dropped from a given height onto the specimen) is taken as the measure of the hardness.

BIBLIOGRAPHY

Batson, R. G., and Hyde, J. H., *Mechanical Testing*, Vol. 1, "Testing of Materials of Construction," Chapman and Hall, Ltd., London (Dutton, N. Y.), 1922, 413 pp.

Davis, H. E., Troxell, G. E., and Wiskocil, C. T., *The Testing and Inspection of Engineering Materials*, McGraw-Hill Book Co., Inc., New York, 1941.

Gibbons, C. H., *Materials Testing Machines*, Instruments Publishing Co., Pittsburgh, 1935.

Gough, H. J., *The Fatigue of Metals*, D. Van Nostrand Co., Inc., New York, 1926.

Lysaght, V. E., *Indentation Hardness Testing*, Reinhold Publishing Corp., New York, 1949.

Manjoine, M. J., "New Machines for Creep and Creep-Rupture Tests," *Trans. A.S.M.E.*, Feb., 1945, p. 111.

Moore, H. F., and Krouse, G. N., "Repeated Stress Testing Machines Used in the Materials Testing Laboratory of the University of Illinois," Circular 23, University of Illinois Engineering Experiment Station, 1934.

Siebel, Erich, *Handbuch der Werkstoffprüfung*, Vol. I, "Pruf und Messeinrichtungen," Julius Springer, Berlin, 1940. Lithoprinted by Edwards Bros., Ann Arbor, Michigan, 1944.

Chapter 12

Strain Gages

12-1. TYPES OF STRAIN GAGES

Strain gages may be classified according to the principles used for the strain measurement. On this basis there are three main types— mechanical, optical, and electrical. Another classification of strain gages may be made based on the type of strain measured as, for example, extensometers for measuring uniaxial tensile strains, compressometers for measuring uniaxial compressive strains, twistometers for measuring angles of twist in torsion, deflectometers for measuring deflections in bending, and strain rosettes for measuring biaxial strains.

12-2. MECHANICAL STRAIN GAGES

There are a number of strain gages used for the measurement of strains along one gage line. Two commonly used gages that measure strains on one gage line are the *Whittemore* and *Berry* strain gages (Figs. 12-1 and 12-2). In the Whittemore gage, members A and B are connected by flexible plates and the dial spindle bears against a lug attached to member B. A change in the gage length will, therefore, produce a change in the relative position of the members A and B that will be indicated by the dial.

In the Berry strain gage (Fig. 12-2) a dial indicator also is used to measure the strains. A bell-crank lever has one arm in contact with the dial and the other constitutes one leg of the gage. The lever ratio is usually five to one. Berry strain gages are available for both 2-in. and 8-in. gage lengths.

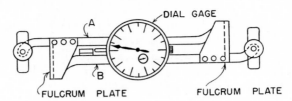

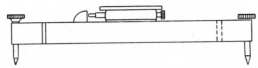

Fig. 12-1. Whittemore strain gage.

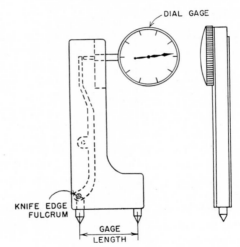

Fig. 12-2. Berry strain gage.

The Berry and Whittemore gages are called "portable" strain gages since one instrument may be used to measure strains along a number of gage lines. When the strain gage is used as a portable gage, readings on an auxiliary unstressed bar, called a "standard bar" are sometimes made at intervals to serve as a base and to provide for temperature correction. In order to correct for temperature effects, the temperature coefficients of expansion of both the object tested and the standard bar must be known.   The Berry and Whittemore type gages are also used clamped to the specimen.   With a 10-in. gage length, strain measurements reliable to 0.000005 in. per in. may be obtained with the Whittemore strain gage.   The precision of a Berry strain gage is probably close to this figure.

Another mechanical strain gage for measuring axial strains on one gage line is the *Huggenberger tensometer* (Fig. 12-3).   In this instrument there is a multiplying lever system, as shown in Fig. 12-3.   A large magnification is used so that for one model of this gage each scale division corresponds to about 0.0001 in.   Huggenberger tensometers are available with gage lengths of $\frac{1}{2}$ in. and 1 in., and their range is about 0.008 in.

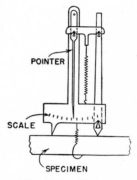

Fig. 12-3.   Huggenberger tensometer.

The friction in the joints of mechanical gages is objectionable.   This friction can be greatly reduced by the use of jeweled bearings, knife edges, or plate fulcrums.

An "averaging" type compressometer or extensometer is most commonly used for measurement of compressive or tensile strains in axially loaded specimens.   A diagrammatic sketch of an averaging-type strain gage is shown in Fig. 12-4.   Even though some bending may occur in the specimen, this gage gives very closely the average strain in the bar.   The deformation, magnified by the lever action of the collars, is usually measured by a dial gage.   When an 8-in. gage length and a dial indicator reading to 0.0001 in. are used, this kind of strain gage will measure strains to 0.0000064 in. per in.

In order to obtain the average strain in a prismatic bar, strains must be measured on at least two diametrically opposite gage lengths. For a member subjected to bending combined with direct stress, strains must be measured on at least three gage lines in order to define completely the strain condition.

There are various types of deflectometers for measuring deflections in bending.   Figure 12-5 shows two types of such instruments. These gages should be designed so that they will not be injured if the test specimen fails.

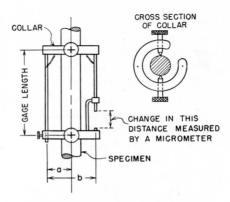

NOTE: MAGNIFICATION RATIO = $^b/_a$

Fig. 12-4.   Averaging-type strain gage.

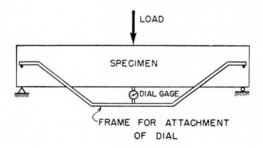

(a)
MEASUREMENT BY DIAL GAGE

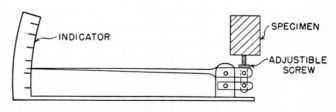

(b)
MEASUREMENT BY MULTIPLYING LEVER
Fig. 12-5.   Measuring devices for deflection.

A twistometer is used to measure the angles of twist (Fig. 12-6). The angle of twist for a given gage length L is obtained by measuring the movement of the indicator I (attached to one end of the gage length) relative to the other end. Usually the movement is measured with a direct-measuring micrometer scale, as indicated in Fig. 12-6. The movement on the arc of the scale divided by the radius of the arc gives the angle of twist value in radians for the given gage length.

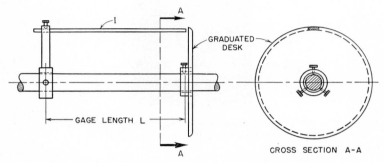

Fig. 12-6.   Twistometer for measurement of angles of twist.

Various types of mechanical gages have been devised for specific purposes and special tests. For example, in Fig. 12-7(a) and 12-7(b), a combined stress gage is shown for measuring both axial strains and angles of twist. The axial strains for specimen S are measured by the dial gages D, and the angles of twist are measured by the indicator I and disks R_1 and R_2. The gage is used for obtaining plastic strains in tubular specimens subjected to large angles of twist and axial strains. Special precautions were necessary in the design of this gage to prevent its loosening during the large lateral contractions accompanying the increase in axial loads in the plastic range of the material. The plunger P and helical spring H at the three locations shown in Fig. 12-7(b) prevent this loosening.

There are also various types of mechanical devices for automatically recording the stress-strain diagrams.

12-3.   OPTICAL STRAIN GAGES

One of the oldest optical strain gages is the *Marten extensometer* illustrated in Fig. 12-8. Strains are measured by the optical arrange-

Fig. 12-7(a).   External view of tension-torsion strain gage.
(Courtesy Pennsylvania State College.)

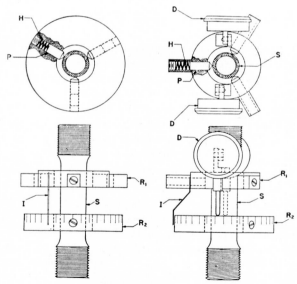

Fig. 12-7(b).   Cross section views of tension-torsion strain gage.

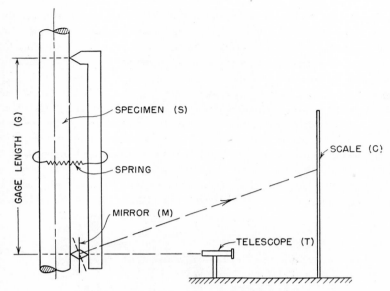

Fig. 12-8.   Marten's optical strain gage.

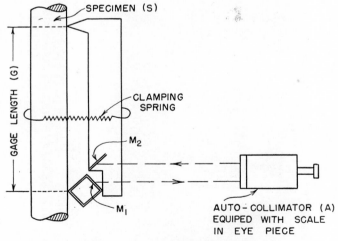

Fig. 12-9.   Tuckerman optical strain gage.

ment shown. That is, a plane mirror (M) is attached to a double knife-edge, which is in contact with one end of the gage length. As the specimen S changes length, the mirror is rotated. Because of the rotation of the mirror, a ray of light from the telescope T, reflected from the mirror onto the scale (C), also moves. The degree of magnification of this movement depends on the length of the long lever (or distance between the mirror and scale) and the length of the short lever (or distance from one corner of the knife-edge to the other). The complete strain gage consists of two units—one attached to each side of the specimen. A roller is sometimes used in place of a double knife-edge for supporting the mirror.

A modern type of optical strain gage capable of great precision is the *Tuckerman optical strain gage* (Fig. 12-9). As in the Marten

Fig. 12-10. Comparator-type optical strain gage.
(Courtesy Pennsylvania State College.)

extensometer, a double knife-edge is attached to one end of the gage length (G).   A mirror (M_1) is attached to the double knife-edge so that it rotates as the gage length (G) changes.   This rotation with respect to another mirror (M_2), fixed in position with respect to the frame, is measured by means of an autocollimator (A), as shown in Fig. 12-9.   The usual standard gage length is 2 in., but attachments are available for gage lengths as small as $\frac{1}{4}$ in.   With the 2-in. gage length, the smallest measurable strain is 0.000002 in. per in. and the range is 0.0025 in. per in.

The *comparator type* of optical strain gage is commonly used for high-temperature and creep tension testing.   The principal features of this device are shown in Fig. 12-10.   The gage consists of two telescopes mounted on a fixed base or bar.   The center crosshair on one of the telescopes is made to coincide with a target on the specimen by moving the comparator or telescope stand.   The other telescope is equipped with a micrometer eyepiece so that the movement of the second target point at the other end of the gage length can be measured.

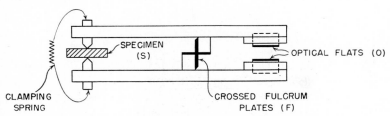

Fig. 12-11.   Vose interferometer strain gage for measurement of lateral strains.

Lateral strains must be measured by means of a lateral strain gage to determine Poisson's ratio.   The *Vose interferometer strain gage* is an optical strain gage for measuring lateral strains.   The use of the interferometer principle for measuring lateral strains optically is illustrated in Fig. 12-11.   The change in thickness of specimen S is translated to the relative displacement between the optical flats (O) by means of a fulcrum F, and the movement between the optical flats is then measured by a micrometer microscope.

There are many other applications of the optical method for measuring strains.   For example, in place of measuring the angle of twist directly with a vernier, the readings may be taken with a micrometer microscope in cases where greater accuracy is desired.   Biaxial strains in combined-stress tests of plates and tubes have sometimes been made by placing a rectangular or other type grid on the specimen and measuring the changes in this grid during loading, by the use of micrometer microscopes.

12-4. ELECTRIC STRAIN GAGES

Electric resistance strain gages are now employed in great numbers for the determination of stresses in machines and structures and for many other purposes.[1] These gages have been established as valuable equipment for both routine testing and for research studies. Although the electric strain gages are more commonly used for the determination of strains and stresses in finished parts, they are also used in tests to determine the mechanical properties of materials by the use of specimens or small samples of the material.

One feature of electric strain gages that makes them extremely useful is that they can be used for measuring strains in inaccessible parts of a structure, as in the interior of a concrete dam or the inside wall of a pressure vessel. Furthermore, a large number of gages can be glued to the stressed surface, thereby making it possible

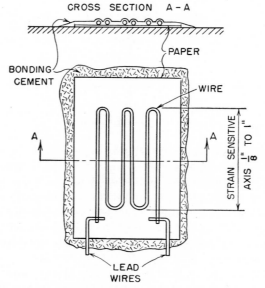

Fig. 12-12.   Schematic drawing of bonded-type
SR-4 electric strain gage.

---

[1] W. B. Dobie and P. C. G. Isaac, *Electric Resistance Strain Gages*, The English Universities Press Ltd., London, 1948.

to make a complete strain survey of various parts of a structure.

One of the earliest types of electric strain gages was the *carbon-pile telemeter,* which consists of a pile of circular carbon disks. The principle used in measuring strains with the carbon pile is that the electric resistance of the pile is a function of the degree of contact between the disks, or the pressure applied to the disks in the direction of the axis of the pile. The electric resistance changes because the contacts between individual disks change with applied pressure. The change in electric resistance is measured with a Wheatstone bridge. The carbon pile has not been found suitable when the load is applied for long periods of time because, with time, the plastic flow of the disk causes changes in the electric resistance.

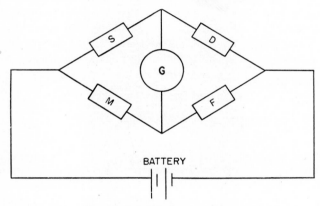

BATTERY

Fig. 12-13.   Wheatstone bridge.

The SR electric strain gage consists essentially of a short length of wire held to the material under test by a glue so that any strain produced in the material is transmitted to the gage (Fig. 12-12). The change in the length and cross-sectional dimensions of the wire produced by the stress applied to it produces a change in electrical resistance as a result of the deformation of the specimen. The strain in the wire and the specimen can be found by measuring the change in electrical resistance.

The change in the electrical resistance of the wire strain gage when stressed is measured by a Wheatstone bridge (Fig. 12-13), where S represents the strain gage and forms one arm of the bridge, while other resistances M, F, and D form the remaining three arms of the bridge. The arm D is called the "dummy." It is a gage of the same type as S, fixed to a similar piece of material but unstrained. The dummy gage is provided to compensate for humidity and temperature changes. The remaining parts in Fig. 12-13 consist of a galvanometer G and a battery B. The balance in the bridge is maintained, when a null method is used, by changing the resistance M as the resistance S varies with strain. By always changing the resistance M to give a zero galvanometer reading, the bridge is balanced and the relation between the resistances is $M/F = S/D$. The Wheatstone bridge is commercially supplied as part of a strain

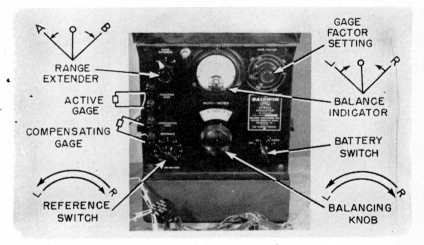

Fig. 12-14. SR-4 electric strain gage indicator. (Courtesy Baldwin-Lima-Hamilton Corp.)

indicator (Fig. 12-14). In using the strain indicator, the readings of the instrument give the strain directly provided the gage-factor dial is set at the gage-factor reading of the strain gage. The gage factors are supplied by the manufacturer with each package of gages. If the gages are used with a material other than steel and for combined-stress applications, correction factors must be applied to the gage readings. For details regarding correction factors, operation of the equipment, and other considerations, see references given in Footnotes 1 and 2.

---

[2] M. Hetenyi, *Handbook for Experimental Stress Analysis*, John Wiley & Sons, Inc., 1950. See also G. H. Lee, *An Introduction to Experimental Stress Analysis*, John Wiley & Sons, Inc., 1950.

Measurements of biaxial stresses on a stressed surface, such as an aeroplane fuselage or wing, have been made by strain rosettes using SR-4 electric strain gages. With three gages, strains are measured in three directions for a given point on the stressed surface. Knowing the directions and magnitudes of these three strains, the magnitudes and directions of the principal stresses can be determined.[1,2]

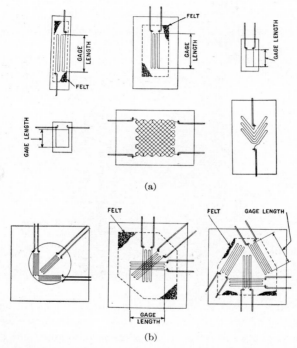

(a)

(b)

Fig. 12-15.   Types of SR-4 electric strain gages: (a) One-dimensional gages.   (b) Two-dimensional gages.

Electric SR-4 strain gages used for both uniaxial and biaxial stress applications are shown in Fig. 12-15.

Although the SR-4 gage is limited to the measurement of strains to about 0.02 in. per in., larger strains can be measured by the use of the clip gage. Figures 12-16 and 12-17 show clip gages that were used to measure large plastic strains in combined-stress tests of tubular specimens subjected to an internal pressure and axial load. A relatively large movement at the base of the clip corresponds to a

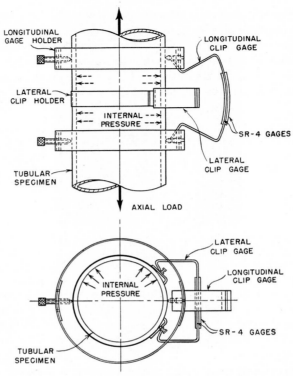

Fig. 12-16.   Clip gage for measurement of combined plastic strains.

relatively small strain in the SR-4 gages attached to the upper and lower surfaces of the top part of the clip.   By using two SR-4 gages in this way, the sensitivity of the gage is increased and a dummy gage for temperature compensation is no longer required.

There are many applications of wire resistance gages in the stress analysis of structural and machine parts.   Residual stresses have been measured in various applications with SR-4 gages.   There have been numerous load-measuring devices developed in which electric gages are used.   Torquemeters for the measurement of torque loads, dynamometers for measuring tensile and compressive loads, and proving rings for calibration of testing machines have been developed using electric strain gages.   Strains can be measured under fluctuating stress conditions, as in a rotating machine part, by the

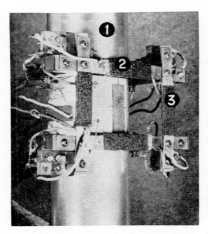

Fig. 12-17. Combined-stress strain gage for measurement of lateral and axial plastic strains. 1, tubular specimen; 2, lateral clip gage; 3, longitudinal clip gage. (Courtesy Pennsylvania State College.)

use of electric strain gages. Under these circumstances the problem is somewhat more complicated than under the static loading condition. It is then necessary to use A.C. current in place of D.C. and not only must the resistance be balanced, but also the capacitance and the inductance.

Stress-strain diagrams under impact loading have been obtained using electric strain gages for the measurement of both the strain on the specimen and the load applied to the specimen.

SR-4 wire resistance gages can also be used for precise weight measurement. A weighing cell used for aircraft purposes consists of a steel block that is about a one-inch cube, to which strain gages are attached. The block is stressed in compression by the object being weighed and the strain measurements give the weight of the object.

Electric strain gages can be used for high-pressure engine indicators and as pressure gages in many applications. The measurement of stresses inside concrete structures and on the inside of tanks and pressure vessels gives electric strain gages a versatility not found with other strain gages.

Electric strain gages have even been used to investigate the mechanical behavior of the skull when subjected to injuring blows. It appears that the field of application of electric strain gages is unlimited and new fields of use are continually being found.

In addition to mechanical, optical, and electric strain gages, special strain gages based on acoustical and pneumatic principles have been developed.[1,2] Space in this text does not permit a consideration of the sensitivity, accuracy, and calibration of strain gages. These subjects are thoroughly discussed in reference given in Footnote 1.

In selecting a strain gage for a particular purpose the testing engineer must consider many factors. The type of specimen, required gage length, accuracy of strain readings, accessibility of location where strain is desired, and rates of straining are some of the factors that influence the type of gage selected. In general, optical and SR electric strain gages are more accurate than mechanical gages. SR-4 electric gages have the advantage that they can be used for short gages, inaccessible locations such as on the inside wall of a pressure vessel, and for dynamic strain measurements. Mechanical and optical gages, although less versatile, do not require the preliminary preparations as do the SR-4 gages. They can be used repeatedly and, hence, are less expensive. For many standard-type tests requiring determination of mechanical properties of specimens, the mechanical and optical type strain gages continue to be the most suitable.

BIBLIOGRAPHY

Davis, H. E., *et al.*, *The Testing and Inspection of Engineering Materials*, McGraw-Hill Book Co., Inc., New York, 1941.

Dobie, W. B., and Isaac, P. C. G., *Electric Resistance Strain Gages*, The English Universities Press, Ltd., London, 1948.

Hetenyi, M., *Handbook on Experimental Stress Analysis*, John Wiley & Sons, Inc., New York, 1950.

Lee, G. H., *An Introduction to Experimental Stress Analysis*, John Wiley & Sons, Inc., 1950.

Withey, M. O., and Aston, James, *Johnson's Materials of Construction*, John Wiley and Sons, Inc., 1939.

Name Index

Abraham, H., 414
Aluminum Company of America, 359, 372
American Magnesium Corporation, 372
American Society of Mechanical Engineers, 131, 229, 257, 267
American Society for Metals, 78, 115, 221, 249, 252, 319, 327, 342, 348, 358, 362, 368, 372
American Society for Testing Materials, 18, 19, 21, 35, 67, 70, 104, 183, 221, 229, 249, 254, 255, 261, 267, 329, 456
Archer, R. F., 319
Arnold, R. N., 241
Aston, J., 78, 115, 482

Bailey, R. W., 271, 295
Barrett, C. S., 319
Battelle Memorial Institute, 211, 221
Batson, R. G., 77, 429, 406
Bauer, E. E., 394, 414
Baumann, K., 272
Bauschinger, J., 63
Beck, A., 371
Bergman, E. O., 77, 115
Blake, J. T., 414
Boyd, J., 273
Bray, J. L., 372
Bridgman, P. W., 438
Brook, R. M., 252

Carpenter, H., 348
Carswell, T. S., 404, 405
Cauzad, R., 221
Chalmers, B., 319
Clapp, W. H., 312
Clark, D. S., 228, 312, 460
Clark, F. H., 295
Clock, L. S., 192
Cook, G., 158

Council for Scientific Research in Australia, 221
Cunningham, D. M., 158

Datwyler, G., 228, 460
Davidenkoff, N. N., 228, 249
Davis, C. C., 414
Davis, E. A., 61
Davis, H. E., 77, 115, 149, 429, 466, **482**
Delmonte, J., 414
Den Hartog, J. P., 236
Desch, H. E., 413
Dobie, W. B., 476, 482
Dorn, J. E., 144, 158
Dumont, C., 267
Dunn, J. A., 338

Eckel, E. C., 414
Eichinger, A., 158
Everett, F. L., 283
Everhart, J. L., 252, 257, 331, 364

Findley, W. N., 267, 407
Fisher, E. G., 238
Forest Products Laboratory, 414
French, H. J., 335, 337
Freudenthal, A. M., 176, 221, 295, **319**
Frocht, M. M., 148
Furman, L., 414

Garafalo, F., 54, 55
Garratt, G. A., 413
Gensamer, M., 144
Gibbons, C. H., 422, 466
Gilkey, H. J., 77, 115
Gillet, H. W., 348, 372
Gough, H. J., 181, 204, 205, 221, **466**
Gregg, J. L., 336
Griffis, Le Van, 206

Griffith, J. H., 383, 386
Grossman, N., 254
Grover, H. J., 221

Hetenyi, M., 478, 482
Hill, R., 177
Hollomon, J. H., 54, 144, 253, 319, 348
Hooke, R., 15, 127
Houwink, R., 319
Howell, F. M., 267, 357
Huntington, W. C., 414
Hyde, J. H., 77, 429, 466

Isaac, P. C. G., 476, 482
Iterson, V., 177

Jackson, L. R., 221
Jaffee, L. D., 253, 319, 348
Jeffries, Z., 319

Kanter, J. J., 271
Kommers, J. B., 187, 221
Krouse, G. N., 466

Lankford, W. T., 149
Lee, G. H., 478, 482
Lessels, J. M., 78, 115
Liddell, D. M., 372
Lipson, C., 186, 192, 213
Low, J. R., 54, 55
Ludwik, P., 48
Lysaght, V. E., 66, 464, 466

MacGregor, C. W., 49, 51, 61, 205, 206,
    254, 256, 258
Majors, H., 205, 206
Manjoine, M. J., 229, 230, 231, 249,
    439, 460, 466
Mark, H., 414
Markwardt, L. S., 413
Marin, J., 128, 199, 201, 206, 269, 272,
    276, 292, 434
Mason, H. L., 241
McCullough, G. H., 276
McMaster, R. C., 221

McMillan, F. R., 396, 414
McVetty, P. G., 267
Memmler, K., 414
Mills, B. D., 206
Mindlin, R. D., 238
Mohr, R., 137, 142
Moore, H. F., 77, 221, 466
Morikawa, G. K., 206
Murphy, G., 77, 115, 327, 328, 352, 367

Nadai, A., 61, 128, 149, 177, 267, 273,
    460
Nason, H. K., 404, 405
Newton, J., 372
Noll, G. C., 186, 213

Odquist, F., 287
O'Neill, H., 66, 464
Osgood, W. R., 158

Parker, E. R., 149
Paul, D. A., 357
Peterson, R. E., 180, 192, 212, 226, 258
Plastics Catalogue Corporation, 402
Pollard, H. V., 205
Portland Cement Association, 391, 395,
    397, 401, 414
Prescott, J., 238
Proskauer, E. S., 414

Reiner, M., 177
Ries, H., 414
Roark, R. J., 192
Robertson, J. M., 348
Robertson, T., 158
Robinson, E. L., 273
Rolle, S., 353
Ros, M., 158
Rotherham, L., 295

Sachs, G., 319, 348
Saibel, E., 149
Salmon, E. H., 249
Samans, C. H., 342, 348, 372
Sanford, E. G., 292, 295
Sauver, A., 82
Sawert, W., 206

Schliecher, H. M., 353
Schulze, R. B., 372
Seigle, L., 252
Seitz, F., 319
Siebel, E., 439, 466
Siebert, C. A., 252
Sisco, F. T., 334, 348
Smith, G. V., 257, 295
Smith, J. O., 186, 194
Society of Automotive Engineers, 332
Soderberg, C. R., 187, 193, 199, 267, 286, 295
Spotts, M. F., 193
Sturm, R. G., 267
Sully, A. H., 292, 295

Tapsell, H. J., 276
Teed, P. L., 249, 252
Templin, R. L., 60, 181, 462
Thomsen, E. G., 158
Timoshenko, S., 78, 115, 123, 128, 177, 221, 236, 249
Troxell, G. E., 77, 115, 429, 466
Tuckerman, L. B., 46

United States Bureau of Standards, 356, 365, 369
United States Forest Service, 375

Van Horn, K. R., 319, 348
Von Heydekampf, G. S., 456

Wahl, A. M., 212
Wangard, F. F., 414
Weibull, W., 179
Welch, L. E., 256, 258
White, A. E., 252, 372
Williams, G. T., 339, 340, 341, 348
Williams, S. R., 66
Wilson, C. L., 372
Wiskocil, C. T., 77, 115, 429, 466
Withey, M. O., 78, 115, 482
Wood, W. A., 181
Worley, W. J., 267

Young, J. F., 78, 312, 319, 325

Zener, C., 64
Zwissler, L., 276

Subject Index

Abrasion tests, 70
Accoustical properties, 66
Admixtures, 393
Aggregate, 393
Alpha iron, 322
Aluminum and its alloys, 355
Angle of twist, 89
Annealing, 328

Babbitt metal, 366
Bauer drill test, 70
Bending properties, 96
Berry strain gage, 467
Bessemer process, 325
Bituminous materials, 410
Blast furnace, 324
Bourdon tube, 421
Brazing, 317
Brick, 384
Brinell hardness test, 67
Bronze, 366
Bulge test, 437

Cartridge brass, 367
Casting, 313, 326
Cast iron, 321, 344
Cementing materials, 386
Cementite, 321
Cements, 390
Charpy impact specimen, 224
Chemical composition, 302
Chemical properties, 66
Clay products, 384
Coefficient of absorption, 66
Coefficient of reflection, 66
Cold bend test, 101
Combined stress machines:
    tension-tension, 435
    tension-torsion, 433
Combined stress specimens, 153
Comparator, 474

Compression specimens, 34
Concrete, 393
Conductivity, 65
Control of properties, 298
Cooling curves, 304
Copper and its alloys, 351
Creep properties, 250
Creep test data, 261
    methods of interpretation, 264
Creep testing machines, 438
    bending, 441
    combined stress, 443
    tension, 439
    torsion, 442
Creep strains and stresses:
    bending, 276
    combined stresses, 286
    torsion, 282
Creep stress-relaxation, in tension, 272

Deformation theory for plastic flow, 147
Design stresses, 38, 162, 189, 208
Distortion energy theory, 134, 201
Drawing, 326
Dropped-weight type impact machine, 459
Ductility, 21, 101
Durability, 65
Dynamic testing machines, 445
Dynamometers, 421

Effective strain, 149
Effective stress, 149
Elastic after effect, 64
Elastic limit, 16
Electric strain gages, 476
Electromagnetic vibrator, 462
Electron, 300
Endurance limit, 181
Endurance strength, 182

Equilibrium diagram, 306
  combination type, 311
  eutectic type, 306, 310
  iron and steel, 322
  layer type, 306
  solid-solution type, 307
Eutectic-type equilibrium diagram, 310
Extrusions, 316

Fabrication of steel, 326
Fabrication methods, 312
Factor of safety, 38
Factors affecting fatigue strength, 210
Factors that modify stress-strain relations, 60
Fatigue limit, 181
Fatigue properties, 178
Fatigue strength, 182, 184, 193, 194, 198
Fatigue-testing machines, 445
  axial stress, 450
  combined tension-tension, 455
  combined tension-torsion, 453
  flexure, 445
  inertia-type, 448
  torsion, 452
Fatigue test specimens, 184
Ferrite, 322
Ferrous metals and alloys, 320
Flexure test loadings, 97
Flux, 325
Forming operations, 342
Forging, 315, 326

Gamma iron, 322
Gerber law, 187
German silver, 370
Glass, 409
Government bronze, 366
Guillery impact machine, 458
Gun metal, 366
Gypsum, 387

Hardening of steel, 327
Hardness testing machines, 463
Hardness tests, 66
Heat treatment of steel, 327, 340
Huggenberger tensometer, 467

Hydraulic universal testing machines, 427
Hyperelastic resilience, 23
Hysteresis, 62
Hysteresis loop, 62

Impact:
  testing, 222
  testing machines, 456
  properties, 222
Inconel, 370
Initial tangent modulus, 19
Internal friction theory, 142
Iron:
  carbon system, 321
  gray, 321
  white, 321
  wrought, 321
Isotope, 300
Izod impact specimen, 224

Johnson's apparent elastic limit, 18

Krouse fatigue testing machine, 451

Laminated constructions, 317
Lattice structures, 308
Lead and its alloys, 364
Liquidus, 307
Lime, 389
Load-deflection diagram, 98
Long-time creep properties in tension, 260
Lumber, 375

Machinability, 65, 70
Machines for tests of members, 460
Manganese bronze, 367
Magnesium and its alloys, 362
Malleability, 65
Mann impact machine, 459
Marten's optical strain gage, 471
Materials testing machines, 417
Maximum shear theory, 121, 129, 140, 199
Maximum strain theory, 131

Maximum strain-energy theory, 131
Maximum stress theory, 128, 140, 199
Mechanical properties:
  under bending, 96
  under combined stresses, 116
  under compression, 31
  under creep, 250
  under impact, 222
  under tension, 4, 8
  under torsion, 82
Mechanical strain gages, 467
Mechanical treatment, 302
Methods of load application, 417
Methods of load measurement, 420
Micrometer microscope, 474
Modified Goodman law, 187
Modified log-log method, 264
Modulus:
  of elasticity, 19, 101
  of resilience, 22
  of resilience in torsion, 88, 90
  of rigidity, 90
  of rupture in bending, 100
  of rupture in torsion, 84
  of toughness, 23
  of toughness in bending, 103
  of toughness in torsion, 90
Mohr's theory, 142
Mohs' scale, 70
Monel metal, 355, 370
Muntz metal, 367

Naval brass, 367
Neutron, 300
Nickel and its alloys, 368
Nickel silver, 370
Non-ferrous metals and alloys, 349
Non-metallic materials, 373
Notch-bar testing, 222
Notch sensitivity, 212

Octahedral strain, 149
Octahedral stress, 149
Open hearth process, 325
Optical strain gages, 471
Overstressing, 214
Oxford impact machine, 458

Pearlite, 324
Pendulum-type impact machine, 456

Percentage elongation, 21
Percentage reduction in area, 21
Phosphor bronze, 366
Pig iron, 324
Plastics, 401
Poisson's ratio, 20
Portland cement, 390
Powder metallurgy, 317
Principal strains, 125
Principal stresses, 117
Proportional limit, 16
Proton, 300

Quicklime, 389

Range of stress, 183
Reduction in area, 21
Resilience, 22, 87, 103
Resistance to scratching, 70
Riveting, 317
Rockwell hardness test, 67
Rockwell hardness testing machine, 465
Rolling, 314, 326
Rotating flywheel-type impact machine, 458
Rubber, 408
Rupture, modulus of, 84, 100

SAE steels, 332
Scleroscope, 67, 466
Screw-gear machine, 423
Shaping of steel, 326
Shear properties, 79
Shear test specimens, 80, 81
Soderberg law, 187
Solid solution, 307
Solidus, 308
Sonntag testing machine, 448
Space lattice, 5
Specific heat, 66
SR-4 strain gages, 477
SR-4 strain indicator, 478
Static properties:
  in bending, 96
  in combined stresses, 116
  in compression, 31
  in shear, 79
  in tension, 3, 8
  in torsion, 82
Steel, 321

Stiffness, 19, 90, 100
Stone, 381
Strain, 9
    creep, 263
    effective, 149
    gages, 467
    octahedral, 149
    plastic, 147
    principal, 125
    significant, 149
Strain energy, 126
Strain hardening exponent, 54
Strength
    A.S.T.M. offset yield, 19
    bending, 98
    breaking, 18
    coefficient, 54
    elastic, 16
    plastic, 16
    tensile, 18
    ultimate, 18
    yield, 17
Strength-density ratio, 350
Strength-weight ratio, 46, 95, 110
Stress, 8
    alternating, 178
    design, 38
    effective, 149
    fatigue, 178
    fluctuating, 178
    impact, 232, 238, 241
    maximum, 183
    mean, 183
    minimum, 183
    octahedral, 149
    principal, 116
    repeated, 178
    significant, 149
    variable, 183
    working, 38
Stress concentration, 169
Stress concentration factors, 172
Stress-relaxation test, 260
Stress-rupture test, 259
Stress-strain diagrams, 12, 13, 26, 27
Structure of materials, 5, 299

Tangent modulus, 20
Temperature properties, 250, 251, 254
Tempering of steel, 327
Tension specimens, 10, 11

Terra Cotta, 384
Testing machines, 417
Theories:
    for combined fatigue stresses, 148
    for ductility, 151
    for plastic stress-strain relations, 147
    for yield strength under combined
        stresses, 127
    for ultimate strength under com-
        bined stresses, 140
Thermal conductivity, 66
Thermal properties, 66
Tin and its alloys, 365
Torsion:
    ductility, 87
    resilience, 87
    stiffness, 87, 89
    strength, 84
    testing machines, 430
    toughness, 90
Toughness, 23, 90, 103
Triaxial stress, 123
True reduction in area, 49
True strain, 48
True stress, 48
True stress-strain relations, 48
Tuckerman optical strain gage, 474
Twistometer, 471

Ultimate strength, 18
Understressing, 214
Universal testing machines, 422
Useful limit point, 18
Utilization of bending properties, 106
Utilization of compression properties,
    43
Utilization of impact properties, 243
Utilization of tension properties, 43
Utilization of theories of failure in de-
    sign, 165

Vickers hardness tester, 67, 465
Vose Interferometer strain gage, 475

Water-cement ratio, 394
Watertown impact machine, 459
Wear tests, 70
Welding, 317
Whittemore strain gage, 467

Wood, 373
Workability, 65
Working stresses, 38
Wrought iron, 321

Yellow brass, 367
Yield strength:
  in bending, 98

Yield strength (*Cont.*):
  in compression, 17
  in tension, 17
  in torsion, 84
Young's modulus, 15

Zamak, 367
Zinc and its alloys, 366

DATE DUE

DEC 1 7 2009			

Demco, Inc. 38-293